THE

Intelligent Man's Guide

TO

SCIENCE

BOOKS BY ISAAC ASIMOV

BIOCHEMISTRY AND HUMAN METABOLISM *(with B. S. Walker and W. C. Boyd)*

RACES AND PEOPLE *(with W. C. Boyd)*

CHEMISTRY AND HUMAN HEALTH *(with B. S. Walker and M. K. Nicholas)*

THE CHEMICALS OF LIFE

INSIDE THE ATOM

BUILDING BLOCKS OF THE UNIVERSE

ONLY A TRILLION

THE CLOCK WE LIVE ON

THE WORDS OF SCIENCE

THE REALM OF NUMBERS

THE LIVING RIVER

KINGDOM OF THE SUN

THE WELLSPRINGS OF LIFE

THE
Intelligent Man's Guide
TO
SCIENCE

ISAAC ASIMOV

VOLUME TWO
The Biological Sciences

BASIC BOOKS, INC.   NEW YORK

Contents

CONTENTS

VOLUME TWO
The Biological Sciences

VOLUME TWO

The Biological Sciences

CHAPTER

10

THE
MOLECULE

ORGANIC MATTER

MODERN SCIENCE has all but wiped out the borderline between life and non-life. Nowadays the question "What is life?" is asked by physicists as often as by biologists. In fact, biology and physics are merged in a new branch of science called biophysics — the study of the physical forces and phenomena involved in living processes. The theory of quantum mechanics has been found to apply to the behavior of matter not only at the level of the atom but also at the level of the molecule, in living as well as non-living forms of matter. And it is to biochemistry ("life chemistry") that biologists today are looking for basic answers to the secrets of reproduction, heredity, evolution, birth, growth, disease, aging, and death.

Just as the atom has furnished the chief excitement in twentieth-

389

century physics, so the molecule has been the subject of equally exciting discoveries in chemistry. Chemists have been able to work out detailed pictures of the structure of even very complex molecules, to identify the roles of specific molecules in living systems, to create elaborate new molecules, and to predict the behavior of a molecule of a given structure with amazing accuracy. Moreover, the technological achievements in chemistry have been fully as impressive as those in physics.

The term molecule (from a Latin word meaning "small mass") originally meant the ultimate, indivisible unit of a substance, and in a sense it *is* an ultimate particle, because it cannot be broken down without losing its identity. To be sure, a molecule of sugar or of water can be divided into single atoms or groups, but then it is no longer sugar or water. Even a hydrogen molecule loses its characteristic chemical properties when it is broken down into its two component hydrogen atoms.

Early in the nineteenth century, chemists separated all matter into two great categories. They had long been aware (even in the days of the alchemists) that substances fell into two sharply distinct classes with respect to their response to heat. One group — for example, salt, lead, water — remained basically unchanged after being heated. Salt might glow red-hot when heated, lead might melt, water might vaporize — but when they were cooled back to the original temperature, they were restored to their original form, none the worse, apparently, for their experience. On the other hand, the second group of substances — for example, sugar, olive oil — were changed permanently by heat. Sugar became charred when heated and remained charred after it was cooled again; olive oil was vaporized and the vapor did not condense on cooling. Eventually the scientists noted that all the heat-resisting substances came from the inanimate world of the air, ocean, and soil, while the combustible substances came from the world of life, either from living matter directly or from dead remains. In 1807 the Swedish chemist Jöns Jakob Berzelius named the combustible substances "organic" (because they were derived, directly or indirectly, from living organisms) and all the rest "inorganic."

Early chemistry focused mainly on the inorganic substances. It
was the study of the behavior of inorganic gases that led to the development of the atomic theory. Once that theory was established,
it soon clarified the nature of inorganic molecules. Analysis showed
that inorganic molecules generally consisted of a small number of
different atoms in definite proportions. The water molecule contained two atoms of hydrogen and one of oxygen; the salt molecule
contained one atom of sodium and one of chlorine; sulfuric acid
contained two atoms of hydrogen, one of sulfur, and four of oxygen,
and so on.

When the chemists began to analyze organic substances, the picture seemed quite different. Two substances might have exactly the
same composition and yet show distinctly different properties. (For
instance, ethyl alcohol is composed of two carbon atoms, one oxygen atom, and six hydrogen atoms; so is dimethyl ether — yet one is
a liquid at room temperature while the other is a gas.) The organic
molecules contained many more atoms than the simple inorganic
ones, and there seemed to be no rhyme or reason in the way they
were combined. Organic compounds simply could not be explained
by the straightforward laws of chemistry that applied so beautifully
to inorganic substances.

Berzelius decided that the chemistry of life was something apart
which obeyed its own set of subtle rules. Only living tissue, he said,
could make an organic compound. His point of view came to be
called "vitalism."

Then in 1828 the German chemist Friedrich Wöhler, a student
of Berzelius, produced an organic substance in the laboratory! He
was heating a compound called ammonium cyanate, made from inorganic substances dug out of the soil. Wöhler was thunderstruck to
discover that, on being heated, this material turned into a white substance identical in properties with "urea," a component of urine.
According to Berzelius, only the living kidney could form urea, and

yet Wöhler had formed it from inorganic material merely by applying a little heat.

Wöhler repeated the experiment many times before he dared publish his discovery. When he finally did, Berzelius and others at first refused to believe it. But other chemists confirmed the results. Furthermore, they proceeded to synthesize many other organic compounds from inorganic precursors, and more and more it became clear that the same chemical laws applied to inorganic and organic molecules alike. Eventually the distinction between organic and inorganic substances was given a simple definition: all substances containing carbon (with the possible exceptions of a few simple compounds such as carbon dioxide) are called organic; the rest are inorganic.

Wöhler is considered the founder of organic chemistry. This is rather ironical, because his main interests were in metallurgy. Until his accidental discovery, he had not been in the least interested in organic substances.

To DEAL WITH THE COMPLEX NEW CHEMISTRY, chemists needed a simple shorthand for representing compounds, and fortunately Berzelius had already suggested a convenient, rational system of symbols. The elements were designated by abbreviations of their Latin names. Thus C would stand for carbon, O for oxygen, H for hydrogen, N for nitrogen, S for sulfur, P for phosphorus, and so on. Where two elements began with the same letter, a second letter was used to distinguish them: *e.g.*, Ca for calcium, Cl for chlorine, Cd for cadmium, Co for cobalt, Cr for chromium, and so on. In only a comparatively few cases are the Latin names (and initials) different from the English, thus: iron ("ferrum") is Fe; silver ("argentum") Ag, gold ("aurum") Au; copper ("cuprum") Cu; tin ("stannum") Sn; mercury ("hydrargyrum") Hg; antimony ("stibium") Sb; sodium ("natrium") Na; and potassium ("kalium") K.

With this system it is easy to symbolize the composition of a molecule. Water is written H_2O (thus indicating the molecule to consist of two hydrogen atoms and an oxygen atom); salt NaCl; sulfuric acid H_2SO_4, and so on. This is called the "empirical formula" of a compound; it tells what the compound is made of but says nothing about its structure, that is, the manner in which the atoms of the molecule are interconnected.

Baron Justus von Liebig, a coworker of Wöhler's, went on to work out the composition of a number of organic chemicals. He would carefully burn a small quantity of an organic substance and trap the gases formed (chiefly CO_2 and water vapor, H_2O) with appropriate chemicals. Then he would weigh the chemicals used to trap the combustion products to see how much weight had been added by the trapped products. From that weight he could determine the amount of carbon, hydrogen, and oxygen in the original substance. It was then an easy matter to calculate, from the atomic weights, the numbers of each type of atom in the molecule. In this way, for instance, he established that the molecule of ethyl alcohol had the formula C_2H_6O.

Liebig's method could not measure the nitrogen present in organic compounds, but the French chemist Jean Baptiste André Dumas devised a combustion method which did collect the gaseous nitrogen released from substances.

Unfortunately, determining the empirical formulas of organic compounds was not very helpful in elucidating their chemistry. In contrast to inorganic compounds, which usually consisted of two or three atoms or at most a dozen, the organic molecules were often huge. Liebig found that the formula of morphine was $C_{17}H_{19}O_3N$, and of strychnine, $C_{21}H_{22}O_2N_2$.

Chemists were pretty much at a loss to deal with such large molecules or make head or tail of their formulas. Several tried to group atoms into smaller collections called "radicals" and to work out theories to show that various compounds were made up of specific radicals in different numbers and combinations. Some of the systems were most ingenious, but none really explained anything. It was particularly difficult to explain why two compounds with the same empirical formula, such as ethyl alcohol and dimethyl ether (to which Berzelius gave the name "isomers"), should have different properties.

The chemists, lost in the jungle of organic chemistry, began to see daylight in the 1850's when they noted that each atom could combine with only a certain number of other atoms. For instance, the hydrogen atom apparently could attach itself to only one atom: it could form hydrogen chloride, HCl, but never HCl_2. Likewise chlorine and sodium could each take only a single partner, so they formed NaCl. An oxygen atom, on the other hand, could take two atoms as partners — for instance, H_2O. Nitrogen could take on three: *e.g.*, NH_3 (ammonia). And carbon could combine with as many as four: *e.g.*, CCl_4 (carbon tetrachloride).

In short, it looked as if each type of atom had a certain number of hooks by which it could hang on to other atoms. The English chemist Edward Frankland called these hooks "valence" bonds, from a Latin word meaning "power," to signify the combining powers of the elements.

The German chemist Friedrich August Kekulé saw that this information could be used to devise a "structural formula" for each compound. For instance, the methane (CH_4), ammonia (NH_3), and water (H_2O) molecules, respectively, could be pictured this way.

$$
\begin{array}{ccc}
\begin{array}{c} H \\ | \\ H-C-H \\ | \\ H \end{array}
&
\begin{array}{c} H \\ | \\ H-N-H \end{array}
&
H-O-H
\end{array}
$$

Further, some large molecules could be represented as chains of carbon atoms with hydrogen atoms attached along the sides. Thus butane (C_4H_{10}) would have the structure:

$$
\begin{array}{c}
H \quad\; H \quad\; H \quad\; H \\
|\quad\;\; |\quad\;\; |\quad\;\; | \\
H-C-C-C-C-H \\
|\quad\;\; |\quad\;\; |\quad\;\; | \\
H \quad\; H \quad\; H \quad\; H
\end{array}
$$

Oxygen or nitrogen might enter the chain in the following manner, picturing the compounds methyl alcohol (CH_4O) and methylamine (CH_5N), respectively:

$$
\begin{array}{cc}
\quad\ \ \text{H} & \qquad\text{H}\ \ \ \text{H} \\
\quad\ \ | & \qquad| \quad\ | \\
\text{H}-\text{C}-\text{O}-\text{H} & \quad\text{H}-\text{C}-\text{N}-\text{H} \\
\quad\ \ | & \qquad| \\
\quad\ \ \text{H} & \qquad\text{H}
\end{array}
$$

An atom possessing more than one hook, such as carbon with its four, need not use each of them for a different atom: it might form a double or triple bond with one of its neighbors, as in ethylene (C_2H_4) or acetylene (C_2H_2):

$$
\begin{array}{cc}
\text{H}\ \ \ \text{H} & \\
| \quad\ | & \\
\text{H}-\text{C}=\text{C}-\text{H} & \qquad \text{H}-\text{C}\equiv\text{C}-\text{H}
\end{array}
$$

Now it became easy to see how two molecules could have the same number of atoms of each element and still differ in properties. The two isomers must differ in the arrangement of those atoms. For instance, the structural formulas of ethyl alcohol and dimethyl ether, respectively, could be written:

$$
\begin{array}{cc}
\text{H}\ \ \ \text{H} & \qquad\text{H}\qquad\ \ \ \text{H} \\
| \quad\ | & \qquad|\qquad\quad\ | \\
\text{H}-\text{C}-\text{C}-\text{O}-\text{H} & \quad\text{H}-\text{C}-\text{O}-\text{C}-\text{H} \\
| \quad\ | & \qquad|\qquad\quad\ | \\
\text{H}\ \ \ \text{H} & \qquad\text{H}\qquad\ \ \ \text{H}
\end{array}
$$

The greater the number of atoms in a molecule, the greater the number of possible arrangements and the greater the number of isomers. For instance, heptane, a molecule made up of seven carbon atoms and 16 hydrogen atoms, can be arranged in nine different ways; in other words, there can be nine different heptanes, each with its own properties. These nine isomers resemble one another fairly closely, but it is only a family resemblance. Chemists have prepared all nine of these isomers but have never found a tenth — good evidence in favor of the Kekulé system.

A compound containing 40 carbon atoms and 82 hydrogen atoms could exist in some 62.5 trillion arrangements, or isomers. And organic molecules of this size are by no means uncommon.

Only carbon atoms can hook to one another to form long chains. Other atoms do well if they can form a chain as long as half a dozen or so. That is why inorganic molecules are usually simple, and why they rarely have isomers. The greater complexity of the organic molecule introduces so many possibilities of isomerism that hundreds of thousands of organic compounds are known, new ones are being formed daily, and a virtually limitless number await discovery.

Structural formulas are now universally used as indispensable guides to the nature of organic molecules. As a short cut, chemists often write the formula of a molecule in terms of the groups of atoms ("radicals") that make it up, such as the methyl (CH_3) and methylene (CH_2) radicals. Thus the formula for butane can be written as $CH_3CH_2CH_2CH_3$.

THE DETAILS OF STRUCTURE

IN THE LATTER HALF of the nineteenth century chemists discovered a particularly subtle kind of isomerism which was to prove very important in the chemistry of life. The discovery emerged from the oddly asymmetrical effect that certain organic compounds had on rays of light passing through them.

A cross-section of a ray of ordinary light would show that the waves of which it consists undulate in all planes — up and down, from side to side, and obliquely. Such light is called "unpolarized." But when light passes through a crystal of the transparent substance called Iceland spar, for instance, it is refracted in such a way that

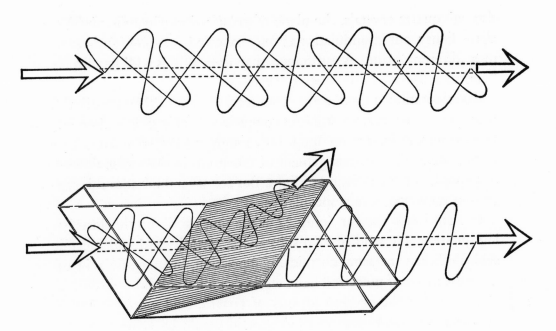

THE POLARIZATION OF LIGHT. *The waves of light normally oscillate in all planes (top). The Nicol prism (bottom) lets through the oscillations in only one plane, reflecting away the others. The transmitted light is plane-polarized.*

the light emerges "polarized." It is as if the array of atoms in the crystal allows only certain planes of undulation to pass through (just as the palings of a fence might allow a person moving sideways to squeeze through but not one coming up to them broadside on). There are devices, such as the "Nicol prism" and the more modern "Polaroid" lenses, that let light through in only one plane. (Reflected light often is partly plane-polarized; this is true of moonlight, for instance. Polaroid sunglasses screen out much of the troublesome reflections of sunlight, because the reflected light is partly polarized.)

Now early in the nineteenth century the French physicist Jean Baptiste Biot had discovered that when plane-polarized light passed through quartz crystals, the plane of polarization was twisted. That is, the light went in undulating in one plane and came out undulating in a different plane. A substance that does this is said to display "optical activity." Some quartz crystals twisted the plane clockwise ("dextrorotation") and some counterclockwise ("levorotation"). Biot found that certain organic compounds, such as camphor and tartaric acid, did the same thing. He thought it likely that some kind of asymmetry in the arrangement of the atoms in the molecules was responsible for the twisting of light. But for several decades this suggestion remained purely speculative.

In 1844 Louis Pasteur (only 22 at the time) took up this interesting question. He studied two substances: tartaric acid and racemic acid. Both had the same chemical composition, but tartaric acid rotated the plane of polarized light while racemic acid did not. Pasteur suspected that the crystals of salts of tartaric acid would prove to be asymmetric and those of racemic acid would be symmetric. Examining both sets of crystals under the microscope, he found to his surprise that both were asymmetric. But the racemate crystals had two versions of the asymmetry. Half of them were the same shape as those of the tartrate and the other half were mirror images. Half of the racemate crystals were left-handed and half right-handed, so to speak.

Pasteur painstakingly separated the left-handed racemate crystals from the right-handed and then dissolved each kind separately and sent light through each solution. Sure enough, the solution of the crystals possessing the same asymmetry as the tartrate crystals twisted the plane of polarized light just as the tartrate did, with the same specific rotation. Those crystals *were* tartrate. The other set twisted the plane of polarized light in the opposite direction, with the same amount of rotation. The reason the original racemate had shown no rotation of light, then, was that the two opposing tendencies canceled each other.

Pasteur next reconverted the two separated types of racemate salt to acid again by adding hydrogen ions to the respective solutions. (A salt, by the way, is a compound in which some hydrogen ions of the acid molecule are replaced by other positively charged ions, such as those of sodium or potassium.) He found that each of these racemic acids was now optically active — one rotating polarized light in the same direction as tartaric acid did (for it *was* tartaric acid) and the other in the opposite direction.

So far, so good, but where did the asymmetry lie? What was there about the two molecules that made them mirror images of each other? Pasteur could not say. And although Biot, who had suggested the existence of molecular asymmetry, lived to be 88, he did not live long enough to see his intuition vindicated.

It was in 1874, twelve years after Biot's death, that the answer was finally presented. Two young chemists, a 22-year-old Dutchman named Jacobus Hendricus Van't Hoff and a 27-year-old Frenchman named Joseph Achille Le Bel, independently advanced a new theory of the carbon valence bonds which explained how mirror-image molecules could be constructed.

Kekulé had drawn the four bonds of the carbon atom all in the same plane, not necessarily because this was the way they were actually arranged but because it was the convenient way of drawing them on a flat piece of paper. Van't Hoff and Le Bel now suggested a three-dimensional model in which the bonds were directed in two mutually perpendicular planes, two in one plane and two in the other. A good way to picture this is to imagine the carbon atom as standing on any three of its bonds as legs, in which case the fourth bond points vertically upward (see the drawing on the next page). If you suppose the carbon atom to be at the center of a tetrahedron (a four-sided geometrical figure with triangular sides), then the four bonds point to the four vertices of the figure. The model is therefore called the "tetrahedral carbon atom."

Now let us attach to these four bonds two hydrogen atoms, a chlorine atom, and a bromine atom. Regardless of which atom we attach to which bond, we will always come out with the same arrangement. Try it and see. With four toothpicks stuck into a marshmallow (the carbon atom) at the proper angles, you could represent the four bonds. Now suppose you stick two black olives (the hydro-

399

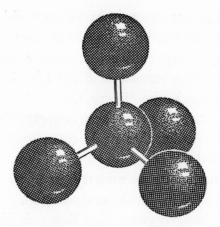

THE TETRAHEDRAL CARBON ATOM.

gen atoms), a green olive (chlorine), and a cherry (bromine) on the ends of the toothpicks in any order. Let us say that when you stand this on three legs with a black olive on the fourth pointing upward, the order on the three standing legs in the clockwise direction is black olive, green olive, cherry. You might now switch the green olive and cherry so that the order runs black olive, cherry, green olive. But all you need to do to see the same order as before is to turn the structure over so that the black olive serving as one of the supporting legs sticks up in the air and the one that was in the air rests on the table. Now the order of the standing legs again is black olive, green olive, cherry.

In other words, when at least two of the four atoms (or groups of atoms) attached to carbon's four bonds are identical, only one structural arrangement is possible. (Obviously this is true when three or all four of the attachments are identical.)

But when all four of the attached atoms (or groups of atoms) are different, the situation changes. Now two different structural arrangements are possible — one the mirror image of the other. For instance, suppose you stick a cherry on the upward leg and a black olive, a green olive, and a cocktail onion on the three standing legs. If you then switch the black olive and green olive so that the clockwise order runs green olive, black olive, onion, there is no way you can turn the structure to make the order come out black olive, green olive, onion, as it was before you made the switch. Thus with four different attachments you can always form two different structures, mirror images of each other. Try it and see.

Van't Hoff and Le Bel thus solved the mystery of the asymmetry of optically active substances. The mirror-image substances that rotated light in opposite directions were substances containing carbon atoms with four different atoms or groups of atoms attached to the bonds. One of the two possible arrangements of these four attachments rotated polarized light to the right; the other rotated it to the left.

More and more evidence beautifully supported Van't Hoff's and Le Bel's tetrahedral model of the carbon atom, and by 1885 their theory was universally accepted.

The two racemic acids that Pasteur had isolated were named *d*-tartaric acid (for "dextrorotatory") and *l*-tartaric acid (for "levorotatory"), and mirror-image structural formulas were written for them. But which was which? Which was actually the right-handed and which the left-handed compound? There was no way of telling at the time.

To provide chemists with a reference, or standard of comparison, for distinguishing right-handed and left-handed substances, Emil Fischer of Germany chose a simple compound called "glyceraldehyde," a relative of the sugars, which were among the most thoroughly studied of the optically active compounds. He arbitrarily assigned left-handedness to one form which he named *L*-glyceraldehyde, and right-handedness to its mirror image, named *D*-glyceraldehyde. His structural formulas for them were:

$$\begin{array}{ccc}
\text{CHO} & \qquad & \text{CHO} \\
| & & | \\
\text{H}-\text{C}-\text{OH} & & \text{HO}-\text{C}-\text{H} \\
| & & | \\
\text{CH}_2\text{OH} & & \text{CH}_2\text{OH}
\end{array}$$

D-glyceraldehyde   *L*-glyceraldehyde

Any compound that could be shown by appropriate chemical methods (rather careful ones) to have a structure related to *L*-glyceraldehyde would be considered in the "*L*-series" and would have the prefix "*L*" attached to its name, regardless of whether it was levorotatory or dextrorotatory as far as polarized light was concerned. As it turned out, the levorotatory form of tartaric acid was found to belong to the *D*-series instead of the *L*-series. (Nowadays, a compound that falls in the *D*-series structurally but rotates light to the left has its name prefixed by "*D*(–)." Similarly, we have "*D*(+)," "*L*(–)," and "*L*(+).")

This preoccupation with the minutiae of optical activity has turned out to be more than a matter of idle curiosity. As it happens, almost all the compounds occurring in living organisms contain asymmetric carbon atoms. And in every such case the organism makes use of only one of the two mirror-image forms of the compound. Furthermore, similar compounds generally fall in the same series. For instance, virtually all the simple sugars found in living tissue belongs to the *D*-series, while virtually all the amino acids (the building blocks of proteins) belong to the *L*-series.

In 1955 a chemist named J. M. Bijvoet finally determined what structure tended to rotate polarized light to the left, and vice versa. It turned out that Fischer had, by chance, guessed right in naming the levorotatory and dextrorotatory forms.

FOR SOME YEARS after the secure establishment of the Kekulé system of structural formulas, one compound with a rather simple molecule resisted formulation. That compound was benzene. Chemical evidence showed that it consisted of six carbon atoms and six hydrogen atoms. What happened to all the extra carbon bonds? (Six carbon atoms linked to one another by single bonds could hold 14 hydrogen atoms, and they do in the well-known compound called hexane, C_6H_{14}.) Evidently the carbon atoms in benzene were linked together by double or triple bonds. Thus benzene might have a structure such as $CH \equiv C - CH = CH - CH = CH_2$. But

the trouble was that the known compounds with that sort of structure had properties quite different from those of benzene. Besides,
all the chemical evidence seemed to indicate that the benzene molecule was very symmetrical, and six carbons and six hydrogens could
not be arranged in a chain in any reasonably symmetrical fashion.

In 1865 Kekulé himself came up with the answer. He related some
years later that the vision of the benzene molecule came to him while
he was riding on a bus and sunk in a reverie, half-asleep. In his dream,
chains of carbon atoms seemed to come alive and dance before his
eyes, and then suddenly one coiled on itself like a snake. Kekulé
awoke from his reverie with a start and could have cried "Eureka!"
He had the solution: the benzene molecule was a ring.

Kekulé suggested that the six carbon atoms of the molecule were
arranged as follows:

$$
\begin{array}{c}
H \\
| \\
H \\ \diagdown \\ C = C \diagdown \diagup H \\
| \qquad \| \\
H \diagup C = C \diagup \diagdown H \\
| \\
H
\end{array}
$$

Here at last was the required symmetry. It explained, among other
things, why the substitution of another atom for one of benzene's
hydrogen atoms always yielded just one unvarying product. Since
all the carbons in the ring were indistinguishable from one another
in structural terms, no matter where you made the substitution for
a hydrogen atom on the ring you would get the same product. Secondly, the ring structure showed that there were just three ways in
which you could replace two hydrogen atoms on the ring: you
could make the substitutions on two adjacent carbon atoms in the

ring, on two separated by a single skip, or on two separated by a double skip. Sure enough, it was found that just three doubly substituted benzene isomers could be made.

Kekulé's blueprint of the benzene molecule, however, presented an awkward question. Generally, compounds with double bonds are more reactive, which is to say more unstable, than those with only single bonds. It is as if the extra bond is ready and more than willing to desert the attachment to the carbon atom and form a new attachment. Double-bonded compounds readily add on hydrogen or other atoms and can even be broken down without much difficulty. But the benzene ring is extraordinarily stable — more stable than carbon chains with only single bonds. (In fact, it is so stable and common in organic matter that molecules containing benzene rings make up an entire class of organic compounds, called "aromatic," all the rest being lumped together as the "aliphatic" compounds.) The benzene molecule resists taking on more hydrogen atoms and is hard to break down.

The nineteenth-century organic chemists could find no explanation for this queer stability of the double bonds in the benzene molecule, and it disturbed them. The point may seem a small one, but the whole Kekulé system of structural formulas was endangered by the recalcitrance of the benzene molecule. The failure to explain this one conspicuous paradox made all the rest uncertain.

The closest approach to a solution prior to the twentieth century was that of the German chemist Johannes Thiele. In 1899 he suggested that when double bonds and single bonds alternated, the nearer ends of a pair of double bands somehow neutralized each other and cancelled each other's reactive nature. Consider, as an example, the compound "butadiene," which contains, in simplest form, the case of two double bonds separated by a single bond ("conjugated double bonds"). Now if two atoms are added to the compound, they add onto the end carbons, as shown in the formula on the next page. Such a view explained the non-reactivity of benzene, since the three double bonds of the benzene rings, being arranged in a ring, neutralize each other completely.

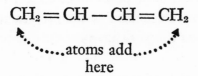

$$CH_2 = CH - CH = CH_2$$

............atoms add............
here

Some forty years later, a better answer was found in the new theory of chemical bonds that pictured atoms as linked together by sharing electrons.

The chemical bond, which Kekulé had drawn as a dash between atoms, came to be looked upon as representing a shared pair of electrons. Each atom that formed a combination with a partner shared one of its electrons with the partner, and the partner reciprocated by donating one of *its* electrons to the bond. Carbon, with four electrons in its outer shell, could form four attachments; hydrogen could donate its one electron to a bond with one other atom, and so on.

Now the question arose: how were the electrons shared? Well, obviously two carbon atoms share the pair of electrons between them equally, because each atom has an equal hold on electrons. On the other hand, in a combination such as H_2O, the oxygen atom, which has a stronger hold on electrons than a hydrogen atom does, takes possession of the greater share of the pair of electrons it has in common with each hydrogen atom. This means that the oxygen atom, by virtue of its excessive portion of electrons, has a slight excess of negative charge. By the same token, the hydrogen atom, suffering from an electron deficiency, has a slight excess of positive charge. A molecule containing an oxygen-hydrogen pair, such as water or ethyl alcohol, possesses a small concentration of negative charge in one part of the molecule and a small concentration of positive charge in another. It possesses two poles of charge, so to speak, and is called a "polar molecule."

This view of molecular structure was first proposed in 1912 by the Dutch chemist Peter Joseph Wilhelm Debye, who later pursued his research in the United States. He used an electric field to measure the amount of separation of poles of electric charge in a molecule. In such a field, polar molecules line themselves up with the negative ends pointing toward the positive pole and the positive ends toward the negative pole, and the ease with which this is done is the measure of the "dipole moment" of the molecule. By the early 1930's, measurements of dipole moments had become routine, and in 1936, for this and other work, Debye was awarded the Nobel Prize in chemistry.

The new picture explained a number of things that earlier views of molecular structure could not. For instance, it explained some anomalies of the boiling points of substances. In general, the greater the molecular weight, the higher the boiling point. But this rule is commonly broken. Water, with a molecular weight of only 18, boils at 100° C., whereas propane, with more than twice this molecular weight (44), boils at the much lower temperature of —42° C. Why should that be? The answer is that water is a polar molecule with a high dipole moment, while propane is "non-polar" — it has no poles of charge. Polar molecules tend to orient themselves with the negative pole of one molecule adjacent to the positive pole of its neighbor. The resulting electrostatic attraction between neighboring molecules makes it harder to tear the molecules apart, and so such substances have relatively high boiling points. This accounts for the fact that ethyl alcohol has a much higher boiling point (78° C.) than its isomer dimethyl ether, which boils at —24° C., although both substances have the same molecular weight (46). Ethyl alcohol has a large dipole moment and dimethyl ether only a small one. Water has a dipole moment even larger than that of ethyl alcohol.

When de Broglie and Schrödinger formulated the new view of electrons not as sharply defined particles but as packets of waves (see Chapter 7), the idea of the chemical bond underwent a further change. In 1939 the American chemist Linus Pauling presented a quantum-mechanical concept of molecular bonds in a book entitled *The Nature of the Chemical Bond*. His theory finally explained, among other things, the paradox of the stability of the benzene molecule.

Pauling pictured the electrons that form a bond as "resonating" between the atoms they join. He showed that under certain conditions it was necessary to view an electron as occupying any one of a number of positions (with varying probability). The electron might then best be presented as being spread out into a kind of blur, representing the weighted average of the individual probabilities of position. The more evenly the electron was spread out, the more stable was the compound. Such "resonance stabilization" was most likely to occur when the molecule possessed conjugated bonds in one plane and when the existence of symmetry allowed a number of alternative positions for the electron (viewed as a particle). The benzene ring is planar and symmetrical, and Pauling showed that the bonds of the ring were not really double and single in alternation but that the electrons were smeared out, so to speak, into an equal distribution which resulted in all the bonds being alike and all being stronger and less reactive than ordinary single bonds.

The resonance structures, though they explain chemical behavior satisfactorily, are difficult to present in simple symbolism on paper. Therefore the old Kekulé structures, although now understood to represent only approximations of the actual electronic situation, are still universally used and will undoubtedly continue to be used through the foreseeable future.

ORGANIC SYNTHESIS

AFTER WÖHLER HAD PRODUCED UREA from ammonium cyanate and chemists had formed various other organic molecules by trial and error, in the 1850's there came a chemist who went systematically and methodically about the business of synthesizing organic substances in the laboratory. He was the Frenchman Pierre Eugène Marcelin Berthelot. He prepared a number of simple organic compounds from still simpler inorganic compounds such as carbon monoxide. Berthelot built his simple organic compounds up through

407

increasing complexity until he finally had ethyl alcohol, among other things. It was "synthetic ethyl alcohol," to be sure, but absolutely indistinguishable from the "real thing," because it *was* the real thing.

Ethyl alcohol is an organic compound familiar to all and highly valued by most. No doubt the thought that the chemist could make ethyl alcohol from coal, air, and water (coal to supply the carbon, air the oxygen, and water the hydrogen), without the necessity of fruits or grain as a starting point, must have created enticing visions and endowed the chemist with a new kind of reputation as a miracle worker. At any rate, it put organic synthesis on the map.

For chemists, however, Berthelot did something even more significant. He began to form products that did not exist in nature. He took "glycerol," a component obtained from the breakdown of the fats of living organisms, and combined it with acids not known to occur naturally in fats (although they occurred naturally elsewhere). In this way he obtained fatty substances which were not quite like those that occurred in organisms.

Thus Berthelot laid the groundwork for a new kind of organic chemistry — the synthesis of molecules that nature could not supply. This meant the possible formation of a kind of "synthetic" which might be a substitute — perhaps an inferior substitute — for some natural compound that was hard or impossible to get in the needed quantity. But it also meant the possibility of "synthetics" which were improvements on anything in nature.

This notion of improving on nature in one fashion or another, rather than merely supplementing it, has grown to colossal proportions since Berthelot showed the way. The first fruits of the new outlook were in the field of dyes.

THE BEGINNINGS OF ORGANIC CHEMISTRY were in Germany. Wöhler and Liebig were both German, and other men of great ability followed them. Before the middle of the nineteenth century, there were no organic chemists in England even remotely comparable to those in Germany. In fact, English schools had so

low an opinion of chemistry that they taught the subject only during
the lunch recess, not expecting (or even perhaps desiring) many students to be interested. It is odd, therefore, that the first feat of synthesis with world-wide repercussions was actually carried through
in England.

It came about in this way. In 1845, when the Royal College of
Science in London finally decided to give a good course in chem-
istry, it imported a young German to do the teaching. He was
August Wilhelm von Hofmann, only 27 at the time, and he was
hired at the suggestion of Queen Victoria's husband, the Prince
Consort Albert (who was himself of German birth).

Hofmann was interested in a number of things, among them coal
tar, which he had worked with on the occasion of his first research
project under Liebig. Coal tar is a black, gummy material given off
by coal when it is heated strongly in the absence of air. The tar is
not an attractive material, but it is a valuable source of organic chemicals. In the 1840's, for instance, it served as a source of large quantities of reasonably pure benzene and of a nitrogen-containing compound called "aniline" which is related to benzene.

About ten years after he arrived in England, Hofmann came
across a 17-year-old boy studying chemistry at the college. His name
was William Henry Perkin. Hofmann had a keen eye for talent and
knew enthusiasm when he saw it. He took on the youngster as an
assistant and set him to work on coal-tar componds. Perkin's enthusiasm was tireless. He set up a laboratory in his home and worked
there as well as at school.

Hofmann, who was also interested in medical applications of
chemistry, mused aloud one day in 1856 on the possibility of synthesizing quinine, a natural substance used in the treatment of
malaria. Now those were the days before structural formulas had
come into their own. The only thing known about quinine was its
composition, and no one at the time had any idea of just how complicated its structure was.

Blissfully ignorant of its complexity, Perkin, at the age of 18,
tackled the problem of synthesizing quinine. He began with allyl-

toluidine, one of his coal-tar compounds. This molecule seemed to have about half the numbers of the various types of atoms that quinine had in its molecule. If he put two of these molecules together and added some missing oxygen atoms (say by mixing in some potassium dichromate, known to add oxygen atoms to chemicals with which it was mixed), Perkin thought he might get a molecule of quinine.

Naturally this approach got Perkin nowhere. He ended with a dirty, red-brown goo. Then he tried aniline in place of allyltoluidine and got a blackish goo. This time, though, it seemed to him that he caught a purplish glint in it. He added alcohol to the mess, and the colorless liquid turned a beautiful purple. At once Perkin thought of the possibility that he had discovered something that might be useful as a dye.

Dyes had always been greatly admired, and expensive, substances. There were only a handful of good dyes — dyes that stained fabric permanently and brilliantly and did not fade or wash out. There was dark blue indigo, from the indigo plant; there was "Tyrian purple," from a snail (so-called because ancient Tyre grew rich on its manufacture — in the later Roman Empire the royal children were born in a room with hangings dyed with Tyrian purple, whence the phrase "born to the purple"); and there was reddish alizarin, from the madder plant ("alizarin" came from Arabic words meaning "the juice"). To these inheritances from ancient and medieval times later dyers had added a few tropical dyes and inorganic pigments (today used chiefly in paints).

This explains Perkin's excitement about the possibility that his purple substance might be a dye. At the suggestion of a friend, he sent a sample to a firm in Scotland which was interested in dyes, and quickly the answer came back that the purple compound had good properties. Could it be supplied cheaply? Perkin proceeded to patent the dye (there was considerable argument as to whether an 18-year-old could obtain a patent, but eventually he obtained it), to quit school, and to go into business.

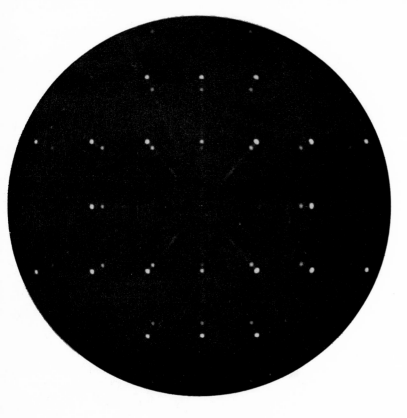

STRUCTURE OF UREA *is indicated in this* X-ray *diffraction picture. It shows the positions of the atoms in a single layer of a urea crystal, looking down at the layer.*

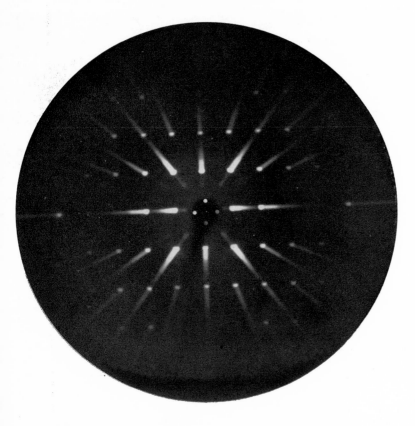

EIGHT-SIDED RING *of an organic compound called cyclo - octa - tetra - ene, shown by* X-ray *diffraction. The ring is similar to the benzene ring, with alternating single and double bonds, but it is eight-sided instead of six-sided.*

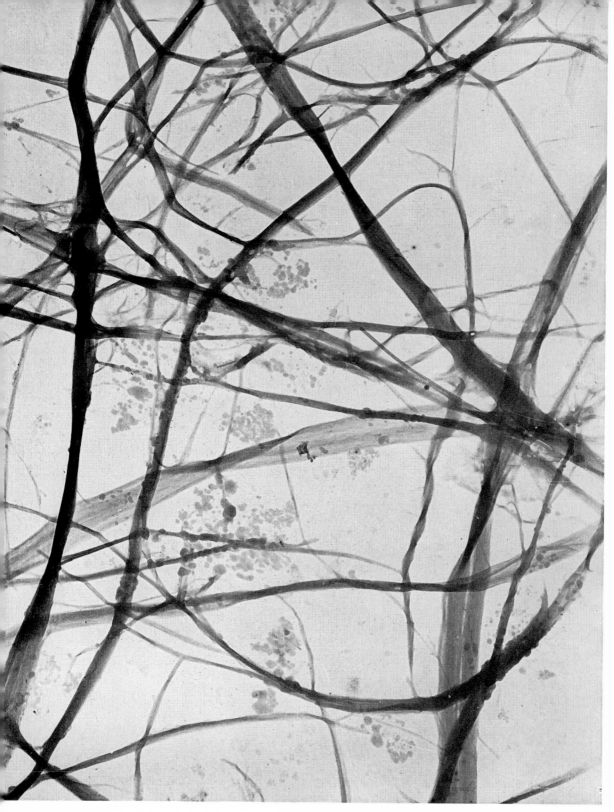

SILK FIBERS *as photographed with the electron microscope. The magnification here is about 6,000 times.*

COLLAGEN FIBERS *shown in an electron micrograph. Note how the fibers are collected in bundles.*

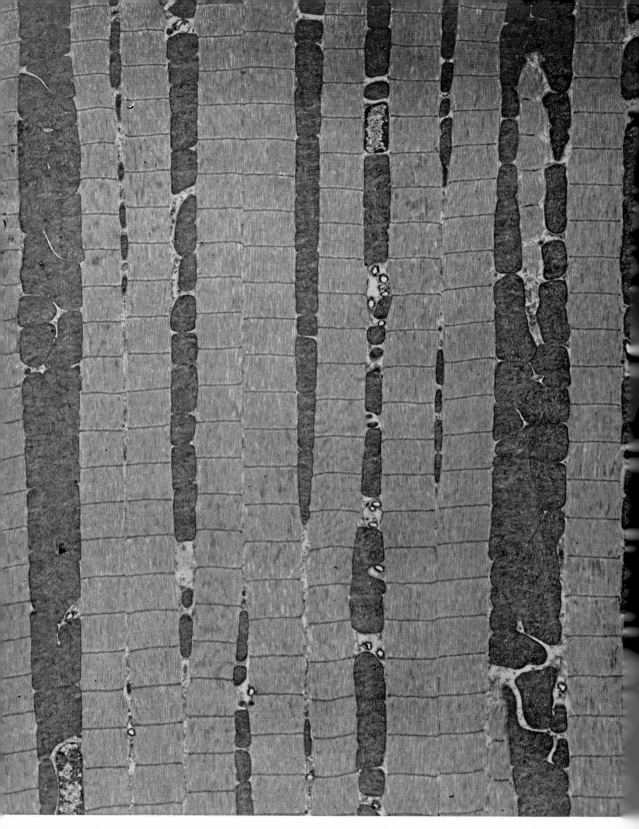

Section of a muscle fiber *under the electron microscope. The gray, striated structures are the fibrils, and the dark bodies are mitochondria, which contain enzymes that carry out energy-yielding reactions. This tissue is from the flight muscles of a beetle.*

His project wasn't easy. Perkin had to start from scratch, preparing his own starting materials from coal tar with equipment of his own design. Within six months, however, he was producing what he named "Aniline Purple" — a compound not found in nature and superior to any natural dye in its color range.

French dyers, who took to the new dye more quickly than did the more conservative English, named the color "mauve," from the mallow (Latin name "malva"), and the dye itself came to be known as "mauveine." Quickly it became the rage (the period being sometimes referred to as the "Mauve Decade"), and Perkin grew rich. At the age of 23 he was the world authority on dyes.

The dam had broken. A number of organic chemists, inspired by Perkin's astonishing success, went to work synthesizing dyes, and many succeeded. Hofmann himself turned to this new field, and in 1858 he synthesized a red-purple dye which was later given the name "magenta" by the French dyers (then, as now, arbiters of the world's fashions). The dye was named for the Italian city where the French defeated the Austrians in a battle in 1859.

Hofmann returned to Germany in 1865, carrying his new interest in dyes with him. He discovered a group of violet dyes still known as "Hofmann's violets."

Chemists also synthesized the natural dyestuffs in the laboratory. Karl Graebe of Germany and Perkin both synthesized alizarin in 1869 (Graebe applying for the patent one day sooner than Perkin), and in 1880 the German chemist Adolf von Baeyer worked out a method of synthesizing indigo. (For his work on dyes von Baeyer received the Nobel Prize in chemistry in 1905.)

Perkin retired from business in 1874, at the age of 35, and returned to his first love, research. By 1875 he had managed to synthesize coumarin (a naturally-occurring substance which has the pleasant odor of new-mown hay); this served as the beginning of the synthetic perfume industry.

Perkin alone could not maintain British supremacy against the great development of German organic chemistry, and by the turn

411

of the century "synthetics" had become virtually a German monopoly. But during World War I, Great Britain and the United States, shut off from the products of the German chemical laboratories, were forced to develop chemical industries of their own.

ACHIEVEMENTS IN SYNTHETIC ORGANIC CHEMISTRY could not have proceeded at anything better than a stumbling pace if chemists had had to depend upon fortunate accidents such as the one that had been seized upon by Perkin. Fortunately the structural formulas of Kekulé, presented three years after Perkin's discovery, made it possible to prepare blueprints, so to speak, of the organic molecule. No longer did chemists have to try to prepare quinine by sheer guesswork and hope; they had methods for attempting to scale the structural heights of the molecule step by step, with advance knowledge of where they were headed and what they might expect.

Chemists learned how to alter one group of atoms to another; to open up rings of atoms and to form rings from open chains; to split groups of atoms in two, and to add carbon atoms one by one to a chain. The specific method of doing a particular architectural task within the organic molecule is still often referred to by the name of the chemist who first described the details. For instance, Perkin discovered a method of adding a two-carbon atom group by heating certain substances with chemicals named acetic anhydride and sodium acetate. This is still called the "Perkin Reaction." Perkin's teacher, Hofmann, discovered that a ring of atoms which included a nitrogen could be treated with a substance called methyl iodide in the presence of silver compound in such a way that the ring was eventually broken and the nitrogen atom removed. This is the "Hofmann Degradation." In 1877 the French chemist Charles Friedel, working with the American chemist James Mason Crafts, discovered a way of attaching a short carbon chain to a benzene ring by the use of heat and aluminum chloride. This is now known as the "Friedel-Crafts Reaction."

In 1900 the French chemist Victor Grignard discovered that magnesium metal, properly used, could bring about a rather large variety of different joinings of carbon chains. For the development of these "Grignard Reactions" he shared in the Nobel Prize in chemistry in 1912. The French chemist Paul Sabatier, who shared it with him, had discovered (with J. B. Senderens) a method of using finely divided nickel to bring about the addition of hydrogen atoms in those places where a carbon chain possessed a double bond. This is the "Sabatier-Senderens Reduction."

In other words, by noting the changes in the structural formulas of substances subjected to a variety of chemicals and conditions, organic chemists worked out a slowly growing set of ground rules on how to change one compound into another at will. It wasn't easy. Every compound and every change had its own peculiarities and difficulties. But the main paths were blazed, and the skilled organic chemist found them clear signs toward progress in what had formerly seemed a jungle.

Knowledge of the manner in which particular groups of atoms behaved could also be used to work out the structure of unknown compounds. For instance, when simple alcohols react with metallic sodium and liberate hydrogen, only the hydrogen linked to an oxygen atom is released, not the hydrogens linked to carbon atoms. On the other hand, some organic compounds will take on hydrogen atoms under appropriate conditions while others will not. It turns out that compounds that add hydrogen generally possess double or triple bonds and add the hydrogen at those bonds. From such information a whole new type of chemical analysis of organic compounds arose; the nature of the atom-groupings was determined, rather than just the numbers and kinds of various atoms present. The liberation of hydrogen by the addition of sodium signified the presence of an oxygen-bound hydrogen atom in the compound; the acceptance of hydrogen meant the presence of double or triple bonds. If the molecule was too complicated for analysis as a whole, it could be broken down into simpler portions by well-defined

4 1 3

methods; the structures of the simpler portions could be worked out and the original molecule deduced from those.

Using the structural formula as a tool and guide, chemists could work out the structure of some useful naturally occurring organic compound (analysis) and then set about duplicating it or something like it in the laboratory (synthesis). One result was that something which was rare, expensive or difficult to obtain in nature might become cheaply available in quantity in the laboratory. Or, as in the case of the coal-tar dyes, the laboratory might create something that fulfilled a need better than did similar substances found in nature.

One startling case of a deliberate improvement on nature involves the drug cocaine. Cocaine is found in the leaves of the coca plant, which is native to Bolivia and Peru (but is now grown chiefly in Java). The South American Indians would chew coca leaves, finding it an antidote to fatigue and a source of happiness-sensation. The Scottish physician Sir Robert Christison introduced the plant to Europe, and eventually cocaine was isolated as the active principle. In 1884 the American physician Carl Koller discovered that cocaine could be used as a local anesthetic when added to the mucous membranes around the eye. Eye operations could then be performed without pain. Cocaine could also be used in dentistry, allowing teeth to be extracted without pain.

Anesthetics had come into general use about 40 years before that. The American surgeon Crawford Williamson Long in 1842 had used ether to put a patient to sleep during tooth extractions. In 1846 the American dentist William Thomas Green Morton conducted a surgical operation under ether at the Massachusetts General Hospital. Morton usually gets the credit for the discovery, because Long did not describe his feat in the medical journals until after Morton's public demonstration. In any case, doctors were quite aware that anesthesia had finally converted surgery from torture-chamber butchery to something that was at least humane and, with the addition of antiseptic conditions, even life-saving. For that reason any further advance in anesthesia was seized upon with great interest, and this included cocaine.

There were several drawbacks to cocaine. In the first place, it induced troublesome side-effects and could even kill patients sensitive to it. Secondly, it could bring about addiction and had to be used skimpily and with caution. (Cocaine is one of the dangerous "dopes." Up to 20 tons of it are produced illegally each year and sold with tremendous profits to a few and tremendous misery to many, despite world-wide efforts to stop the traffic.) Thirdly, the molecule is fragile, and heating cocaine to sterilize it of any bacteria leads to changes in the molecule that interfere with its anesthetic effects.

The structure of the cocaine molecule is rather complicated:

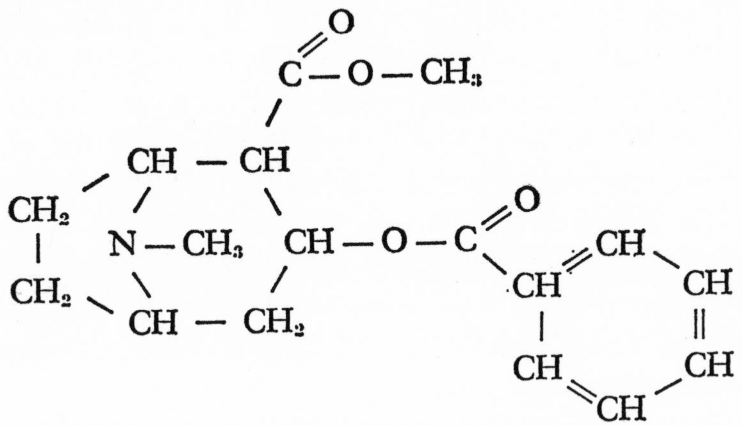

The double ring on the left is the fragile portion, and that is the difficult one to synthesize. (The synthesis of cocaine wasn't achieved until 1923, when the German chemist Richard Willstätter managed it.) However, it occurred to chemists that they might synthesize similar compounds in which the double ring was not closed. This would make the compound both easier to form and more stable. The synthetic substance might possess the anesthetic properties of cocaine, perhaps without the undesirable side-effects.

For some 20 years German chemists tackled the problem, turning out dozens of compounds, some of which were pretty good. The most successful modification was obtained in 1909, when a compound with the following formula was prepared:

$$CH_3 \diagup \begin{matrix} CH_2 \\ | \\ N \\ | \\ CH_2 \end{matrix} \diagdown \begin{matrix} CH_2 - O - C \diagup \diagdown \\ | \\ CH_2 \end{matrix} \begin{matrix} O \\ \diagup \\ CH \diagdown \\ CH \\ | \\ CH \diagdown \\ CH \end{matrix} \begin{matrix} CH \\ \diagup \\ CH \\ \| \\ CH \\ \diagdown \\ NH_2 \end{matrix}$$

Compare this with the formula for cocaine and you will see the similarity, and also the important fact that the double ring no longer exists. This simpler molecule — stable, easy to synthesize, with good anesthetic properties and very little in the way of side-effects — does not exist in nature. It is a "synthetic substitute" far better than the real thing. It is called "procaine," but is better known to the public by the trade-name Novocaine.

A series of other anesthetics have been synthesized in the half-century since, and, thanks to chemistry, doctors and dentists have an assortment of effective and safe pain-killers at hand.

MAN NOW HAS AT HIS DISPOSAL all sorts of synthetics of great potential use and misuse: explosives, poison gases, insecticides, weed-killers, antiseptics, disinfectants, detergents, drugs — almost no end of them, really. But synthesis is not merely the handmaiden of consumer needs. It can also be placed at the service of pure chemical research.

It often happens that a complex compound, produced either by living tissue or by the apparatus of the organic chemist, can only be assigned a tentative molecular structure, after all possible deductions have been drawn from the nature of the reactions it undergoes. In that case, a way out is to synthesize a compound by means of reactions designed to yield a molecular structure like the one that has been deduced. If the properties of the resulting compound are identical with the compound being investigated in the first place, the assigned structure becomes something in which a chemist can place his confidence.

An impressive case in point involves hemoglobin, the main component of the red blood cells and the pigment that gives the blood its red color. In 1831 the French chemist L. R. LeCanu split hemoglobin into two parts, of which the smaller portion, called "heme," made up 4 per cent of the mass of hemoglobin. Heme was found to have the empirical formula $C_{34}H_{32}O_4N_4Fe$. Compounds like heme were known to occur in other vitally important substances, both in the plant and animal kingdoms, and so the structure of the molecule was a matter of great moment to biochemists. For nearly a century after LeCanu's isolation of heme, however, all that could be done was to break it down into smaller molecules. The iron atom (Fe) was easily removed, and what was left then broke up into pieces roughly a quarter the size of the original molecule. These fragments were found to be "pyrroles" — molecules built on rings of five atoms, of which four are carbon and one nitrogen. Pyrrole itself has the following structure:

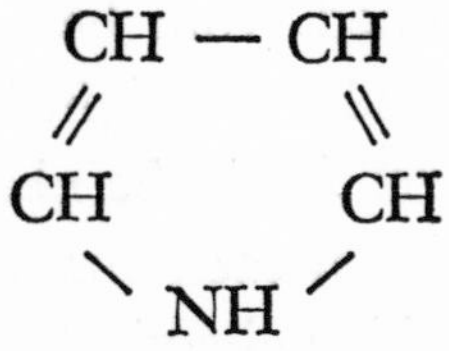

$$CH - CH$$

CH — CH
 //   \\
CH   CH
  \ NH /

The pyrroles actually obtained from heme possessed small groups of atoms containing one or two carbon atoms attached to the ring in place of one or more of the hydrogen atoms.

In the 1920's the German chemist Hans Fischer tackled the problem further. Since the pyrroles were one quarter the size of the original heme, he decided to try to combine four pyrroles and see what he got. What he finally succeeded in getting was a four-ring compound which he called "porphin" (from a Greek word meaning "purple," because of its purple color). Porphin would look like this:

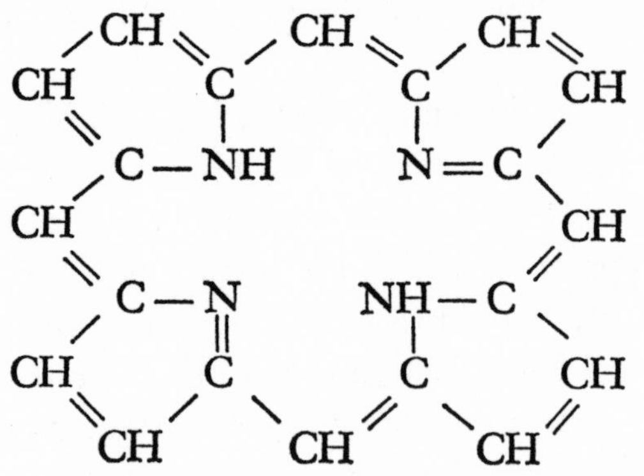

However, the pyrroles obtained from heme in the first place contained small "side-chains" attached to the ring. These remained in place when the pyrroles were joined to form porphin. The porphin with various side-chains attached make up a family of compounds called the "porphyrins." It was obvious to Fischer upon comparing the properties of heme with those of the porphyrins he had synthesized that heme (minus its iron atom) was a porphyrin. But which one? No fewer than 15 different compounds could be formed from the various pyrroles obtained from heme, according to Fischer's reasoning, and any one of those 15 might be heme itself.

A straightforward answer could be obtained by synthesizing all 15 and testing the properties of each one. Fischer put his students to work preparing, by painstaking chemical reactions that allowed only a particular structure to be built up, each of the 15 possibilities. As each different porphyrin was formed, he compared its properties with those of the natural porphyrin of heme.

In 1928 he discovered that the porphyrin numbered nine in his series was the one he was after. The natural variety of porphyrin is therefore called "porphyrin IX" to this day. It was a simple procedure to convert porphyrin IX to heme by adding iron. Chemists at last felt confident that they knew the structure of that important compound. Here is the structure of heme, as worked out by Fischer:

For this achievement Fischer was awarded the Nobel Prize in chemistry in 1930.

As a postscript to the story of organic chemical synthesis, let me say that in 1945 two young chemists at Harvard, Robert B. Woodward and William E. von Doering, succeeded in synthesizing quinine, the hopeless objective of Perkin that had started it all. And here, if you are curious, is the structural formula of quinine:

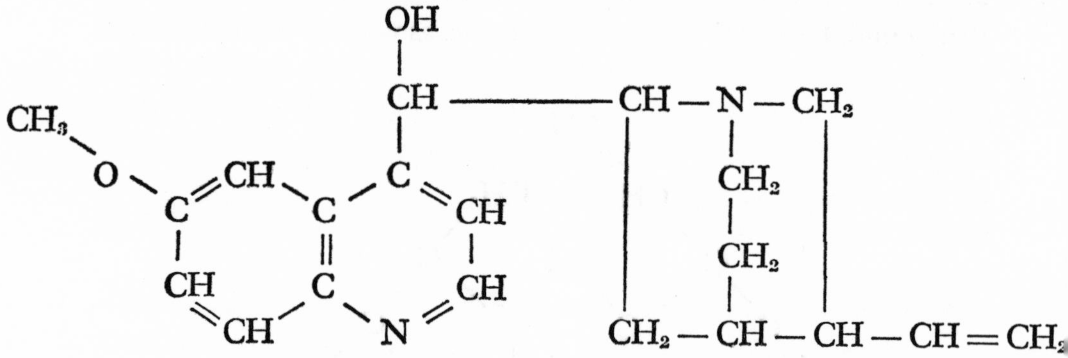

$$
\begin{array}{c}
\text{OH} \\
|\\
\text{CH} \longrightarrow \text{CH} - \text{N} - \text{CH}_2
\end{array}
$$

CH_3
O
$C = CH - C - C = CH$
$CH \quad C \quad CH$
$CH \quad C \quad CH$
$CH \quad N \quad CH$
$CH_2 \quad CH_2$
CH_2
$CH_2 - CH - CH - CH = CH_2$

POLYMERS AND PLASTICS

WHEN WE CONSIDER MOLECULES like those of heme and quinine, we are approaching a complexity with which even the
modern chemist can cope only with great difficulty. The synthesis
of such a compound requires so many steps and such a variety of
procedures that we can hardly expect to produce it in quantity without the help of some living organism (other than the chemist). This
is nothing about which to get an inferiority complex, however. Living tissue itself approaches the limit of its capacity at this level of
complexity. Few molecules in nature are more complex than heme
and quinine.

To be sure, there are natural substances composed of hundreds of
thousands, even millions, of atoms, but these are not really individual
molecules, constructed in one piece, so to speak. Rather, these large
molecules are built up of units strung together like beads in a neck-
lace. Living tissue usually synthesizes some small, fairly simple compound and then merely hooks the units together in chains. And that,
as we shall see, the chemist also is capable of doing.

In living tissue this union of small molecules ("condensation") is
usually accompanied by the over-all elimination of two hydrogen
atoms and an oxygen atom (which combine to form a water mole-

cule) at each point of junction. Invariably the process can be reversed (both in the body and in the test-tube): by the addition of water, the units of the chain can be loosened and separated. This reverse of condensation is called "hydrolysis," from Greek words meaning "loosening through water." In the test-tube the hydrolysis of these long chains can be hastened by a variety of methods, the most common being the addition of a certain amount of acid to the mixture.

The first investigation of the chemical structure of a large molecule dates back to 1812, when a Russian chemist, G. S. C. Kirchhoff, found that boiling starch with acid produced a sugar identical in properties with glucose, the sugar obtained from grapes. In 1819 the French chemist M. H. Braconnot also obtained glucose by boiling various plant products such as sawdust, linen, and bark, all of which contain a compound called "cellulose." It was easy to guess that both starch and cellulose were built of glucose units, but the details of the molecular structure of starch and cellulose had to await knowledge of the molecular structure of glucose. At first, before the days of structural formulas, all that was known of glucose was its empirical formula, $C_6H_{12}O_6$. This proportion suggested that there was one water molecule, H_2O, attached to each of the six carbon atoms. Hence glucose, and compounds similar to it in structure, were called "carbohydrates" ("watered carbon").

The structural formula of glucose was worked out in 1886 by the German chemist Heinrich Kiliani. He showed that its molecule consisted of a chain of six carbon atoms, to which hydrogen atoms and oxygen-hydrogen groups were separately attached. There were no intact water combinations anywhere in the molecule.

Over the next decade or so the German chemist Emil Fischer (no relation to the Hans Fischer of later porphyrin fame) studied glucose in detail and worked out the exact arrangement of the oxygen-hydrogen groups around the carbon atoms, four of which were asymmetric. There are 16 possible arrangements of these groups, and therefore 16 possible optical isomers, each with its own properties. Chemists have, indeed, made all 16, only a few of which actually occur in nature. It was as a result of his work on the optical activity of these sugars that Fischer suggested the establishment of the *L*-series and *D*-series of compounds. For putting carbohydrate chemistry on a firm structural foundation, Fischer received the Nobel Prize in chemistry in 1902.

Here are the structural formulas of glucose and of two other common sugars, fructose and galactose:

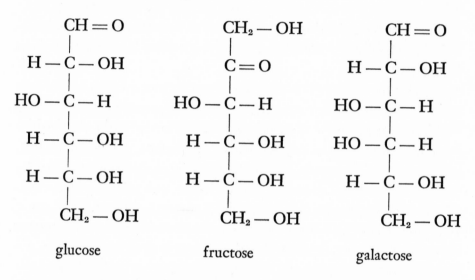

| glucose | fructose | galactose |

Once chemists knew the structure of the simple sugars, it was relatively easy to work out the manner in which they were built up into more complex compounds. For instance, a glucose molecule and a fructose can be condensed to the "double-sugar" sucrose — the sugar we use at the table. Glucose and galactose combine to form lactose, which occurs in nature only in milk.

There is no reason why such condensations cannot continue indefinitely, and in starch and cellulose they do. Each consists of long chains of glucose units, condensed in a particular pattern.

The details of the pattern are important, because although both compounds are built up of the same unit, they are profoundly different. Starch in one form or another forms the major portion of humanity's diet, while cellulose is completely inedible. The difference in the pattern of condensation, as painstakingly worked out by chemists, is analogous to the following: Suppose a glucose molecule is viewed as either right-side-up (when it may be symbolized as "u") or upside down (symbolized as "n"). The starch molecule can then be viewed as consisting of a string of glucose molecules after this fashion ".... uuuuuuuuu ....", while cellulose consists of ".... unununununu ...." The body's digestive juices possess the ability to hydrolyze the "uu" linkage of starch, breaking it up to glucose, which we can then absorb and from which we can obtain energy. Those same juices are helpless to touch the "un" linkage of cellulose, and any cellulose we ingest travels through the alimentary canal and out.

There are certain microorganisms that can digest cellulose, though none of the higher animals can. Some of these microorganisms live in the intestinal tracts of ruminants and termites, for instance. It is thanks to these small helpers that cows can live on grass, and termites live on wood. The microorganisms form glucose from cellulose in quantity, use what they need, and the host uses the overflow. The microorganisms supply the processed food, while the host supplies the raw material and the living quarters. This form of cooperation between two forms of life for mutual benefit is called "symbiosis," from Greek words meaning "life together."

CHRISTOPHER COLUMBUS discovered South American natives playing with balls of a hardened plant juice. Columbus and the other explorers who visited South America over the next two centuries were fascinated by these bouncy balls (obtained from the sap of trees in Brazil). Samples were brought back to Europe eventually as a curiosity. About 1770 the English chemist Joseph Priestley found that a lump of this bouncy material would rub out pencil marks, so he invented the uninspired name of "rubber," still the English word for the substance. The British call it "India rubber," because it came from the "Indies" (the original name of Columbus's new world).

People eventually found other uses for rubber. In 1823 a Scots-

423

man named Charles Macintosh patented garments made of a layer of rubber between two layers of cloth for use in rainy weather, and raincoats are still sometimes called "mackintoshes" (with an added "k").

The trouble with rubber as used in this way, however, was that in warm weather it became gummy and sticky, while in cold weather it was leathery and hard. A number of individuals tried to discover ways of treating rubber so as to remove these undesirable characteristics. Among them was an American named Charles Goodyear, who was innocent of chemistry but worked stubbornly along by trial and error. One day in 1839 he accidentally spilled a mixture of rubber and sulfur on a hot stove. He scraped it off as quickly as he could and found, to his amazement, that the heated rubber-sulfur mixture was dry even while it was still warm. He heated it and cooled it and found that he had a sample of rubber which did not turn gummy with heat or leathery with cold but remained soft and springy throughout.

This process of adding sulfur to rubber is now called "vulcanization" (after Vulcan, the Roman god of fire). Goodyear's discovery founded the rubber industry. It is sad to have to report that Goodyear himself never reaped a reward despite this multi-million dollar discovery. He spent his life fighting for patent rights and died deeply in debt.

Knowledge of the molecular structure of rubber dates back to 1879, when a French chemist, G. Bouchardat, heated rubber in the absence of air and obtained a liquid he called "isoprene." Its molecule turned out to be composed of five carbon atoms and eight hydrogen atoms, arranged as follows:

$$CH_2 = \overset{\displaystyle CH_3}{\overset{\displaystyle |}{C}} - CH = CH_2$$

A second type of plant juice ("latex"), obtained from certain trees in southeast Asia, yields a substance called "gutta percha." This

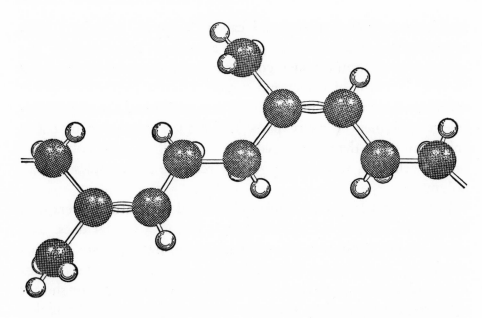

THE GUTTA PERCHA MOLECULE, *a portion of which is shown here, is made up of thousands of isoprene units. The first five carbon atoms at the left* (black balls), *and the eight hydrogen atoms bonded to them, make up an isoprene unit.*

lacks the elasticity of rubber, but when it is heated in the absence of air it, too, yields isoprene.

Both rubber and gutta percha are made up of thousands of isoprene units. As in the case of starch and cellulose, the difference between them lies in the pattern of linkage. In rubber the isoprene units are joined in the "...uuuuu..." fashion and in such a way that they form coils, which can straighten out when pulled, thus allowing stretching. In gutta percha the units join in the "...unun-ununun..." fashion, and these form chains that are straighter to begin with and therefore much less stretchable.

A simple sugar molecule such as glucose is a "monosaccharide" (Greek for "one sugar"); sucrose and lactose are "disaccharides" ("two sugars"); and starch and cellulose are "polysaccharides" ("many sugars"). Because two isoprene molecules join to form a

4 2 5

well-known type of compound called "terpene" (obtained from turpentine), rubber and gutta percha are called "polyterpenes."

The general term for such compounds was invented by Berzelius (a great inventor of names and symbols) as far back as 1830. He called the basic unit a "monomer" ("one part") and the large molecule a "polymer" ("many parts"). Polymers consisting of many units (say more than a hundred) are now called "high polymers." Starch, cellulose, rubber, and gutta percha are all examples of high polymers.

In 1913 two Japanese chemists discovered that natural fibers such as those of cellulose diffracted X-rays, just as a crystal does. The fibers are not crystals in the ordinary sense, but they are "microcrystalline" in character. That is, the long chains of units making up their molecules tend to run in parallel bundles for longer or shorter distances, here and there. Over the course of those parallel bundles, atoms are arranged in a repetitive order as they are in crystals, and X-rays striking those sections of the fiber are diffracted.

So polymers have come to be divided into two broad classes — crystalline and amorphous.

In a crystalline polymer such as cellulose, the strength of the individual chains is increased by the fact that parallel neighbors are joined together by chemical bonds. The resulting fibers have considerable tensile strength. Starch is crystalline, too, but far less so than is cellulose. It therefore lacks the strength of cellulose or its capacity for fiber formation.

Rubber is an amorphous polymer. Since the individual chains do not line up, cross-links do not occur. If heated, the various chains can vibrate independently and slide freely over and around one another. Consequently rubber or a rubber-like polymer will grow soft and sticky and eventually melt with heat. (Stretching rubber straightens the chains and introduces a certain amount of microcrystalline character. Stretched rubber has considerable tensile strength, therefore.) Cellulose and starch, in which the individual molecules are bound together here and there, cannot undergo the same independence of vibration, so there is no softening with heat. They remain

THE RUBBER MOLECULE *has a structure which is indicated here by a model of a portion of the molecule containing four isoprene units.*

VULCANIZATION OF RUBBER *in one of the early plants of the mid-nineteenth century. At the left is a pile of solid rubber tires.*

A MODERN PLASTICS PLANT. *This one produces vinyl resins.*

GLASSWARE *in an industrial chemical laboratory.*

stiff until the temperature is high enough to induce vibrations that shake the molecule apart so that charring and smoke emission take place.

At temperatures below the gummy, sticky stage, amorphous polymers are often soft and springy. At still lower temperatures, however, they become hard and leathery, even glassy. Raw rubber is dry and elastic only over a rather narrow temperature range: The addition of sulfur to the extent of 5 to 8 per cent provides flexible sulfur links from chain to chain, which reduce the independence of the chains and thus prevent gumminess at moderate heat. They also increase the free play between the chains at moderately low temperatures; therefore the rubber does not harden. The addition of greater amounts of sulfur, up to 30 to 50 per cent, will bind the chains so tightly that the rubber grows hard. It is then known as "hard rubber" or "ebonite."

(Even vulcanized rubber will turn glassy if the temperature is lowered sufficiently. An ordinary rubber ball, dipped in liquid air for a few moments, will shatter if thrown against a wall. This is a favorite demonstration in introductory chemistry courses.)

Various amorphous polymers show different physical properties at a given temperature. At room temperature natural rubber is elastic, various resins are glassy and solid, and chicle (from the sapodilla tree of South America) is soft and gummy (it is the chief ingredient of chewing gum).

ASIDE FROM OUR FOOD, which is mainly made up of high polymers (meat, starch, and so on), probably the one polymer that man has depended on longest is cellulose. It is the major component of wood, which has been indispensable as a fuel and a construction material. Wood's cellulose is also used to make paper. In the pure fibrous forms of cotton and linen, cellulose has been man's most important textile material. And the organic chemists of the mid-nineteenth century naturally turned to cellulose as a raw material for making other giant molecules.

One way of modifying cellulose is by attaching the "nitrate group" of atoms (a nitrogen atom and two oxygen atoms) to the oxygen-hydrogen combinations ("hydroxyl groups") in the glucose units. When this was done, by treating cellulose with a mixture of nitric acid and sulfuric acid, an explosive of until-then unparalleled ferocity was created. The explosive was discovered by accident in 1846 by a German-born Swiss chemist named Christian Friedrich Schönbein. He had spilled an acid mixture in the kitchen (where he was forbidden to experiment but where he had taken advantage of his wife's absence to do just that), and he snatched up his wife's cotton apron, so the story goes, to wipe up the mess. When he hung the apron over the fire to dry, it went poof, leaving nothing behind.

Schönbein recognized the potentialities at once, as can be told from the name he gave the compound, which in English translation is "guncotton." (It is also called "nitrocellulose.") Schönbein peddled the recipe to several governments. Ordinary gunpowder was so smoky that it blackened the gunners, fouled the cannon so that it had to be swabbed between shots, and raised such a pall of smoke that after the first volleys battles had to be fought by dead reckoning. War offices therefore leaped at the chance to use an explosive which was not only more powerful but also smokeless. Factories for the manufacture of guncotton began to spring up. And almost as fast as they sprang up, they blew up. Guncotton was too eager an explosive; it wouldn't wait for the cannon. By the early 1860's the abortive guncotton boom was over, figuratively as well as literally.

Later, however, methods were discovered for removing the small quantities of impurities that encouraged guncotton to explode. It then became reasonably safe to handle. It was mixed with nitroglycerine, and vaseline was added to the mixture to make it moldable into cords (the mixture was called "cordite"). That, finally, was a useful smokeless powder. The Spanish-American War of 1898 was the last of any consequence fought with ordinary gunpowder.

Nitroglycerine, by the way, was discovered in the same year as was guncotton. An Italian chemist named Ascanio Sobrero treated glycerol with a mixture of nitric acid and sulfuric acid and knew he had something when he nearly killed himself in the explosion that followed. Sobrero, lacking Schönbein's promotional impulses, felt nitroglycerine to be too dangerous a substance to deal with and virtually suppressed information about it. But within ten years a Swedish family, the Nobels, took to manufacturing it as a "blasting oil" for use in mining and construction work. After a series of accidents, including one which took the life of a member of the family, Alfred Bernhard Nobel, the brother of the victim, discovered a method of mixing nitroglycerine with an absorbent earth called "kieselguhr." A stick of this impregnated earth could be dropped, hammered, even burned, without explosion. When set off by a percussion cap, however, it displayed virtually all the shattering force of the pure nitroglycerine.

These sticks of "dynamite" eventually made it possible to carve the American West into railroads, mines, highways, and dams at a rate unprecedented in history. Dynamite, and other explosives he discovered, made a millionaire of the lonely and unpopular Nobel (who found himself, against his humanitarian will, regarded as a "merchant of death"). When he died in 1896, he left behind a fund out of which the famous Nobel Prizes were to be granted each year in five fields: chemistry, physics, medicine and physiology, literature, and peace.

But let's get back to modified cellulose. Clearly it was the addition of the nitrate group that made for explosiveness. In guncotton all of the available hydroxyl groups were nitrated. What if only some of them were nitrated? Would they not be less explosive? Actually such partly nitrated cellulose proved not to be explosive at all. However, it did burn very readily; the material was eventually named "pyroxylin" (from Greek words meaning "firewood").

Pyroxylin could be dissolved in mixtures of alcohol and ether. (This was discovered independently by the French scholar Louis Nicolas Ménard and an American medical student named J. Parkers Maynard — and an odd similarity in names that is.) When the alcohol and ether evaporated, the pyroxylin was left behind as a tough, transparent film, which was named "collodion." Its first use was as a coating over minor cuts and abrasions; it was called "new skin." However, the adventures of pyroxylin were only beginning. Much more lay ahead.

Pyroxylin itself is brittle in bulk. But the English chemist Alexander Parkes found that if it was dissolved in alcohol and ether and mixed with a substance such as camphor, the evaporation of the solvent left behind a hard solid that became soft and malleable when heated. It could then be modeled into some desired shape which it would retain when cooled and hardened. So nitrocellulose was transformed into the first artificial "plastic," and the year in which this was done was 1865. Camphor, which introduced the plastic properties into an otherwise brittle substance, was the first "plasticizer."

What brought plastics to the attention of the public and made it more than a chemical curiosity was its dramatic introduction into the billiard parlor. Billiard balls were then made from ivory, a commodity which could be obtained only over an elephant's dead body —a point that naturally produced problems. In the early 1860's a prize of $10,000 was offered for the best substitute for ivory that would fulfill the billiard ball's manifold requirements of hardness, elasticity, resistance to heat and moisture, lack of grain, and so on. The American inventor John Wesley Hyatt was one of those who went out for the prize. He didn't get far until he heard of Parkes' trick of plasticizing pyroxylin to a moldable material that would set as a hard solid. He set about working out improved methods of manufacturing the material, using less of the expensive alcohol and ether and more in the way of heat and pressure. By 1869 Hyatt was turning out cheap billiard balls of this material, which he called "celluloid." It won him the prize.

Celluloid turned out to have significance away from the pool table. It was versatile indeed. It could be molded at the temperature of boiling water; it could be cut, drilled, and sawed at lower temperatures; it was strong and hard in bulk but could also be produced in the form of thin flexible films that served for shirt-collars, baby-rattles, and so on. In the form of still thinner and more flexible films it could be used as a base for silver compounds in gelatin, and thus it became the first practical photographic film.

The one fault of celluloid was that, thanks to its nitrate groups, it had a tendency to burn with appalling quickness, particularly when in the form of thin film. It was the cause of a number of fire tragedies.

The substitution of acetate groups (CH_3COO^-) for nitrate groups led to the formation of another kind of modified cellulose called "cellulose acetate." Properly plasticized, this has properties as good or almost as good as those of celluloid, plus the saving grace of being much less apt to burn. Cellulose acetate came into use just before World War I, and after the war it completely replaced celluloid in the manufacture of photographic film and many other items.

WITHIN HALF A CENTURY after the development of celluloid, chemists emancipated themselves from dependence on cellulose as the base for plastics. As early as 1872, Baeyer (who was later to synthesize indigo) had noticed that when phenols and aldehydes were heated together, a gooey, resinous mass resulted. Since he was interested only in the small molecules he could isolate from the reaction, he ignored this mess at the bottom of the flask (as nineteenth-century organic chemists typically tended to do when goo fouled up their glassware). Thirty-seven years later the Belgian-born American chemist Leo Hendrik Baekeland, experimenting with formaldehyde, found that under certain conditions the reaction would yield a resin which on continued heating under pressure became first a soft solid, then a hard, insoluble substance. This resin could be molded while soft and then be allowed to set into a hard, permanent shape. Or, once hard, it could be powdered, poured into a mold and set into one piece by heat and pressure. Very complex forms could be cast easily and quickly. Furthermore, the product was inert and impervious to most environmental vicissitudes.

Baekeland named his product "Bakelite," after his own name. Bakelite belongs to the class of "thermosetting plastics," which, once they set on cooling, cannot be softened again by heating (though, of course, they can be destroyed by intense heat). Materials such as the cellulose derivatives, which can be softened again and again, are called "thermoplastics." Bakelite has numerous uses — as an insulator, an adhesive, a laminating agent, and so on. Although the oldest of the thermosetting plastics, it is still the most used.

Bakelite was the first production, in the laboratory, of a useful high polymer from small molecules. For the first time the chemist had taken over this particular task completely. It does not, of course, represent synthesis in the sense of the synthesis of heme or quinine, where chemists must place every last atom into just the proper position, almost one at a time. Instead, the production of high polymers requires merely that the small units of which they are composed be mixed under the proper conditions. A reaction is then set up in which the units form a chain automatically, without the specific point-to-point intervention of the chemist. The chemist can, however, alter the nature of the chain indirectly by varying the starting materials or the proportions among them, or by the addition of small quantities of acids, alkalies, or various substances that act as "catalysts" and tend to guide the precise nature of the reaction.

With the success of Bakelite, chemists naturally turned to other possible starting materials in search of more synthetic high polymers which might be useful plastics. And, as time went on, they succeeded many times over.

British chemists discovered in the 1930's, for instance, that the gas ethylene ($CH_2 = CH_2$), under heat and pressure, would form very long chains. One of the two bonds in the double bond between the carbon atoms opens up and attaches itself to a neighboring molecule. With this happening over and over again, the result is a long-chain molecule called "polythene" in England and "polyethylene" in the United States.

The paraffin-wax molecule is a long chain made up of the same units, but the molecule of polyethylene is even longer. Polyethylene is therefore like wax, but more so. It has the cloudy whiteness of wax, the slippery feel, the electrical insulating properties, the water-proofness, and the lightness (it is about the only plastic that will float on water). It is, however, at its best, much tougher than paraffin and much more flexible.

As it was first manufactured, polyethylene required dangerous pressures, and the product had a rather low melting point — just above the boiling point of water. It softened to uselessness at temperatures below the melting point. Apparently this was due to the fact that the carbon chain had branches which prevented the molecules from forming close-packed, crystalline arrays. In 1953 a German chemist named Karl Ziegler found a way to produce un-branched polyethylene chains, and without the need for high pressures. The result was a new variety of polyethylene, tougher and stronger than the old, and capable of withstanding boiling-water temperatures without softening too much. Ziegler accomplished this by using a new type of catalyst — a resin with ions of metals such as aluminum or titanium attached to negatively charged groups along the chain. Chemists have not been able to explain how these catalysts work, but they have proved effective in promoting various kinds of polymerizations.

The atomic-bomb project contributed another useful high polymer in the form of an odd relative of polyethylene. In the separation of uranium 235 from natural uranium, the nuclear physicists had to combine the uranium with fluorine in the gaseous compound uranium hexafluoride. Fluorine is the most active of all substances and will attack almost anything. Looking for lubricants and seals for their vessels that would be impervious to attack by fluorine, the physicists resorted to "fluorocarbons" — substances in which the carbon was already combined with fluorine (replacing hydrogen). Up to then the fluorocarbons had been only laboratory curiosities, but the chemistry of these interesting substances was now pursued intensively. Among the new fluorocarbons discovered was "tetrafluoroethylene" ($CF_2 = CF_2$), which is, as you see, ethylene with its four hydrogens replaced by four fluorines. It was bound to occur to someone that tetrafluoroethylene might polymerize as ethylene

433

itself did. After the war Du Pont chemists produced a long-chain polymer which was as monotonously $CF_2CF_2CF_2 \ldots$ as polyethylene was $CH_2CH_2CH_2. \ldots$ Its trade name is Teflon, the "tefl" being an abbreviation of "tetrafluoro-".

Teflon is like polyethylene, only more so. The carbon-fluorine bonds are stronger than the carbon-hydrogen bonds and offer even less of a loophole for the interference of the environment. Teflon is insoluble in everything, unwettable by anything, an extremely good electrical insulator, and considerably more resistant to heat than is even the new and improved polyethylene. However, it is also more expensive.

The fluorocarbons showed that organic chemistry, after more than a century of study, still offered new fields for development. And in 1958 another was opened up. This time a new class of substances was created by substituting the so-called cyanide group (CN) for hydrogen atoms on the carbon chain. These simple new compounds, called "cyano-carbons," have become agents for establishing some interesting new syntheses, and it seems reasonable to expect that useful developments will follow.

Plastic properties do not, of course, belong solely to the organic world. One of the most ancient of all plastic substances is glass. The large molecules of glass are essentially chains of silicon and oxygen atoms; that is, -Si-O-Si-O-Si-O-Si-, and so on indefinitely. Each silicon atom in the chain has two unoccupied bonds to which other groups can be added. The silicon atom, like the carbon atom, has four valence bonds. The silicon-silicon bond, however, is weaker than the carbon-carbon bond, so only short silicon chains can be formed, and those (in compounds called "silanes") are unstable. The silicon-oxygen bond is a strong one, however, and such chains are even more stable than those of carbon. In fact, since the earth's crust is half oxygen and a quarter silicon, the solid ground we stand upon may be viewed as essentially a silicon-oxygen chain.

Although the beauties and usefulness of glass (a kind of sand, made transparent) are infinite, it possesses the great disadvantage of being breakable. And in the process of breaking, it produces hard, sharp pieces which can be dangerous, even deadly. With untreated glass in the windshield of a car, a crash may convert the auto into a shrapnel bomb.

Plastics are the answer. Glass can be prepared as a double sheet between which is placed a thin layer of a transparent polymer, which hardens and acts as an adhesive. This is "safety glass," for when it is shattered, even into powder, each piece is held firmly in place by the polymer. None goes flying out on death-dealing missions. Originally collodion was used as the powder, but nowadays that has been replaced for the most part by polymers built of small molecules such as vinyl chloride. (Vinyl chloride is like ethylene, except that one of the hydrogen atoms is replaced by a chlorine atom.) The "vinyl resin" is not discolored by light, so safety glass can be trusted not to develop a yellowish cast with time.

Then there are the transparent plastics that can completely replace glass, at least in some applications. In the middle 1930's Du Pont polymerized a small molecule called methyl methacrylate and cast the polymer that resulted (a "polyacrylic plastic") into clear, transparent sheets. The trade names of these products are Plexiglas and Lucite. Such "organic glass" is lighter than ordinary glass, more easily molded, less brittle, and simply snaps instead of shattering when it does break. During World War II molded transparent plastic sheets came into important use as windows and transparent domes in airplanes, where lightness and non-brittleness are particularly useful. To be sure, the polyacrylic plastics have their disadvantages. They are affected by organic solvents, are more easily softened by heat than glass is, and are easily scratched. Polyacrylic plastics used in the windshields of cars, for instance, would quickly scratch under the impact of dust particles and become dangerously hazy. So glass is not likely ever to be replaced entirely. In fact, it is actually developing new versatility. Glass fibers have been spun into textile material which has all the flexibility of organic fibers and the inestimable further advantage of being absolutely fireproof.

In addition to glass substitutes, there is also what might be called a glass compromise. As I said, each silicon atom in a silicon-oxygen

4 3 5

chain has two spare bonds for attachment to other atoms. In glass those other atoms are oxygen atoms, but they need not be. What if carbon-containing groups are attached instead of oxygen? You will then have an inorganic chain with organic offshoots, so to speak — a compromise between an organic and an inorganic material. As long ago as 1908 the English chemist Frederic Stanley Kipping formed such compounds, and they have come to be known as "silicones."

During World War II, long-chain "silicone resins" came into prominence. Such silicones are essentially more resistant to heat than purely organic polymers. By varying the length of the chain and the nature of the side-chains, a list of desirable properties not possessed by glass itself can be obtained. For instance, some silicones are liquid at room temperature and change very little in viscosity over large ranges of temperature. (That is, they don't thin out with heat or thicken with cold.) This is a particularly useful property for a hydraulic fluid — the type of fluid used to lower landing-gear on airplanes, for instance. Other silicones form soft, putty-like sealers which do not harden or crack at the low temperatures of the strato-sphere and are remarkably water-repellent. Still other silicones serve as acid-resistant lubricants, and so on.

FIBERS

IN THE STORY OF ORGANIC SYNTHESIS, a particularly interesting chapter is that of the synthetic fibers. The first artificial fibers (like the first bulk plastics) were made from cellulose as the starting material. Naturally the chemists began with cellulose nitrate, since it was available in reasonable quantity. In 1884 Hilair Bernigaud de Chardonnet, a French chemist, dissolved cellulose nitrate in a mixture of alcohol and ether and forced the resulting thick solution through small holes. As the solution sprayed out, the alcohol and ether evaporated, leaving behind the cellulose nitrate as a thin thread of collodion. (This is essentially the manner in which spiders and

silkworms spin their threads. They eject a liquid through tiny ori-
fices and this becomes a solid fiber on exposure to air.) The cellulose-
nitrate fibers were too inflammable for use, but the nitrate groups
could be removed by appropriate chemical treatment, and the result
was a glossy cellulose thread which resembled silk.

De Chardonnet's process was expensive, of course, what with nitrate groups being first put on and then taken off, to say nothing of
the dangerous interlude while they were in place and of the fact
that the alcohol-ether mixture used as solvent was also dangerously
inflammable. In the early 1890's methods were discovered for dissolving cellulose itself. The English chemist Charles Frederick Cross,
for instance, dissolved it in carbon disulfide and formed a thread
from the resulting viscous solution (named "viscose"). The trouble
was that carbon disulfide is inflammable, toxic, and evil-smelling.
In 1903 a competing process employing acetic acid as part of the
solvent, and forming a substance called cellulose acetate, came into
use.

These artificial fibers were first called "artificial silk" but later
named "rayon," because their glossiness reflected rays of light. The
two chief varieties of rayon are usually distinguished as "viscose
rayon" and "acetate rayon."

Viscose, by the way, can be squirted through a slit to form a thin,
flexible, waterproof, transparent sheet — "cellophane." Some synthetic polymers also can be extruded through a slit for the same purpose. Vinyl resins, for instance, yielded the covering material known
as Saran.

IT WAS IN THE 1930's that the first completely synthetic fiber
was born.

Let me begin by saying a little about silk. Silk is an animal product,
made by certain caterpillars which are exacting in their requirements
for food and care. The fiber must be tediously unraveled from their
cocoons. For these reasons, silk is expensive and cannot be turned
out on a mass-production basis. It was first produced in China more

than 2,000 years ago, and the secret of its preparation was jealously guarded by the Chinese, so that it could be kept a lucrative monopoly for export. However, secrets cannot be kept forever, despite all security measures. The secret spread to Korea, Japan, and India. Ancient Rome received silk by the long overland route across Asia, with middlemen levying tolls every step of the way; thus the fiber was beyond the reach of anyone except the most wealthy. In 550 A.D. silkworm eggs were smuggled into Constantinople, and silk production in Europe got its start. Nevertheless, silk has always remained more or less a luxury item. Moreover, until recently there was no good substitute for it. Rayon could imitate its glossiness but not its sheerness or strength.

After World War I, when silk stockings became an indispensable item of the feminine wardrobe, the pressure for greater supplies of silk or of some adequate substitute became very strong. This was particularly true in the United States, where silk was used in greatest quantity and where relations with the chief supplier, Japan, were steadily deteriorating. Chemists dreamed of somehow making a fiber that could compare with it.

Silk is a protein. Its molecule is built up of monomers called "amino acids," which in turn contain "amino" ($-NH_2$) and "carboxyl" ($-COOH$) groups. The two groups are joined by a carbon atom between them; labeling the amino group a and the carboxyl group c, and symbolizing the intervening carbon by a hyphen, we can write an amino acid like this: a - c. These amino acids polymerize in head-to-tail fashion; that is, the amino group of one condenses with the carboxyl group of the next. Thus the structure of the silk molecule runs like this: ...a - c . a - c . a - c . a - c...

In the 1930's a Du Pont chemist named Wallace Hume Carothers inadvertently put together a structure of this sort. He was investigating molecules containing amine groups and carboxyl groups in the hope of discovering a good method of making them condense in such a way as to form molecules with large rings. (Such molecules are of importance in perfumery.) Instead, he found them condensing to form long-chain molecules.

Carothers lost little time in following up this lucky development. He eventually formed fibers from adipic acid and hexamethylene-diamine. The adipic acid molecule contains two carboxyl groups separated by four carbon atoms, so it can be symbolized as: c - - - - c. Hexamethylene diamine consists of two amine groups separated by six carbon atoms, thus: a - - - - - - a. When Carothers mixed the two substances together, they condensed to form a polymer like this:
. . . . a - - - - - - a . c - - - - c . a - - - - - - a . c - - - - c . a - - - - - - a . . . .
The points at which condensation took place had the a . c configuration found in silk, you will notice.

At first the fibers produced were not much good. They were too weak. Carothers decided the trouble lay in the presence of the water produced in the condensation process. The water set up a counteracting hydrolysis reaction which prevented polymerization from going very far. Carothers found a cure for this: he arranged to carry on the polymerization under low pressure, so that the water vaporized (and was easily removed by letting it condense on a cooled glass surface). Now the polymerization could continue indefinitely. It formed nice long, straight chains, and in 1935 Carothers finally had the basis for a dream fiber.

The polymer formed from adipic acid and hexamethylene diamine was melted and extruded through holes. It was then stretched so that the fibers would lie side by side in crystalline bundles. The result was a glossy, silk-like thread which could be used to weave a fabric as sheer and beautiful as silk, and even stronger. This first of the completely synthetic fibers was named "Nylon." Carothers did not live to see his discovery come to fruition, however. He died in 1937.

Du Pont announced the existence of the synthetic fiber in 1938 and began producing it commercially in 1939. During World War II the United States Armed Forces took all the production of nylon for parachutes and for a hundred other purposes. But after the war nylon completely replaced silk for hosiery; indeed, women's stockings are now called "nylons."

Nylon opened the way to the production of many other synthetic fibers. Acrylonitrile, or vinyl cyanide ($CH_2 = CHCN$), can be made to polymerize into a long chain like that of polyethylene but with cyanide groups (completely non-poisonous in this case) attached to every other carbon. The result, introduced in 1950, is "Orlon." If vinyl chloride ($CH_2 = CHCl$) is added, so that the eventual chain contains chlorine atoms as well as cyanide groups, "Dynel" results. Or the addition of acetate groups, through the use of vinyl acetate ($CH_2 = CHOOCCH_3$), produces "Acrilan."

The British in 1941 made a "polyester" fiber, in which the carboxyl group of one monomer condenses with the hydroxyl group of another. The result is the usual long chain of carbon atoms, broken in this case by the periodic insertion of an oxygen in the chain. The British call it "Terylene," but in the United States it has appeared under the name "Dacron."

These new synthetic fibers are more water-repellent than most of the natural fibers; thus they resist dampness and are not easily stained. They are not subject to destruction by moths or beetles. Some are crease-resistant and can be used to prepare "wash-and-wear" fabrics.

RUBBERS

IT IS A BIT STARTLING to realize that man has been riding on rubber wheels for only about a hundred years. For thousands of years he had ridden on wooden or metal rims. When Goodyear's discovery made vulcanized rubber available, it occurred to a number of people that rubber rather than metal might be wrapped around wheels. In 1845 a British engineer, Robert William Thomson, went this idea one better: he patented a device consisting of an inflated rubber tube which would fit over a wheel. By 1890 "tires" were routinely used for bicycles, and in 1895 they were placed on horseless carriages.

Amazingly enough, rubber, though a soft, relatively weak substance, proved to be much more resistant to abrasion than wood or metal. This durability, coupled with its shock-absorbing qualities and the air-cushioning idea, introduced man to unprecedented riding comfort.

As the automobile increased in importance, the demand for rubber for tires grew astronomical. You can judge the quantity of rubber in use for tires today when I tell you that, in the United States, they leave no less than 200,000 tons of abraded rubber on the highways each year, in spite of the relatively small amount abraded from the tires of an individual car.

The increasing demand for rubber introduced a certain insecurity in the war resources of many nations. As war was mechanized, armies and supplies began to move on rubber, and rubber could be obtained in significant quantity only from the Malayan peninsula, far removed from the "civilized" nations most apt to engage in "civilized" warfare. (The Malayan peninsula is not the natural habitat of the rubber tree. The tree was transplanted there, with great success, from Brazil, where the original rubber supply steadily diminished.) The supply of the United States was cut off at the beginning of its entry into World War II when the Japanese overran Malaya. American apprehensions in this respect were responsible for the fact that the very first object rationed during the war emergency, even before the attack on Pearl Harbor, was rubber tires.

Even in World War I, when mechanization was just beginning, Germany was hampered by being cut off from rubber supplies by Allied sea-power.

By the time of World War I, then, there was reason to consider the possibility of constructing a synthetic rubber. The natural starting material for such a synthetic rubber was isoprene, the building block of natural rubber. As far back as 1880, chemists had noted that isoprene, on standing, tended to become gummy and, if acidified, would set into a rubber-like material. Kaiser Wilhelm II eventually had the tires of his official automobile made of such material, as a kind of advertisement of Germany's chemical virtuosity.

However, there were two catches to the use of isoprene as the starting material for synthesizing rubber. First, the only major source of isoprene was rubber itself. Secondly, when isoprene polymerizes, it is most likely to do so in a completely random manner. The rubber chain possesses all the isoprene units oriented in the same fashion: - - - uuuuuuuuu - - -. The gutta percha chain has them oriented in strict alternation: - - - - unununununun - - - -. When isoprene is polymerized in the laboratory under ordinary conditions, however, the *u*'s and *n*'s are mixed randomly, forming a material which is neither rubber nor gutta percha. Lacking the flexibility and resilience of rubber, it is useless for automobile tires (except possibly for imperial automobiles used on state occasions).

Eventually catalysts like those that Ziegler introduced in 1953 for manufacturing polyethylene made it possible to polymerize isoprene to a product almost identical with natural rubber, but by that time many useful synthetic rubbers, very different chemically from natural rubber, had been developed.

THE FIRST EFFORTS, naturally, concentrated on attempts to form polymers from readily available compounds resembling isoprene. For instance, during World War I, under the pinch of the rubber famine, Germany made use of dimethylbutadiene:

$$CH_2 = C - C = CH_2$$
$$| \quad |$$
$$CH_3 \ CH_3$$

Dimethylbutadiene differs from isoprene (see page 424) only in containing a methyl group (CH_3) on both middle carbons of the four-carbon chain instead of on but one of them. The polymer built of dimethylbutadiene, called "methyl rubber," could be formed cheaply and in quantity. While it did not stand up well under stress, it was nonetheless the first of the usable synthetic rubbers.

About 1930 both Germany and the Soviet Union tried a new tack. They used as the monomer, butadiene, which has no methyl group at all:

$$CH_2 = CH - CH = CH_2$$

With sodium metal as a catalyst, they formed a polymer called "Buna" (from "*bu*tadiene" and *Na* for sodium).

Buna rubber was a synthetic rubber which could be considered satisfactory in a pinch. It was improved by the addition of other monomers, alternating with butadiene at intervals in the chain. The most successful addition was "styrene," a compound resembling ethylene but with a benzene ring attached to one of the carbon atoms. This product was called Buna S. Its properties were very similar to those of natural rubber and, in fact, thanks to it, Germany's armed forces suffered no serious rubber shortage in World War II. The Soviet Union also supplied itself with rubber in the same way. The raw materials could be obtained from coal or petroleum.

The United States was later in developing synthetic rubber in commercial quantities, perhaps because it was in no danger of a rubber famine before 1941. But after Pearl Harbor it took up synthetic rubber with a vengeance. It began to produce buna rubber and another type of synthetic rubber called "Neoprene," built up of "chloroprene":

$$CH_2 = C - CH = CH_2$$
$$|$$
$$Cl$$

This molecule, as you see, resembles isoprene except for the substitution of a chlorine atom for the methyl group.

The chlorine atoms, attached at intervals to the polymer chain, confer upon neoprene certain resistances that natural rubber does not have. For instance, it is more resistant to organic solvents such as gasoline: it doesn't soften and swell nearly as much as would natural rubber. Thus neoprene is actually preferable to rubber for such uses as gasoline hoses. Neoprene first clearly demonstrated that in the field of synthetic rubbers, as in many other fields, the product of the test-tube need not be a mere substitute for nature but could be an improvement.

Amorphous polymers with no chemical resemblance to natural rubber but with rubbery qualities have now been produced, and

443

they offer a whole constellation of desirable properties. Since they are not actually rubbers, they are called "elastomers" (an abbreviation of "elastic polymer"). This term was first suggested in 1939 by the American chemist Harry L. Fisher for all polymers with rubbery properties.

The first rubber-unlike elastomer had been discovered in 1918 by Fisher himself. This was a "polysulfide rubber;" its molecule was a chain composed of pairs of carbon atoms alternating with groups of four sulfur atoms. The substance was given the name "thiokol," the prefix coming from the Greek word for sulfur. The odor involved in its preparation held it in abeyance for a long time, but eventually it was put into commercial production.

Thiokol is even more resistant to the action of organic solvents than is neoprene. It is also more resistant to the action of oxygen, and especially of ozone, which ruins ordinary rubbers and rubber substitutes quickly. This makes thiokol useful in missiles and rockets, which have to pass through the ozone layer in the upper atmosphere. Thiokol has therefore become prominent as a "space-age polymer." More prosaically, thiokol has found employment as an outer coating on tire treads, because it is even more resistant to abrasion than rubber.

Elastomers have also been formed from acrylate monomers, fluorocarbons, and silicones. Here, as in almost every field he touches, the organic chemist works as an artist, using materials to create new forms and improve upon Nature.

CHAPTER

II

THE
PROTEINS

KEY MOLECULES OF LIFE

EARLY IN THEIR STUDY of living matter, chemists noticed that there was a large group of substances which behaved in a peculiar manner. Heating changed these substances from the liquid to the solid state, instead of the other way round. The white of eggs, a substance in milk (casein), and a component of the blood (globulin) were among the things that showed this property. In 1777 the French chemist Pierre Joseph Macquer put all the substances that coagulated on heating into a special class which he called "albuminous," after "albumen," the name the Roman encyclopedist Pliny had given to egg-white.

When the nineteenth-century organic chemists undertook to analyze the albuminous substances, they found these compounds con-

445

siderably more complicated than other organic molecules. In 1839 the Dutch chemist Gerardus Johannes Mulder worked out a basic formula, $C_{40}H_{62}O_{12}N_{10}$, which he thought the albuminous substances had in common. He believed that the various albuminous compounds were formed by the addition of small sulfur-containing groups or phosphorus-containing groups to this central formula. Mulder named his root formula "protein" (a word suggested to him by the inveterate word-coiner Berzelius), from a Greek word meaning "of first importance." Presumably the term was merely meant to signify that this core formula was of first importance in determining the structure of the albuminous substances, but as things turned out, it proved to be a very apt word for the substances themselves. The "proteins," as they came to be known, were soon found to be of key importance to life.

Within a decade after Mulder's work, the great German organic chemist Justus von Liebig had established that proteins were even more essential for life than carbohydrates or fats; they supplied not only carbon, hydrogen, and oxygen, but also nitrogen, sulfur, and often phosphorus, which were absent from fats and carbohydrates.

The attempts of Mulder and others to work out complete empirical formulas for proteins were doomed to failure at the time they were made. The protein molecule was far too complicated to be analyzed by the methods available. However, a start had already been made on another line of attack which was eventually to reveal not only the composition but also the structure of proteins. Chemists had begun to learn something about the building blocks of which they were made.

In 1820 M. H. Braconnot, having succeeded in breaking down cellulose into its glucose units by heating the cellulose in acid (see Chapter 10), decided to try the same treatment with gelatin, an albuminous substance. The treatment yielded a sweet, crystalline substance. Braconnot quickly learned it was not a sugar but a nitrogen-containing compound, for ammonia (NH_3) could be obtained from it. Nitrogen-containing substances are conventionally given names ending in "-ine," and the compound isolated by Braconnot is now called "glycine," from the Greek word for "sweet."

Shortly afterward Braconnot obtained a white, crystalline substance by heating muscle tissue with acid. He named this one "leucine," from the Greek word for "white."

Eventually, when the structural formulas of glycine and leucine were worked out, they were found to have a basic resemblance:

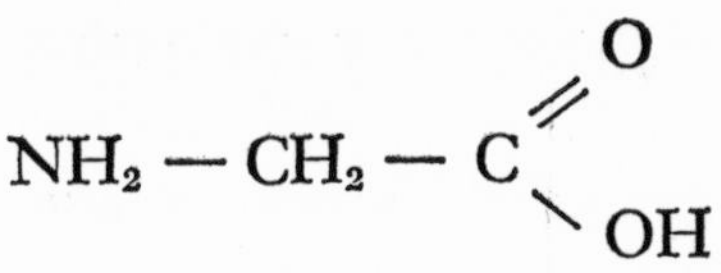

$$NH_2 - CH_2 - C \overset{O}{\underset{OH}{}}$$

glycine

$$\begin{array}{c} CH_3 \quad CH_3 \\ CH \\ | \\ CH_2 \\ | \\ NH_2 - CH - C \overset{O}{\underset{OH}{}} \end{array}$$

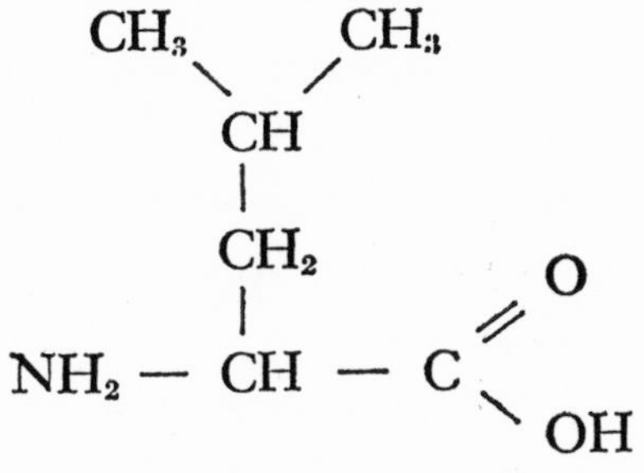

leucine

Each compound, as you see, has at its ends an amine group (NH_2) and a carboxyl group (COOH). Because the carboxyl group gives acid properties to any molecule that contains it, molecules of this kind were named "amino acids." Those that have the amine group and carboxyl group linked together by a single carbon atom between them, as both these molecules have, are called "alpha-amino acids."

As time went on, chemists isolated other amino acids from proteins. For instance, Liebig obtained one from the protein of milk (casein), which he called "tyrosine" (from the Greek word for "cheese;" casein itself comes from the Latin word for "cheese"). Its formula is shown at the top of the next page.

The differences among the various alpha-amino acids lie entirely in the nature of the atom grouping attached to that single carbon atom between the amine and the carboxyl groups. Glycine, the simplest of all the amino acids, has only a pair of hydrogen atoms

447

$$
\begin{array}{c}
OH \\
| \\
C \\
CH \qquad CH \\
| \qquad || \\
CH \qquad CH \\
C \\
| \\
CH_2 \\
| \\
NH_2 - CH - C \overset{O}{\underset{OH}{}}
\end{array}
$$

attached there. The others all possess a carbon-containing "side-chain" attached to that carbon atom.

I will give the formula of just one more amino acid, which will be useful in connection with matters to be discussed later in the chapter. It is "cystine," discovered in 1899 by the German chemist K. A. H. Mörner. This is a double-headed molecule containing two atoms of sulfur:

$$
\begin{array}{c}
NH_2 - CH - C \overset{O}{\underset{OH}{}} \\
| \\
CH_2 \\
| \\
S \\
| \\
S \\
| \\
CH_2 \\
| \\
NH_2 - CH - C \overset{O}{\underset{OH}{}}
\end{array}
$$

Actually, cystine had first been isolated in 1810 by the English chemist William Hyde Wollaston from a bladder stone, and it had been named cystine from the Greek word for "bladder" in consequence. What Mörner did was to show that this century-old compound was a component of protein as well as the substance in bladder stones.

Altogether, 19 important amino acids (that is, occurring in most proteins) have now been identified. The last of these was discovered in 1935 by the American chemist William C. Rose. It is unlikely that any other common ones remain to be found.

BY THE END OF THE NINETEENTH CENTURY, biochemists had become certain that proteins were giant molecules built up of amino acids, just as cellulose was constructed of glucose and rubber of isoprene units. But there was this important difference: whereas cellulose and rubber were made with just one kind of building block, a protein was built from a number of different amino acids. That meant that working out its structure would pose special and subtle problems.

The first problem was to find out just how the amino acids were joined together in the protein chain molecule. Emil Fischer made a start on the problem by linking amino acids together in chains, in such a way that the carboxyl group of one amino acid was always joined to the amine group of the next. In 1901 he achieved his first such condensation, linking one glycine molecule to another with the elimination of a molecule of water:

$$NH_2 - CH_2 - C \overset{O}{\underset{}{\diagup}} OH + NH_2 - CH_2 - C \overset{O}{\underset{OH}{\diagup}}$$

$$\downarrow$$

$$NH_2 - CH_2 - C \overset{O}{\underset{}{\diagup}} NH - CH_2 - C \overset{O}{\underset{OH}{\diagup}} + H_2O$$

449

This is the simplest condensation possible. By 1907 Fischer had synthesized a chain made up of 18 amino acids, 15 of them glycine and the remaining three leucine. This molecule did not show any of the obvious properties of proteins, but Fischer felt that was only because the chain was not long enough. He called his synthetic chains "peptides," from a Greek word meaning "digest," because he believed that proteins broke down into such groups when they were digested. Fischer named the combination of the carboxyl's carbon with the amine group a "peptide link."

In 1932 the German biochemist Max Bergmann (a pupil of Fischer's) devised a method of building up peptides from various amino acids. Using Bergmann's method, the American biochemist Joseph S. Fruton prepared peptides which could be broken down into smaller fragments by digestive juices. Since there was good reason to believe that digestive juices would hydrolyze (split by the addition of water) only one kind of molecular bond, this meant that the bond between the amino acids in the synthetic peptides must be of the same kind as the one joining amino acids in true proteins. The demonstration laid to rest any lingering doubts as to the validity of Fischer's peptide theory of protein structure.

Still, the synthetic peptides were very small and nothing like proteins in their properties. Fischer had made one consisting of 18 amino acids, as I have said; in 1916 the Swiss chemist Emil Abderhalden went him one better by preparing a peptide with 19 amino acids, but that held the record for 30 years. And chemists knew that such a peptide must be a tiny fragment indeed compared with the size of a protein molecule, because the molecular weights of proteins were enormous.

Consider, for instance, hemoglobin, a protein of the blood. Hemoglobin contains iron, making up just 0.34 per cent of the weight of the molecule. Chemical evidence indicates that the hemoglobin molecule has four atoms of iron, so the total molecular weight must be about 67,000; four atoms of iron, with a total weight of 4×55.85, would come to 0.34 per cent of such a molecular weight. Consequently hemoglobin must contain about 550 amino acids (the average molecular weight of the amino acids being about 120). Compare that with Abderhalden's puny 19. And hemoglobin is only an average-sized protein.

The best measurement of the molecular weights of proteins has been obtained by whirling them in a centrifuge, a spinning device that pushes particles outward from the center by centrifugal force.

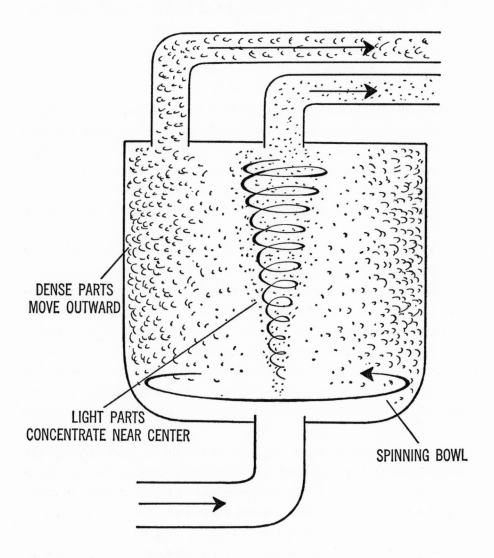

DENSE PARTS
MOVE OUTWARD

LIGHT PARTS
CONCENTRATE NEAR CENTER

SPINNING BOWL

PRINCIPLE OF THE CENTRIFUGE.

451

When the centrifugal force is more intense than the earth's gravitational force, particles suspended in a liquid will settle outward away from the center at a faster rate than they would settle downward under gravity. For instance, red blood corpuscles will settle out quickly in such a centrifuge, and fresh milk will separate into two fractions, the fatty cream and the denser skim-milk. These particular separations will take place slowly under ordinary gravitational forces, but centrifugation speeds them up.

Now protein molecules, though very large for molecules, are not heavy enough to settle out of solution under gravity; nor will they settle out rapidly in an ordinary centrifuge. But in the 1920's the Swedish chemist Theodor Svedberg developed an "ultracentrifuge" capable of separating molecules according to their weight. This high-speed device whirls at more than 10,000 revolutions per second and produces centrifugal forces hundreds of thousands of times as intense as the gravitational force at the earth's surface. For his contributions to the study of suspensions, Svedberg received the Nobel Prize in chemistry in 1926.

With the ultracentrifuge, chemists were able to determine the molecular weights of a number of proteins on the basis of their rate of sedimentation (measured in "svedbergs" in honor of the chemist). The smallest proteins turned out to have molecular weights of only a few thousand and to contain perhaps not more than 50 amino acids (still decidedly more than 19). Other proteins have molecular weights in the hundreds of thousands and even in the millions, which means that they must consist of thousands or tens of thousands of amino acids.

The protein chemists naturally were eager to synthesize long, "polypeptide" chains, with the hope of producing proteins. But the methods of Fischer and Bergmann allowed only one amino acid to be added at a time — a procedure which would have been completely impractical. What was needed was a procedure which would cause amino acids to join up in a kind of chain reaction, such as Baekeland had used in forming his high-polymer plastics. Then, in

1947, the Israeli chemist E. Katchalski and the Harvard chemist Robert Woodward (who had synthesized quinine) both reported success in producing polypeptides through chain-reaction polymerization. Their starting material was a slightly modified amino acid. (The modification eliminated itself neatly during the reaction.) From this beginning they built up synthetic polypeptides consisting of as many as a hundred or even a thousand amino acids.

These chains are usually composed of only one kind of amino acid, such as glycine or tyrosine, and are therefore called "polyglycine" or "polytyrosine." It is also possible, by beginning with a mixture of two modified amino acids, to form a polypeptide containing two different amino acids in the chain. But these synthetic constructions resemble only the very simplest kind of protein: for example, "fibroin," the protein in silk. The complex proteins are still beyond the reach of the synthesizer.

SOME PROTEINS are as fibrous and crystalline as cellulose or nylon. Examples are fibroin; keratin, the protein in hair and skin; and collagen, the protein in tendons and in connective tissue. The German physicist R. O. Herzog proved the crystallinity of these substances by showing that they diffracted X-rays. Another German physicist, R. Brill, analyzed the pattern of the diffraction and determined the spacing of the atoms in the polypeptide chain. The British biochemist W. T. Astbury and others in the 1930's obtained further information about the structure of the chain. They were able to calculate with reasonable precision the distances between adjacent atoms and the angles at which adjacent bonds were set. And they learned that the chain of fibroin was fully extended: that is, the atoms were in as nearly a straight line as the angles of the bonds between them would permit.

This full extension of the polypeptide chain is the simplest possible arrangement. It is called the "beta configuration." When hair is stretched, its keratin molecule, like that of fibroin, takes up this configuration. (If hair is moistened, it can be stretched up to three times its original length.) But in its ordinary, unstretched state, keratin shows a more complicated arrangement, called the "alpha configuration."

In 1951 Linus Pauling and Robert B. Corey of Caltech suggested that in the alpha-configuration, polypeptide chains took a helical shape (a shape like that of a spiral staircase). After building various models to see how the structure would arrange itself if all the bonds between atoms lay in their natural directions without strain, they decided that each turn of the helix would have the length of 3.6 amino acids, or 5.4 angstrom units.

Many lines of evidence, mostly derived from X-ray diffraction data, seem to support this helical theory. For instance, the Indian physicist G. N. Ramachandran has presented X-ray evidence indicating that collagen molecules are made up of three such helices, neatly intertwined like vines wound around one another.

What enables a helix to hold its structure? Pauling suggested that the agent is the so-called "hydrogen bond." As we have seen, when a hydrogen atom is attached to an oxygen or a nitrogen atom, the latter holds the major share of the bonding electrons, so that the hydrogen atom has a slight positive charge and the oxygen or nitrogen a slight negative charge. In the helix, it appears, a hydrogen atom periodically occurs close to an oxygen or nitrogen atom on the turn of the helix immediately above or below it. The slightly positive hydrogen atom is attracted to its slightly negative neighbor. This attraction is only one-twentieth of the force of an ordinary chemical bond, but it is strong enough to hold the helix in place. However, a pull on the fiber easily uncoils the helix and thereby stretches the fiber.

We have considered so far only the "backbone" of the protein molecule — the chain that runs ...CCNCCNCCNCCN.... But the various side-chains of the amino acids also play an important part in protein structure.

All the amino acids except glycine have at least one asymmetric carbon atom — the one between the carboxyl group and the amine group. Thus each could exist in two optically active isomers, one levorotatory and one dextrorotatory. The general formulas of the two isomers are:

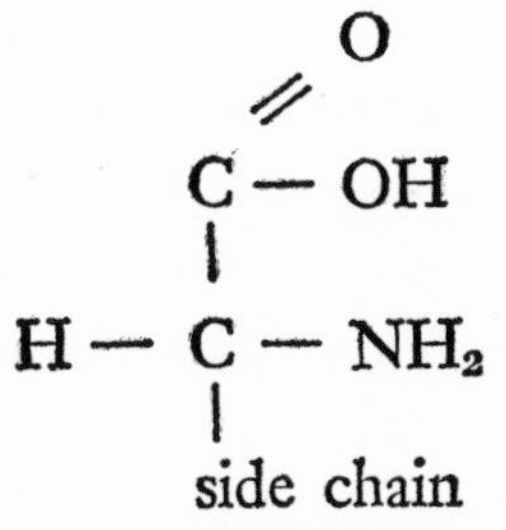

O
//
C — OH
|
H — C — NH₂
|
side chain

D-amino acid

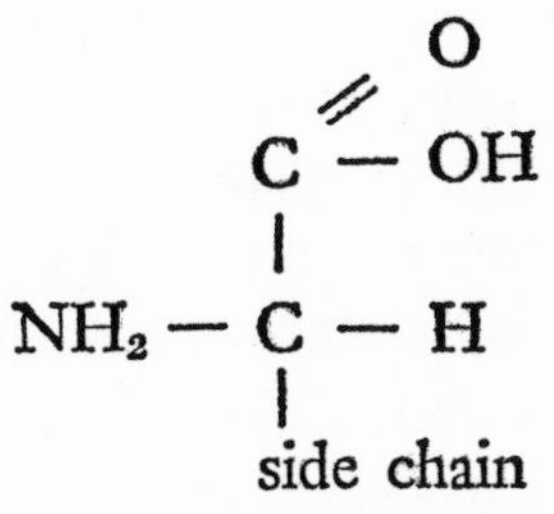

O
//
C — OH
|
NH₂ — C — H
|
side chain

L-amino acid

However, it seems quite certain from both chemical and X-ray analysis that polypeptide chains are made up only of *L*-amino acids. In this situation the side-chains stick out alternately on one side of the backbone and then the other. A chain composed of a mixture of both isomers would not be stable, because then, whenever an *L*-amino acid and a *D*-amino acid were next to each other, there would be two side-chains sticking out on the same side, which would crowd them and strain the bonds.

The side-chains are important factors in holding neighboring peptide chains together. Wherever a negatively charged side-chain on one chain is near a positively charged side-chain on its neighbor, they will form an electrostatic link. The side-chains also provide hydrogen bonds that can serve as links. And the double-headed amino acid cystine (see page 448) can insert one of its amine-carboxyl sequences in one chain and the other in the next. The two chains are then tied together by the two sulfur atoms in the side-chain (the "disulfide link"). The binding together of polypeptide chains accounts for the strength of protein fibers. It explains the remarkable toughness of

4 5 5

the apparently fragile spider web and the fact that keratin can form structures as hard as fingernails, tiger claws, alligator scales, and rhinoceros horns.

All this nicely describes the structure of protein fibers. What about proteins in solution? What sort of structure do they have?

They certainly possess a definite structure, but it is extremely delicate, for gentle heating or stirring of the solution or the addition of a bit of acid or alkali or any of a number of other environmental stresses will "denature" a dissolved protein. That is, the protein loses its ability to perform its natural functions, and many of its properties change. Furthermore, denaturation usually is irreversible: for instance, a hard-boiled egg can never be un-hard-boiled again.

It seems certain that denaturation involves the loss of some specific configuration of the polypeptide backbone. Just what feature of the structure is destroyed? The Harvard chemists Paul Doty and Elkan R. Blout tackled this problem. They used solutions of synthetic polypeptides, and they examined these by the technique called "light-scattering." Molecules in solution, if they are large enough, will scatter the light of a beam shined through the solution. Protein molecules are large enough to show light-scattering effects. Now the positions of the atoms forming a molecule determine the directions in which the light is scattered. Therefore light scattering can give the same kind of analytical information about atomic positions that X-ray diffraction does, and it works in solutions, whereas X-rays do not.

Doty and Blout found that their synthetic polypeptides in solution had a helical structure. By changing the acidity of the solution, they could break down the helices into randomly curved coils; by readjusting the acidity, they could restore the helices. And they showed that the conversion of the helices to random coils reduced the amount of the solution's optical activity. It was even possible to show which way a protein helix is twisted: it runs in the direction of a right-handed screw-thread.

All this suggests that the denaturation of a protein involves the destruction of its helical structure.

AMINO ACIDS IN THE CHAIN

WHAT I HAVE DESCRIBED so far represents an over-all look at the structure of the protein molecule — the general shape of the chain. Now what about the details of its construction? For instance, how many amino acids of each kind are there in a given protein molecule?

We might break down a protein molecule into its amino acids (by heating it with acid) and then determine how much of each amino acid is present in the mixture. Unfortunately, some of the amino acids resemble each other chemically so closely that it is almost impossible to get clear-cut separations by ordinary chemical methods. The amino acids can, however, be separated neatly by chromatography. In 1941 the British biochemists A. J. P. Martin and R. L. M. Synge pioneered the application of chromatography to this purpose. They introduced the use of starch as the packing material in the column. In 1948 the American biochemists Stanford Moore and William H. Stein brought the starch chromatography of amino acids to a high pitch of efficiency.

After the mixture of amino acids has been poured into the starch column and all the amino acids have attached themselves to the starch particles, they are washed slowly down the column with fresh solvent. Each amino acid moves down the column at its own characteristic rate. As each emerges at the bottom separately, the drops of solution of that amino acid are caught in a container. The solution in each container is then treated with a chemical that turns the amino acid into a colored product. The intensity of the color is a measure of the amount of the particular amino acid present. This color intensity is measured by an instrument called a "spectrophotometer," which indicates the intensity by means of the amount of light of that particular wavelength that is absorbed.

(Spectrophotometers can be used for other kinds of chemical analysis, by the way. If light of successively increased wavelength

4 5 7

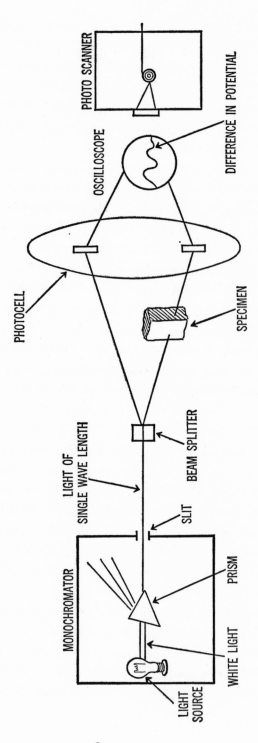

A SPECTROPHOTOMETER. *The beam of light is split into two so that one beam passes through the specimen being analyzed and the other goes directly to the photocell. Since the weakened beam that has passed through the specimen liberates fewer electrons in the photocell than the unabsorbed beam does, the two beams create a difference in potential which measures the amount of absorption of the light by the specimen.*

is sent through a solution, the amount of absorption changes smoothly, rising to maxima at some wavelengths and falling to minima at
others. The result is an "absorption spectrum." A given atomic
group has its own characteristic absorption peak or peaks. This is
especially true in the region of the infrared. Since World War II
the "infrared spectrophotometer" has come into increasing use for
analysis of the structure of complex compounds.)

The measurement of amino acids with starch chromatography is
quite satisfactory, but by the time this procedure was developed,
Martin and Synge had worked out a simpler method of chromatography. It is called "paper chromatography." The amino acids are
separated on a sheet of filter paper (an absorbent paper made of particularly pure cellulose). A drop or two of a mixture of amino acids
is deposited near a corner of the sheet, and this edge of the sheet is
then dipped into a solvent, such as butyl alcohol. The solvent slowly
creeps up the paper through capillary action. (Dip the corner of a
blotter into water and see it happen yourself.) The solvent picks up
the molecules in the deposited drop and sweeps them along the paper. As in column chromatography, each amino acid moves up the
paper at a characteristic rate. After a while the amino acids in the
mixture become separated in a series of spots on the sheet. Some of
the spots may contain two or three amino acids. To separate these,
the filter paper, after being dried, is turned around 90 degrees from
its first position and the new edge is now dipped into a second solvent which will deposit the components in separate spots. Finally,
the whole sheet, after once again being dried, is washed with chemicals that cause the patches of amino acids to show up as colored or
darkened spots. It is a dramatic thing to see: all the amino acids,
originally mixed in a single solution, are now spread out over the
length and breadth of the paper in a mosaic of colorful spots. Experienced biochemists can identify each amino acid by the spot it
occupies, and thus they can read the composition of the original
protein almost at a glance. By dissolving a spot they can even measure how much of that particular amino acid was present in the
protein.

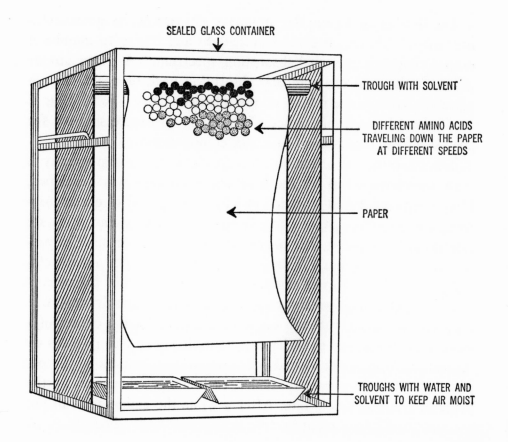

SEALED GLASS CONTAINER

TROUGH WITH SOLVENT

DIFFERENT AMINO ACIDS
TRAVELING DOWN THE PAPER
AT DIFFERENT SPEEDS

PAPER

TROUGHS WITH WATER AND
SOLVENT TO KEEP AIR MOIST

PAPER CHROMATOGRAPHY.

Chromatographic analysis yielded accurate estimates of the amino-acid contents of various proteins. For instance, the molecule of a blood protein called "serum albumin" was found to contain 15 glycines, 45 valines, 58 leucines, 9 isoleucines, 31 prolines, 33 phenylalanines, 18 tyrosines, 1 tryptophan, 22 serines, 27 threonines, 16 cystines, 4 cysteines, 6 methionines, 25 arginines, 16 histidines, 58 lysines, 46 aspartic acids, and 80 glutamic acids — a total of 526 amino acids of 18 different types built into a protein with a molecular weight of about 69,000. (In addition to these 18, there is one other common amino acid — alanine.)

The biochemist Erwin Brand suggested a system of symbols for the amino acids which is now in general use. To avoid confusion with the symbols of the elements, he designated each amino acid by the first three letters of its name, instead of just the initial. There are a few special variations: cystine is symbolized CyS, to show that its two halves are usually incorporated in two different chains; cysteine is CySH, to distinguish it from cystine; and isoleucine is Ileu rather than Iso, for "iso" is the prefix of many chemical names.

In this shorthand, the formula of serum albumin can be written: $Gly_{15}Val_{45}Leu_{58}Ileu_9Pro_{31}Phe_{33}Tyr_{18}Try_1Ser_{22}Thr_{27}CyS_{32}CySH_4-Met_6Arg_{25}His_{16}Lys_{58}Asp_{46}Glu_{80}$. This is, you will admit, more concise, though certainly nothing to be rattled off.

DISCOVERING THE EMPIRICAL FORMULA of a protein was only half the battle — in fact, much less than half. Now came the far more difficult task of deciphering the structure of a protein molecule. There was every reason to believe that the properties of every protein depended on exactly how — in what order — all those amino acids are arranged in the molecular chain. This presents the biochemist with a staggering problem. The number of possible arrangements in which 19 amino acids can be placed in a chain (even assuming that only one of each is used) comes to nearly 120,000,000,000,000,000. If you find this hard to believe, try multiplying out 19 times 18 times 17 times 16, etc., which is the way the number of possible arrangements is calculated. And if you don't trust the arithmetic, get 19 checkers, number them 1 to 19, and see in how many different orders you can arrange them. I guarantee you won't continue the game long.

When you have a protein of the size of serum albumin, composed of more than 500 amino acids, the number of possible arrangements comes out to something like 10^{600} — that is, 1 followed by 600 zeroes. This is a completely fantastic number — far more than the number of subatomic particles in the entire known Universe, or, for that matter, far more than the Universe could hold if it were packed solid with such particles.

Nevertheless, although the task of finding out which one of all those possible arrangements a serum albumin molecule actually possesses may seem hopeless, this sort of problem has actually been tackled and solved.

In 1945 the British biochemist Frederick Sanger set out to determine the order of amino acids in a peptide chain. He started by trying to identify the amino acid at one end of the chain — the amine end.

Obviously the amine group of this end amino acid (called the "N-terminal amino acid") is free: that is, not attached to another amino acid. Sanger made use of a reagent called DNP, which combines with a free amine group but not with an amine group that is bound to a carboxyl group. With DNP he could label the N-terminal amino acid, and since the bond holding this combination together is stronger than those linking the amino acids in the chain, he could break up the chain into its individual amino acids and isolate the one with the DNP label. As it happens, DNP has a yellow color, so this particular amino acid, with its DNP label, shows up as a yellow spot on a paper chromatogram.

Thus Sanger was able to separate and identify the amino acid at the amine end of a peptide chain. In a similar way, he identified the amino acid at the other end of the chain — the one with a free carboxyl group, called the "C-terminal amino acid." He was also able to peel off a few other amino acids one by one and identify the "end sequence" of a peptide chain in several cases.

Now Sanger proceeded to attack the peptide chain all along its length. He worked with insulin, a protein which has the merit of being very important to the functioning of the body and which has the added virtue of being rather small for a protein, having a molecular weight of only 6,000 in its simplest form. DNP treatment showed this molecule to consist of two peptide chains, for it contained two different N-terminal amino acids. The two chains were joined together by cystine molecules. By a chemical treatment that broke the bond between the two sulfur atoms in the cystine, Sanger split the insulin molecule into its two peptide chains, each intact. One of the chains had glycine as the N-terminal amino acid (call it the G-chain), and the other had phenylalanine as the N-terminal amino acid (the P-chain.) The two could now be worked on separately.

Sanger and a co-worker, Hans Tuppy, first broke up the chains into individual amino acids and identified the 21 amino acids that made up the G-chain and the 30 that composed the P-chain. Next, to learn some of the sequences, they broke the chains not into individual amino acids but into fragments consisting of two or three. This could be done by partial hydrolysis, breaking only the weaker bonds in the chain, or by attacking the insulin with certain digestive substances which broke only certain links between amino acids and left the others intact.

By these devices Sanger and Tuppy broke each of the chains into a large number of different pieces. For instance, the P-chain yielded 48 different fragments, 22 of which were made up of two amino acids (dipeptides), 14 of three, and 12 of more than three.

The various small peptides, after being separated, could then be broken down into their individual amino acids by paper chromatography. Now the investigators were ready to determine the order of the amino acids in these fragments. Suppose they had a dipeptide consisting of valine and isoleucine. The question would be: was the order Val-Ileu or Ileu-Val? In other words, was valine or isoleucine the N-terminal amino acid? (The amine group, and consequently the N-terminal unit, is conventionally considered to be at the left end of a chain.) Here DNP could provide the answer. If it combined with the valine, that would be the N-terminal amino acid, and the arrangement in the dipeptide would then be established to be Val-Ileu. If it combined with the isoleucine, it would be Ileu-Val.

The arrangement in a fragment consisting of three amino acids also could be worked out. Say its components were leucine, valine, and glutamic acid. The DNP test could first identify the N-terminal amino acid. If it was, say, leucine, the order had to be either Leu-Val-Glu or Leu-Glu-Val. Each of these combinations was then synthesized and deposited as a spot on a chromatogram to see which would occupy the same place on the paper as did the fragment being studied.

As for peptides of more than three amino acids, these could be broken down to smaller fragments for analysis.

After thus determining the structures of all the fragments into which the insulin molecule had been divided, the next step was to put the pieces together in the right order in the chain — in the fashion of a jigsaw puzzle. There were a number of clues to work with. For instance, the G-chain was known to contain only one unit of the amino acid alanine. In the mixture of peptides obtained from the breakdown of G-chains, alanine was found in two combinations: alanine-serine and cystine-alanine. This meant that in the intact G-chain the order must be CyS-Ala-Ser.

By means of such clues, Sanger and Tuppy gradually put the pieces together. It took a couple of years to identify all the fragments definitely and arrange them in a completely satisfactory sequence, but by 1952 they had worked out the exact arrangement of all the amino acids in the G-chain and the P-chain. They then went on to establish how the two chains were joined together. In 1953 their final triumph in deciphering the structure of insulin was announced. The complete structure of an important protein molecule had been worked out for the first time. For this achievement Sanger was awarded the Nobel Prize in chemistry in 1958.

Biochemists immediately adopted Sanger's methods to determine the structure of other protein molecules. Ribonuclease, a protein molecule consisting of a single peptide chain with 121 amino acids, was conquered by 1959, and chemists were well on the way to deciphering several others.

Meanwhile the first synthesis of a protein molecule — albeit a very simple one — had been announced. It was "oxytocin," a hormone with important functions in the body. Oxytocin is extremely small for a protein molecule: it consists only of eight amino acids. In 1953 the American biochemist Vincent du Vigneaud succeeded in synthesizing a peptide chain exactly like that thought to represent the oxytocin molecule. And, indeed, the synthetic peptide showed all the properties of the natural hormone. Du Vigneaud was awarded the Nobel Prize in chemistry in 1955.

ENZYMES

THERE IS GOOD REASON, of course, for the complexity and almost infinite variety of protein molecules. Proteins have a multitude of different functions to perform in living organisms.

One major function is to provide the structural framework of the body. Just as cellulose serves as the framework of plants, so fibrous proteins act in the same capacity for the complex animals. Spiders spin gossamer threads and insect larvae spin cocoon threads of protein fibers. The scales of fish and reptiles are made up mainly of the protein keratin. Hair, feathers, horns, hooves, claws, and finger nails — all merely modified scales — also contain keratin. Skin owes its strength and toughness to its high content of keratin. The internal supporting tissues — cartilage, ligaments, tendons, even the organic framework of bones — are made up largely of protein molecules such as collagen and elastin. Muscle is made of a complex fibrous protein called actomyosin.

In all these cases the protein fibers are more than a cellulose substitute. They are an improvement; they are stronger and more flexible. Cellulose will do to support a plant, which is not called on for any motion more complex than swaying with the wind. But protein fibers must be designed for the bending and flexing of the appendages of the body, for rapid motions and vibrations, and so on.

The fibers, however, are among the simplest of the proteins, in form as well as function. Most of the other proteins have more subtle and more complicated jobs to do.

To maintain life in all its aspects, numerous chemical reactions must proceed in the body. These must go on at high speed and in great variety, each reaction meshing with all the others, for it is not upon any one reaction, but upon all together, that life's smooth workings must depend. Moreover, all the reactions must proceed under the mildest of environments: without high temperatures, strong chemicals or great pressures. The reactions must be under strict yet flexible control, and they must be constantly adjusted to the changing characteristics of the environment and the changing needs of the body. The undue slowing down, or speeding up, of even one reaction out of the many thousands would more or less seriously disorganize the body.

All this is accomplished by protein molecules.

TOWARD THE END OF THE EIGHTEENTH CENTURY, chemists, following the leadership of Lavoisier, began to study reactions in a quantitative way — in particular, to measure the rates at which chemical reactions proceeded. They quickly noted that reaction rates could be changed drastically by comparatively minor changes in the environment. For instance, when Kirchhoff found that starch could be converted to sugar in the presence of acid, he noticed that while the acid greatly speeded up this reaction, it was not itself consumed in the process. Other examples of this were soon discovered. The German chemist Johann Wolfgang Döbereiner found that finely divided platinum (called "platinum black") encouraged the combination of hydrogen and oxygen to form water — a reaction which without this help could take place only at a high temperature. Döbereiner even designed a self-igniting lamp in which a jet of hydrogen, played upon a surface coated with platinum black, caught fire.

Because the "hastened reactions" were usually in the direction of breaking down a complex substance to a simpler one, Berzelius named the phenomenon "catalysis" (from Greek words essentially meaning "break down"). Thus platinum black came to be called a catalyst for the combination of hydrogen and oxygen and acid a catalyst for the hydrolysis of starch to glucose.

Catalysis has proved of the greatest importance in industry. For instance, the best way of making sulfuric acid (the most important single inorganic chemical next to air, water and, perhaps, salt) involves the burning of sulfur, first to sulfur dioxide (SO_2), then to sulfur trioxide (SO_3). The step from the dioxide to the trioxide would not proceed at more than a snail's pace without the help of a catalyst such as platinum black. Finely divided nickel (which has replaced platinum black in most cases, because it is cheaper) and compounds such as copper chromite, vanadium pentoxide, ferric oxide, and manganese dioxide also are important catalysts. In fact, a great deal of the success of an industrial chemical process depends on finding just the right catalyst for the reaction involved. It was the discovery of a new type of catalyst by Ziegler that revolutionized the production of polymers.

How is it possible for a substance, sometimes present only in very small concentrations, to bring about large quantities of reaction without itself being changed?

Well, one kind of catalyst does in fact take part in the reaction, but in a cyclic fashion, so that it is continually restored to its original form. An example is vanadium pentoxide (V_2O_5), which can catalyze the change of sulfur dioxide to sulfur trioxide. Vanadium pentoxide passes on one of its oxygen atoms to SO_2, forming SO_3 and changing itself to vanadyl oxide (V_2O_4). But the vanadyl oxide rapidly reacts with oxygen in the air and is restored to V_2O_5. The vanadium pentoxide thus acts as a middleman, handing an oxygen atom to sulfur dioxide, taking another from the air, handing that to sulfur dioxide, and so on. The process is so rapid that a small quantity of vanadium pentoxide will suffice to bring about the conversion of large quantities of sulfur dioxide, and in the end we will appear still to have the vanadium pentoxide unchanged.

In 1902 the German chemist George Lunge suggested that this sort of thing was the explanation of catalysis in general. In 1916 Irving Langmuir went a step farther and advanced an explanation for the catalytic action of substances such as platinum, which are so non-reactive that they cannot be expected to engage in ordinary chemical reactions. Langmuir suggested that excess valence bonds at the surface of platinum metal would seize hydrogen and oxygen

467

molecules. While held imprisoned in close proximity on the platinum surface, the hydrogen and oxygen molecules would be much more likely to combine to form water molecules than in their ordinary free condition as gaseous molecules. Once a water molecule was formed, it would be displaced from the platinum surface by hydrogen and oxygen molecules. Thus the process of seizure of hydrogen and oxygen, their combination into water, release of the water, seizure of more hydrogen and oxygen, and formation of more water could continue indefinitely.

This is called "surface catalysis." Naturally, the more finely divided the metal, the more surface a given mass will provide and the more effectively catalysis can proceed. Of course, if any extraneous substance attaches itself firmly to the surface bonds of the platinum, it will "poison" the catalyst.

All surface catalysts are more or less selective, or "specific." Some easily absorb hydrogen molecules and will catalyze reactions involving hydrogen; others easily absorb water molecules and catalyze condensations or hydrolyses, and so on.

THE ORGANIC WORLD, too, has its catalysts. Indeed, some of them have been known for thousands of years, though not by that name. They are as old as bread-making and wine-making.

Bread dough, left to itself and kept from contamination by outside influences, will not rise. Add a lump of "leaven" (from a Latin word meaning "rise"), and bubbles begin to appear, lifting and lightening the dough. The common English word for leaven is "yeast," possibly descended from a Sanskrit word meaning "to boil."

Yeast also hastens the conversion of fruit juices and grain to alcohol. Here again, the conversion involves the formation of bubbles, so the process is called "fermentation," from a Latin word meaning "boil." The yeast preparation is often referred to as "ferment."

It was not until the seventeenth century that the nature of leaven was discovered. In 1680, for the first time, van Leeuwenhoek saw yeast cells under his microscope. A century and a half later a French physicist, Charles Cagniard de la Tour, demonstrated that the little blobs were alive. Then in the 1850's yeast became a dramatic subject of study.

France's wine industry was in trouble. Aging wine was going sour and becoming undrinkable, and millions of francs were being lost. The problem was placed before the young dean of the Faculty of Sciences at the University of Lille, in the heart of the vineyard area. The young dean was Louis Pasteur, who had already made his mark by being the first to separate optical isomers in the laboratory.

Pasteur studied the yeast cells in the wine under the microscope. It was obvious to him that the cells were of varying types. All the wine contained yeast that brought about fermentation, but those wines that went sour contained another type of yeast in addition. It seemed to Pasteur that the souring action did not get under way until the fermentation was completed. Since there was no need for yeast after the necessary fermentation, why not get rid of all the yeast at that point and avoid letting the wrong kind make trouble?

He therefore suggested to a horrified wine industry that the wine be heated gently after fermentation, in order to kill all the yeast in it. Aging, he predicted, would then proceed without souring. The industry reluctantly tried his outrageous proposal, and found to its delight that souring ceased, while the flavor of the wine was not in the least damaged by the heating. The wine industry was saved. Furthermore, the process of gentle heating ("pasteurization") was later applied to milk also, to kill any disease germs present.

Other organisms besides yeast hasten breakdown processes. In fact, a process analogous to fermentation takes place in the intestinal tract. The first man to study digestion scientifically was the French physicist René Antoine Ferchault de Réaumur. He used a hawk as his experimental subject, and he made it swallow small metal tubes containing meat; the tubes protected the meat from any mechanical grinding action, but they had openings, covered by gratings, so that chemical processes in the stomach could act on the meat. Réaumur found that when the hawk regurgitated these tubes, the meat was partly dissolved, and a yellowish fluid was present in the tubes.

Clearly the stomach juices contained something that hastened the breakdown of meat. In 1834 the German naturalist Theodor Schwann added mercuric chloride to the stomach juice and precipitated a white powder. After freeing the powder of the mercury compound, and dissolving what was left, he found he had a very concentrated digestive juice. He called the powder he had dissolved "pepsin," from the Greek word meaning "digest."

Meanwhile two French chemists, A. Payen and J. F. Persoz, had found in malt extract a substance which could bring about the conversion of starch to sugar more rapidly than acid could. They called this "diastase," from a Greek word meaning "to separate," because they had separated it from malt.

For a long time chemists made a sharp distinction between living ferments such as yeast cells and non-living, or "unorganized," ferments such as pepsin. But in 1878 the Germany physiologist Wilhelm Kühne suggested that the latter be called "enzymes," from Greek words meaning "in yeast," because their activity was similar to that brought about by the catalyzing substances in yeast. Kühne did not realize how important, indeed universal, that term "enzyme" was to become.

In 1897 the German chemist Eduard Buchner ground yeast cells with sand to break up all the cells and succeeded in extracting a juice which he found could perform the same fermentative tasks that the original yeast cells could. Suddenly the distinction between the ferments inside and outside of cells vanished. It was one more breakdown of the vitalists' semi-mystical separation of life from non-life. The term "enzyme" was now applied to all ferments.

For this discovery Buchner received the Nobel Prize in chemistry in 1907.

NOW IT WAS POSSIBLE to define an enzyme simply as an organic catalyst. Chemists began to try to isolate enzymes and find out what sort of substances they were. The trouble was that the amount of enzyme in cells and natural juices was very small, and the extracts obtained were invariably mixtures in which it was hard to tell what was an enzyme and what was not.

Many biochemists suspected that enzymes were proteins, because enzyme properties could easily be destroyed, as proteins could be denatured, by gentle heating. But in the 1920's the German biochemist Richard Willstätter reported that certain purified enzyme solutions, from which he believed he had eliminated all protein, showed marked catalytic effects. He concluded from this that enzymes were not proteins but were relatively simple chemicals, which might, indeed, utilize a protein as a "carrier molecule." Most biochemists went along with Willstätter, who was a Nobel Prize winner and had great prestige.

However, the Cornell University biochemist James Batcheller Sumner produced strong evidence against this theory almost as soon as it was advanced. From jackbeans (the white seeds of a tropical American plant), Sumner isolated crystals which, in solution, showed the properties of an enzyme called "urease." This enzyme catalyzed the breakdown of urea to carbon dioxide and ammonia. Sumner's crystals showed definite protein properties, and he could find no way to separate the protein from the enzyme activity. Anything that denatured the protein also destroyed the enzyme. All this seemed to show that what he had was an enzyme in pure and crystalline form and that that enzyme was a protein.

Willstätter's greater fame for a time minimized Sumner's discovery. But in 1930 the chemist John Howard Northrop and his co-workers at the Rockefeller Institute clinched Sumner's case. They crystallized a number of enzymes, including pepsin, and found all to be proteins. Northrop, furthermore, showed that these crystals were pure proteins and retained their catalytic activity even when dissolved and diluted to the point where the ordinary chemical tests, such as those used by Willstätter, could no longer detect the presence of protein.

Enzymes were thus established to be "protein catalysts." By now nearly a hundred enzymes have been crystallized, and all without exception are proteins.

For their work, Sumner and Northrop shared in the Nobel Prize in chemistry in 1946.

Enzymes are remarkable as catalysts in two respects — efficiency and specificity. There is an enzyme known as catalase, for instance, which catalyzes the breakdown of hydrogen peroxide to water and oxygen. Now the breakdown of hydrogen peroxide in solution can also be catalyzed by iron filings or manganese dioxide. However, weight for weight, catalase speeds up the rate of breakdown far more than any inorganic catalyst can. Each molecule of catalese can bring about the breakdown of 44,000 molecules of hydrogen peroxide per second at 0° C. Moreover, catalase is highly specific: it breaks down only hydrogen peroxide, whereas iron filings and manganese dioxide can catalyze various other reactions as well.

What accounts for the remarkable specificity of enzymes? Lunge's and Langmuir's theories about the behavior of a catalyst as a middleman suggested an answer. Suppose we consider that an enzyme forms a temporary combination with the "substrate" — the substance whose reaction it catalyzes. The form, or configuration, of the particular enzyme may therefore play a highly important role. Plainly each enzyme must present a very complicated surface, for it has a number of different side-chains sticking out of the peptide backbone. Some of these side-chains have a negative charge, some positive, some no charge. Some are bulky, some small. One can imagine that each enzyme may have a surface that just fits a particular substrate. In other words, it fits the substrate as a key fits a lock. Therefore it will combine readily with that substance but only clumsily or not at all with others. This would explain the high specificity of enzymes: each has a surface made to order, so to speak, for combining with a particular compound. That being the case, no wonder that proteins are built of so many different units and are constructed by living tissue in such great variety.

This view of enzyme action was borne out by the discovery that the presence of a substance similar in structure to a given substrate would slow down or inhibit the substrate's enzyme-catalyzed reaction. The best-known case involves an enzyme called succinic acid dehydrogenase, which catalyzes the removal of two hydrogen atoms from succinic acid. That reaction will not proceed if a substance called malonic acid, which is very similar to succinic acid, is present. The structures of succinic acid and malonic acid are:

$$
\begin{array}{ccc}
CH_2-C{\overset{\displaystyle O}{\diagup}}_{\diagdown OH} & & C{\overset{\displaystyle O}{\diagup}}_{\diagdown OH} \\
| & CH_2 & \\
CH_2-C{\overset{\displaystyle O}{\diagup}}_{\diagdown OH} & & C{\overset{\displaystyle O}{\diagup}}_{\diagdown OH}
\end{array}
$$

succinic acid   malonic acid

The only difference between these two molecules is that succinic acid has one more CH_2 group at the left. Presumably the malonic acid, because of its structural similarity to succinic acid, can attach itself to the surface of the enzyme. Once it has pre-empted the spot on the surface to which the succinic acid would attach itself, it remains jammed there, so to speak, and the enzyme is out of action. The malonic acid "poisons" the enzyme, so far as its normal function is concerned. This sort of thing is called "competitive inhibition."

The most positive evidence in favor of the enzyme-substrate-complex theory has come from spectrographic analysis. Presumably if an enzyme combines with its substrate, there should be a change in the absorption spectrum: the combination's absorption of light should be different from that of the enzyme or the substrate alone. In 1936 the British biochemists David Keilin and Thaddeus Mann actually detected a change of color in a solution of the enzyme peroxidase after its substrate, hydrogen peroxide, was added. The American biophysicist Britton Chance made a spectral analysis and found that there were two progressive changes in the absorption

473

pattern, one following the other. He attributed the first change in pattern to the formation of the enzyme-substrate complex at a certain rate and the second to the decline of this combination as the reaction moved to completion.

Now the question arises: is the entire enzyme molecule necessary for catalysis, or would some part of it be sufficient? This is an important question from a practical as well as a theoretical standpoint. Enzymes are in wide use today; they have been put to work in the manufacture of drugs, citric acid, and many other chemicals. If the entire enzyme molecule is not essential and some small fragment of it would do the job, perhaps this active portion could be synthesized, so that the processes would not have to depend on the use of living cells, such as yeasts, molds, and bacteria.

Some promising advances toward this goal have been made. For instance, Northrop found that when a few acetyl groups (CH_3CO) were added to the side-chains of the amino acid tyrosine in the pepsin molecule, the enzyme lost some of its activity. There was no loss, however, when acetyl groups were added to the lysine side-chains in pepsin. Tyrosine, therefore, must contribute to pepsin's activity while lysine obviously did not. This was the first indication that an enzyme might possess portions not essential to its activity.

Recently the "active region" of another digestive enzyme was pinpointed with more precision. This enzyme is chymotrypsin. The pancreas first secretes it in an inactive form called "chymotrypsinogen." This inactive molecule is converted into the active one by the splitting of a single peptide link (accomplished by the digestive enzyme trypsin). That is to say, it looks as if the uncovering of a single amino acid endows chymotrypsin with its activity. Now it turns out that the attachment of a molecule known as DFP to chymotrypsin stops the enzyme's activity. Presumably the DFP attaches itself to the key amino acid. Thanks to its tagging by DFP, that amino acid has been identified as serine. In fact, DFP has also been found to attach itself to serine in other digestive enzymes. In each case the serine is in the same position in a sequence of four amino acids: gly-cine-aspartic acid-serine-glycine.

It turns out that a peptide consisting of those four amino acids alone will not display catalytic activity. In some way, the rest of the enzyme molecule plays a role, too. We can think of the four-acid sequence — the active center — as analogous to the cutting edge of a knife which is useless without a handle.

We cannot tamper with the cutting edge, but could we modify the handle without impairing the usefulness of the tool? The existence of different varieties of a protein such as insulin, for instance, encourages us to believe that we might. Insulin is a hormone, not an enzyme, but its function is highly specific. At a certain position in the G-chain of insulin there is a three-amino-acid sequence which differs in different animals: in cattle it is alamine-serine-valine; in swine, threonine-serine-isoleucine; in sheep, alanine-glycine-valine; in horses, threonine-glycine-isoleucine; and so on. Yet any of these insulins can be substituted for any other and still perform the same function.

What is more, a protein molecule can sometimes be cut down drastically without any serious effect on its activity (as the handle of a knife or an axe might be shortened without much loss in effectiveness). A case in point is the hormone called ACTH. This is a peptide chain made up of 39 amino acids, the order of which has now been fully determined. Up to 15 of the amino acids have been removed from the C-terminal end without destroying the hormone's activity. On the other hand, the removal of one or two amino acids from the N-terminal end (the cutting edge, so to speak) kills activity at once.

The same sort of thing has been done to an enzyme called "papain," from the fruit and sap of the papaya tree. Its enzymatic action is similar to that of pepsin. Removal of 80 of the pepsin molecule's 180 amino acids, from the N-terminal end, does not reduce its activity to any detectable extent.

So it is at least conceivable that enzymes may yet be simplified to

475

the point where they will fall within the region of practical synthesis. Synthetic enzymes, in the form of fairly simple organic compounds, may then be made on a large scale for various purposes. This would be a form of "chemical miniaturization." Chemists are even now at work on such possibilities. The outlook is hopeful.

METABOLISM

AN ORGANISM, such as the human body, is a chemical plant of great diversity. It breathes in oxygen and drinks water. It takes in as food carbohydrates, fats, proteins, minerals, and other raw materials. It eliminates various indigestible materials plus bacteria and the products of the putrefaction they bring about. It also excretes carbon dioxide via the lungs, gives up water both by way of the lungs and the sweat glands, and excretes urine, which carries off a number of compounds in solution, the chief of these being urea. These chemical reactions determine the body's metabolism.

By examining the raw materials that enter the body and the waste products that leave it, we can tell a few things about what goes on within the body. For instance, since protein supplies most of the nitrogen entering the body, we know that urea (NH_2CONH_2) must be a product of the metabolism of proteins. But between protein and urea lies a long, devious, complicated road. Each enzyme of the body catalyzes only a specific small reaction, rearranging perhaps no more than two or three atoms. Every major conversion in the body involves a multitude of steps and many enzymes. Even an apparently simple organism such as the tiny bacterium must make use of many thousands of separate enzymes and reactions.

All this may seem needlessly complex, but it is the very essence of life. The vast complex of reactions in tissues can be controlled delicately by increasing or decreasing the production of appropriate enzymes. The enzymes control body chemistry as the intricate movements of fingers on the strings control the playing of a violin, and without this intricacy the body could not perform its manifold functions.

To trace the course of the myriads of reactions that make up the body's metabolism is to follow the outline of life. The attempt to follow it in detail, to make sense of the intermeshing of countless reactions all taking place at once, may indeed seem a formidable and even hopeless undertaking. Formidable it is, but not hopeless.

The chemists' study of metabolism began modestly with an effort to find out how yeast cells converted sugar to ethyl alcohol. In 1905 two British chemists, Arthur Harden and W. J. Young, suggested that this process involved the formation of sugars bearing phosphate groups. They were the first to note that phosphorus played an important role in metabolism (and phosphorus has been looming larger and larger ever since). Harden and Young even found in living tissue a sugar-phosphate ester consisting of the sugar fructose with two phosphate groups (PO_3H_2) attached. This "fructose diphosphate" is called the "Harden-Young ester" still. In 1929 Harden shared the Nobel Prize in chemistry. He had, after all, placed students of carbohydrate metabolism on the right track.

What began by involving only the yeast cell became of far broader importance when the German chemist Otto Meyerhof demonstrated in 1918 that animal cells, such as those of muscle, broke down sugar in much the same way as yeast did. The chief difference was that in animal cells the breakdown did not proceed so far in this particular route of metabolism. Instead of converting the six-carbon glucose molecule all the way down to the two-carbon ethyl alcohol (CH_3-CH_2OH), they broke it down only as far as the three-carbon lactic acid ($CH_3CHOHCOOH$).

Meyerhof's work made clear for the first time a general principle which has since become commonly accepted: that, with only minor differences, metabolism follows the same routes in all creatures, from the simplest to the most complex. For his studies on the lactic acid in muscle, Meyerhof shared the Nobel Prize in physiology and medicine in 1922.

The details of the individual steps involved in the transition from

477

sugar to lactic acid were worked out between 1937 and 1941 by Carl Cori and his wife Gerty, working at Washington University in St. Louis. They used tissue extracts and purified enzymes to bring about changes in various sugar-phosphate esters, then put all the changes together like a jigsaw puzzle. The scheme of step-by-step changes that they presented has stood with little modification to this day, and the Coris were awarded a share in the Nobel Prize in physiology and medicine in 1947.

In the path from sugar to lactic acid, a certain amount of energy is produced and is utilized by the cells. The yeast cell lives on it when it is fermenting sugar, and so, when necessary, does the muscle cell. It is important to remember that this energy is obtained without the use of oxygen from the air. Thus a muscle is capable of working even when it must expend more energy than can be replaced by reactions involving the oxygen brought to it at a relatively slow rate by the blood. As the lactic acid accumulates, however, the muscle grows weary, and eventually it must rest until oxygen breaks up the lactic acid.

Next comes the question: in what form is the energy from the sugar-to-lactic-acid breakdown supplied to the cells, and how do they use it? The German-born American chemist Fritz Lipmann found an answer in researches beginning in 1941. He showed that certain phosphate compounds formed in the course of carbohydrate metabolism store unusual amounts of energy in the bond that connects the phosphate group to the rest of the molecule. This "high-energy phosphate bond" is transferred to energy carriers present in all cells. The best known of these carriers is "adenosine triphosphate" (ATP). The ATP molecule and certain similar compounds represent the small currency of the body's energy. They store the energy in neat, conveniently-sized, readily negotiable packets. When the phosphate bond is hydrolyzed off, the energy is available to be converted into chemical energy for the building of proteins from amino acids, or into electrical energy for the transmission of a nerve impulse, or into kinetic energy via the contraction of muscle, and so on. Although the quantity of ATP in the body is small at any one time, there is always enough (while life persists), for as fast as the ATP molecules are used up, new ones are formed.

For his key discovery, Lipmann shared the Nobel Prize in physiology and medicine in 1953.

The mammalian body cannot convert lactic acid to ethyl alcohol (as yeast can); instead, by another route of metabolism, it by-passes ethyl alcohol and breaks lactic acid down all the way to carbon dioxide (CO_2) and water. In so doing, it consumes oxygen and produces a great deal more energy than is produced by the non-oxygen-requiring conversion of glucose to lactic acid.

The fact that consumption of oxygen is involved offers a convenient means of tracing a metabolic process — that is, finding out what intermediate products are created along the route. Let's say that at a given step in a sequence of reactions a certain substance (*e.g.*, succinic acid) is suspected to be the intermediate substrate. We can mix this with living tissue (or in many cases with a single enzyme) and measure the rate at which the mixture consumes oxygen. If it shows a rapid uptake of oxygen, we can be confident that this particular substance can indeed further the process.

The German biochemist Otto Heinrich Warburg devised the key instrument used to measure the rate of uptake of oxygen. Called the "Warburg manometer," it consists of a small flask (where the substrate and the tissue or enzyme are mixed) connected to one end of a thin U-tube, the other end of which is open. A colored fluid fills the lower part of the U. As the mixture of enzyme and substrate absorbs oxygen from the air in the flask, a slight vacuum is created there, and the colored liquid in the U-tube rises on the side of the U connected to the flask. The rate at which the liquid rises can be used to calculate the rate of oxygen uptake.

Warburg's experiments on the uptake of oxygen by tissues won him the Nobel Prize in physiology and medicine in 1931.

Warburg and another German biochemist, Heinrich Wieland, identified the reactions that yield energy during the breakdown of lactic acid. In the course of the series of reactions, pairs of hydrogen atoms are removed from intermediate substances by means of en-

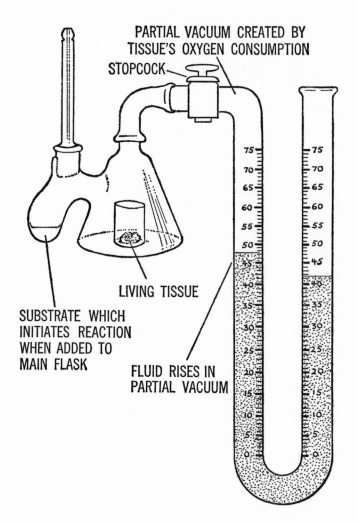

PARTIAL VACUUM CREATED BY
TISSUE'S OXYGEN CONSUMPTION

STOPCOCK

LIVING TISSUE

SUBSTRATE WHICH
INITIATES REACTION
WHEN ADDED TO
MAIN FLASK

FLUID RISES IN
PARTIAL VACUUM

WARBURG MANOMETER.

zymes called "dehydrogenases." These hydrogen atoms then combine with oxygen, with the catalytic help of enzymes called "cytochromes." In the late 1920's Warburg and Wieland argued strenuously over which of these reactions was the important one, Warburg contending that it was the uptake of oxygen and Wieland that it was the removal of hydrogen. Eventually David Keilin of England showed that both steps were essential.

The German biochemist Hans Adolf Krebs went on to work out the complete sequence of reactions and intermediate products from lactic acid to carbon dioxide and water. This is called the Krebs cycle, or the citric-acid cycle, citric acid being one of the key products formed along the way. For this achievement, completed in 1940, Krebs received a share in the Nobel Prize in physiology and medicine in 1953.

Meanwhile biochemists were beginning to make a little headway in solving the metabolism of fats. It was known that the fat molecules were carbon chains, that they could be hydrolyzed to "fatty acids" (most commonly 16 or 18 carbon atoms long), and that the molecules were broken down two carbons at a time. In 1947 Fritz Lipmann discovered a rather complex compound which played a part in "acetylation" — that is, transfer of a two-carbon fragment from one compound to another. He called the compound "coenzyme A" (the A standing for acetylation). Three years later the German biochemist Feodor Lynen found that coenzyme A was deeply involved in the breakdown of fats. Once it attached itself to a fatty acid, there followed a series of four steps which ended in lopping off the two carbons at the end of the chain to which the coenzyme A was attached. Then another coenzyme A molecule would attach itself to what was left of the fatty acid, chop off two more atoms, and so on. This is called the "fatty-acid oxidation cycle."

The breakdown of proteins obviously must be, in general, more complicated than that of carbohydrates or fats, because some 20 different amino acids are involved. In some cases it turns out to be rather simple: one minor change in an amino acid may convert it into a compound which can enter the citric-acid cycle (as the two-carbon fragments from fatty acids can). But many amino acids are decomposed by complex routes.

We can now go back to the conversion of protein into urea — the question that we considered at the start. This conversion happens to be comparatively simple.

A group of atoms which is essentially the urea molecule forms part of a side-chain of the amino acid arginine. This group can be chopped off by an enzyme called "arginase," and it leaves behind a kind of truncated amino acid, called "ornithine." Now in 1932 Krebs and a coworker, K. Henseleit, while studying the formation of urea by rat-liver tissue, discovered that when they added arginine to the tissue, it produced a flood of urea — much more urea, in fact, than the splitting of every molecule of arginine they had added could have produced. Krebs and Henseleit decided that the arginine molecules must be acting as agents which produced urea over and over again. In other words, after an arginine molecule had its urea combination chopped off by arginase, the ornithine that was left picked up amine groups from other amino acids (plus carbon dioxide from the body) and formed arginine again. So the arginine molecule was repeatedly split, reformed, split again, and so on, each time yielding a molecule of urea. This is called the "urea cycle," the "ornithine cycle" or the "Krebs-Henseleit cycle."

After the removal of nitrogen, by way of arginine, the remaining "carbon skeletons" of the amino acids can be broken down by various routes to carbon dioxide and water, producing energy.

TRACERS

THE INVESTIGATIONS OF METABOLISM by all these devices still left biochemists in the position of being on the outside looking in, so to speak. They could work out general cycles, but to find out what was really going on in the living animal they needed some means of tracing the course of events through the stages of metabolism — to follow the fate of particular molecules, as it were. Actually, techniques for doing this had been discovered early in the century, but the chemists were rather slow in making full use of them.

The first to pioneer along these lines was a German biochemist named Franz Knoop. In 1904 he conceived the idea of feeding labeled fat molecules to dogs to see what happened to the molecules. He labeled them by attaching a benzene ring at one end of the chain; he used the benzene ring because mammals possess no enzymes that can break it down. Knoop expected that what the benzene ring carried with it when it showed up in the urine might tell something about how the fat molecule broke down in the body — and he was right. The benzene ring invariably turned up with a two-carbon side-chain attached. From this he deduced that the body must split off the fat molecule's carbon atoms two at a time. (As we have seen, more than 40 years later the work with coenzyme A confirmed his deduction.)

The carbon chains in ordinary fats all contain an even number of carbon atoms. What if you used a fat whose chain had an odd number of carbon atoms? In that case, if the atoms were chopped off two at a time, you should end up with just one carbon atom attached to the benzene ring. Knoop fed this kind of fat molecule to dogs and did indeed end up with that result.

Knoop had employed the first "tracer" in biochemistry. In 1913 the Hungarian chemist Georg von Hevesy and his coworker F. A. Paneth hit upon another way to tag molecules: radioactive isotopes. They began with radioactive lead, and their first biochemical experiment was to measure how much lead, in the form of a lead-salt solution, a plant would take up. The amount was certainly too small to be measured by any available chemical method, but if radiolead was used, it could easily be measured by its radioactivity. Hevesy and Paneth fed the radioactively tagged lead-salt solution to plants, and at periodic intervals they would burn a plant and measure the radioactivity of its ash. In this way they were able to determine the rate of absorption of lead by plant cells.

But the benzene ring and lead were very "unphysiological" substances to use as tags. They might easily upset the normal chemistry of living cells. It would be much better to use as tags atoms that actually took part in the body's ordinary metabolism — atoms such as oxygen, nitrogen, carbon, hydrogen, phosphorus, and so on.

Radioactive isotopes of these elements were not available in pre-fission days, and anyway, the radioisotopes of some of them — notably nitrogen and oxygen — are not usable, because they are very short-lived, having a half-life of only a few minutes at most. But the most important elements do have *stable* isotopes that can be used as tags. These isotopes are carbon 13, nitrogen 15, oxygen 18, and hydrogen 2. Ordinarily they occur in very small amounts (about 1 per cent or less); consequently, by "enriching" natural hydrogen, say, in hydrogen 2, it can be made to serve as a distinguishing tag in a hydrogen-containing molecule fed to the body. The presence of the heavy hydrogen in any compound can be detected by means of the mass spectrograph, which separates it by virtue of its extra weight. Thus the fate of the tagged hydrogen can be traced through the body.

Hydrogen, in fact, served as the first physiological tracer. It became available for this purpose when Harold Urey isolated hydrogen 2 (deuterium) in 1931. One of the first things brought to light by the use of deuterium as a tracer was that hydrogen atoms in the body were much less fixed to their compounds than had been thought. It turned out that they shuttled back and forth from one compound to another, exchanging places on the oxygen atoms of sugar molecules, water molecules, and so on. Since one ordinary hydrogen atom cannot be told from another, this shuttling had not been detected before the deuterium atoms disclosed it. What the discovery implied was that hydrogen atoms hopped about throughout the body, and if deuterium atoms were attached to oxygen they would spread through the body regardless of whether or not the compounds involved underwent chemical change. Consequently the investigator must make sure that a deuterium atom found in a compound got there by some definite enzyme-catalyzed reaction and not just by the shuttling, or exchange, process. Fortunately, hydrogen atoms attached to carbon atoms do not exchange, so deuterium found along carbon chains has metabolic significance.

The roving habits of atoms were further emphasized in 1937 when the German-born American biochemist Rudolf Schoenheimer and his associates began to use nitrogen 15. They fed rats on amino acids tagged with nitrogen 15, killed the rats after a set period, and analyzed the tissues to see which compounds carried nitrogen 15. Here again, exchange was found to be important. After one tagged amino acid had entered the body, almost all the amino acids were shortly found to carry nitrogen 15. In 1942 Schoenheimer published a book entitled *The Dynamic State of Body Constituents*. That title describes the new look in biochemistry that the isotopic tracers brought about. A restless traffic in atoms goes on ceaselessly, quite aside from actual chemical changes.

Little by little the use of tracers filled in the details of the metabolic routes. It corroborated the general pattern of such things as sugar breakdown, the citric-acid cycle, and the urea cycle. It resulted in the addition of new intermediates, in the establishment of alternate routes of reaction, and so on.

When, thanks to the nuclear reactor, radioactive isotopes became available in quantity after World War II, tracer work went into high gear. Ordinary compounds could be bombarded by neutrons in a reactor and come out loaded with radioactive isotopes. Almost every biochemical laboratory in the United States (I might almost say in the world, for the United States soon made isotopes available to other countries for scientific use) started research programs involving radioactive tracers.

The stable tracers were now joined by radioactive hydrogen (tritium), radiophosphorus (phosphorus 32), radiosulfur (sulfur 35), radiopotassium (potassium 42), radiosodium, radioiodine, radioiron, radiocopper, and, most important of all, radiocarbon (carbon 14). To everyone's surprise, carbon 14 turned out to have a half-life of more than 5,000 years — unexpectedly long for a radioisotope among the light elements.

Carbon 14 solved problems that had defied chemists for years and against which they had seemed to be able to make no headway at all. One of the riddles to which it gave the beginning of an answer was the production of the substance known as "cholesterol." Cholesterol's formula, worked out by many years of painstaking investigation, had been found to be:

4 8 5

The function of cholesterol in the body is not yet completely understood, but the substance is clearly of central importance. Cholesterol is found in large quantity in the fatty sheaths around nerves, in the adrenal glands, and in combination with certain proteins. An excess of it can cause gallstones and atherosclerosis. Most significant of all, cholesterol is the prototype of the whole family of "steroids," the steroid nucleus being the four-ring combination you see in the formula. The steroids are a group of solid, fat-like substances which include the sex hormones and the adrenocortical hormones. All of them undoubtedly are formed from cholesterol. But how is cholesterol itself synthesized in the body?

Until tracers came to their help, biochemists had not the foggiest notion. The first to tackle the question with a tracer were Rudolf Schoenheimer and his coworker David Rittenberg. They gave rats heavy water to drink and found that its deuterium turned up in the cholesterol molecules. This in itself was not significant, because the deuterium could have got there merely by exchanges. But in 1942 (after Schoenheimer tragically had committed suicide) Rittenberg and another coworker, K. Bloch, discovered a more definite clue. They fed rats acetate ion (a simple two-carbon group, CH_3COO^-) with the deuterium tracer attached to the carbon atom in the CH_3 group. The deuterium again showed up in cholesterol molecules, and this time it could not have arrived there by exchange; it must have been incorporated in the molecule as part of the CH_3 group.

Two-carbon groups (of which the acetate ion is one version) seem to represent a general crossroads of metabolism. Such groups, then, might very well serve as the pool of material for building cholesterol. But just how did they form the molecule?

In 1950, when carbon 14 had become available, Bloch repeated the experiment, this time labeling the two carbons of the acetate ion, each with a different tag. He marked the carbon of the CH_3 group with the stable tracer carbon 13, and he labeled the carbon of the COO^- group with radioactive carbon 14. Then, after feeding the compound to a rat, he analyzed its cholesterol to see where the two tagged carbons would appear in the molecule. The analysis was a task that called for delicate chemical artistry, and Bloch and a number of other experimenters worked at it for years, identifying the source of one after another of the cholesterol carbon atoms. The pattern that developed suggested eventually that the acetate groups probably first formed a substance called "squalene," a rather scarce 30-carbon compound in the body to which no one had ever dreamed of paying serious attention before. Now it appeared to be a way-station on the road to cholesterol, and biochemists have begun to study it with intense interest.

In much the same way as they tackled the synthesis of cholesterol, biochemists have gone after the construction of the porphyrin ring of heme, a key structure in hemoglobin and in many enzymes. David Shemin of Columbia University fed ducks the amino acid glycine, labeled in various ways. Glycine (NH_2CH_2COOH) has two carbon atoms. When he tagged the CH_2 carbon with carbon 14, that carbon showed up in the porphyrin extracted from the ducks' blood. When he labeled the COOH carbon, the radioactive tracer did not appear in the porphyrin. In short, the CH_2 group entered into the synthesis of porphyrin but the COOH group did not.

Shemin, working with Rittenberg, found that the incorporation of glycine's atoms into porphyrin could take place just as well in red blood cells in the test tube as it could in living animals. This simplified matters, gave more clear-cut results, and avoided sacrificing or inconveniencing the animals.

(I would like to interrupt myself here to comment on a subject that has been greatly confused by the propaganda of emotional individuals with more sentiment than understanding. Scientists must often experiment with animals, and even at times kill them, if they are to gain knowledge. The incidence of sadism among scientists is no higher than it is in any other calling. If they can avoid using animals, they will. Even leaving considerations of humanity and decency to one side, animal experimentation is expensive and inconvenient. If a scientist must use an animal, he will avoid hurting or killing the animal if he can. If he must kill an animal, it is done as humanely as possible. And he never conducts such an experiment unless there is a reasonable expectation that the results gained will outweigh the necessary harm done the animal. There are those, I am sure, who firmly believe that no possible gain in knowledge can make up for killing an animal, but logic would require that such people be vegetarians. I wonder how many of them are.)

To get on with Shemin's studies of porphyrin. He labeled glycine's nitrogen with nitrogen 15 and its CH_2 carbon with carbon 14, then mixed the glycine with duck blood. Later he carefully took apart the porphyrin produced and found that all four nitrogen atoms in the porphyrin molecule came from the glycine. So did an adjacent carbon atom in each of the four small pyrrole rings (see the formula on page 418), and also the four carbon atoms that serve as bridges between the pyrrole rings. This left 12 other carbon atoms in the porphyrin ring itself and 14 in the various side-chains. These were shown to arise from acetate ion, some from the CH_3 carbon and some from the COO^- carbon.

From the distribution of the tracer atoms it was possible to deduce the manner in which the acetate and glycine entered into the porphyrin. First they formed a one-pyrrole ring; then two such rings combined, and finally two two-ring combinations joined to form the four-ring porphyrin structure.

In 1952 a compound called "porphobilinogen" was isolated in

pure form, as a result of an independent line of research by the English chemist R. G. Westall. This compound occurs in the urine of persons with defects in porphyrin metabolism, so it was suspected of having something to do with porphyrins. Its structure turned out to be just about identical with the one-pyrrole-ring structure that Shemin and his coworkers had postulated as one of the early steps in porphyrin synthesis. Porphobilinogen was a key way-station.

It was next shown that "delta-aminolevulinic acid," a substance with a structure like that of a porphobilinogen molecule split in half, could supply all the atoms necessary for incorporation into the porphyrin ring by the duck blood cells. The most plausible conclusion is that the cells first form delta-aminolevulinic acid from glycine and acetate (eliminating the COOH group of glycine as carbon dioxide in the process), that two molecules of delta-aminolevulinic acid then combine to form porphobilinogen (a one-pyrrole ring), and that the latter in turn combines first into a two-pyrrole ring and finally into the four-pyrrole ring of porphyrin.

PHOTOSYNTHESIS

OF ALL THE TRIUMPHS OF TRACER RESEARCH, perhaps the greatest has been the tracing of the complex series of steps that builds green plants — on which all life on this planet depends.

The animal kingdom could not exist if animals could feed only on one another, any more than a community of people could grow rich solely by taking in one another's washing or a man could lift himself by yanking upward on his belt buckle. A lion that eats a zebra or a man who eats a steak is consuming precious substance that was obtained at great pains and with considerable attrition from the plant world. The second law of thermodynamics tells us that at each stage of the cycle something is lost. No animal stores all of the carbohydrate, fat, and protein contained in the food it eats, nor can it make use of all the energy available in the food. Inevitably a large part, indeed most, of the energy is wasted in unusable heat. At each level of eating, then, some chemical energy is frittered away. Thus if all animals were strictly carnivorous, the whole animal kingdom would die off in a very few generations. In fact, it would never have come into being at all.

The fortunate fact is that most animals are herbivorous. They feed on the grass of the field, on the leaves of trees, on seeds, nuts and fruit, or on the seaweed and microscopic green plant-cells that fill the upper layers of the oceans. Only a minority of animals can be supported in the luxury of being carnivorous.

As for the plants themselves, they would be in no better plight were they not supplied with an external source of energy. They build carbohydrates, fats, and proteins from simple molecules, such as carbon dioxide and water. This synthesis calls for an input of energy, and the plants get it from just one source: sunlight. Green plants convert the energy of sunlight into the chemical energy of complex compounds, and that chemical energy supports all life forms (except for certain bacteria). This was first clearly pointed out in 1845 by the German physicist Julius Robert von Mayer, who was one of those who pioneered the law of conservation of energy and who was therefore particularly aware of the problem of energy balance. The process by which green plants make use of sunlight is called "photosynthesis," from Greek words meaning "put together by light."

The first attempt at a scientific investigation of plant growth was made early in the seventeenth century by the Flemish chemist Jean Baptiste Van Helmont. He grew a small willow tree in a tub containing a weighed amount of soil, and he found, to everyone's surprise, that although the tree grew large, the soil weighed just as much as before. It had been taken for granted that plants derived their substance from the soil. (Actually plants do take some minerals and ions from the soil, but not in any weighable amount.) If they did not get it there, where did they get it from? Van Helmont decided that plants must manufacture their substance from water, with which he had supplied the soil liberally. He was only partly right.

A century later the English physiologist Stephen Hales showed that plants built their substance in great part from a material more ethereal than water, namely, air. Half a century later the Dutch physician Jan Ingen-Housz identified the nourishing ingredient in air as carbon dioxide. He also demonstrated that a plant did not absorb carbon dioxide in the dark; it needed light (the "photo" of photosynthesis). Meanwhile Priestley, the discoverer of oxygen, had learned that green plants gave off oxygen. And in 1804 the Swiss chemist Nicholas Théodore de Saussur proved that water was incorporated in plant tissue, as Van Helmont had suggested.

Now the skeleton of the process was established. In sunlight, a plant took up carbon dioxide and combined it with water to form its tissues, giving off "left-over" oxygen in the process. Thus it became plain that green plants not only provided food but also renewed the earth's oxygen supply. Were it not for this, within a matter of centuries the oxygen would fall to a low level and the atmosphere would be loaded with enough carbon dioxide to asphyxiate animal life.

The scale on which the earth's green plants manufacture organic matter and release oxygen is enormous. The Russian-born American biochemist Eugene I. Rabinowitch, a leading investigator of photosynthesis, estimates that each year the green plants of the earth combine a total of 150 billion tons of carbon (from carbon dioxide) with 25 billion tons of hydrogen (from water) and liberate 400 billion tons of oxygen. Of this gigantic performance, the plants of the forests and fields on land account for only 10 per cent; for 90 per cent we have to thank the one-celled plants and seaweed of the oceans.

In 1817 Pierre Joseph Pelletier and Joseph Bienaimé Caventou of France, the discoverers of quinine, strychnine and several other specialized plant products, isolated the most important plant product of all — the one that gives the green color to green plants. They called the compound "chlorophyll," from Greek words meaning "green leaf."

It became apparent that chlorophyll was the catalyst that enabled plants to use the energy of sunlight, but for nearly a century this complex substance resisted all efforts to analyze its structure. Finally in 1906 Richard Willstätter of Germany (who was later to rediscover chromatography and to insist, incorrectly, that enzymes were not proteins) identified a central component of the chlorophyll molecule. It was the metal magnesium. (Willstätter received the Nobel Prize in chemistry in 1915 for this discovery and other work on plant pigments.) Willstätter and Hans Fischer went on to work on the structure of the molecule — a task which took a full generation to complete. By the 1930's it had been determined that chlorophyll had a porphyrin ring structure basically like that of heme (a molecule which Fischer had deciphered). Where heme had an iron atom at the center of the porphyrin ring, chlorophyll had a magnesium atom.

Exactly what reaction in the plant did chlorophyll catalyze? All that was known was that carbon dioxide and water went in and oxygen came out. As a first guess, biochemists assumed that the plant cells synthesized glucose ($C_6H_{12}O_6$) from the carbon dioxide and water and then went on to build from this the various plant substances, adding nitrogen, sulfur, phosphorus, and other inorganic elements from the soil.

On paper, it seemed that glucose might be formed by a series of steps which first combined the carbon atom of carbon dioxide with water (releasing the oxygen atoms of CO_2), and then polymerized the combination, CH_2O (formaldehyde), into glucose. Six molecules of formaldehyde would make one molecule of glucose.

This synthesis of glucose from formaldehyde could indeed be performed in the laboratory, in a tedious sort of way. Presumably the plant might possess enzymes that speeded the reactions. To be sure, formaldehyde is a very poisonous compound, but the chemists assumed that the formaldehyde was turned into glucose so quickly that at no time did the plant contain more than a very small amount of it. This formaldehyde theory, first proposed in 1870 by Baeyer (the synthesizer of indigo), lasted for two generations, simply because there was nothing better to take its place.

A fresh attack on the problem began in 1938, when Samuel

Ruben, together with Martin D. Kamen and other coworkers at the University of California, undertook to probe the chemistry of the green leaf with tracers. By the use of oxygen 18, the uncommon stable isotope of oxygen, they made one clear-cut finding. It turned out that when the water given a plant was labeled with oxygen 18, the oxygen released by the plant carried this tag, but the oxygen did not carry the tag when only the carbon dioxide supplied to the plant was labeled. In short, the experiment showed that the oxygen given off by plants came from the water molecule and not from the carbon dioxide molecule, as had been mistakenly assumed in the formaldehyde theory.

Ruben and his associates tried to follow the fate of the carbon atoms in the plant by labeling the carbon dioxide with the radioactive isotope carbon 11 (the only radiocarbon known at the time). But this attempt failed. For one thing, carbon 11 has a half-life of only 20.5 minutes. For another, they had no available method at the time for separating individual compounds in the plant cell quickly and thoroughly enough.

But in the early 1940's the necessary tools came to hand. Ruben and Kamen discovered carbon 14, the long-lived radioisotope, which made it possible to trace carbon through a series of leisurely reactions. And the development of paper chromatography provided a means of separating complex mixtures easily and cleanly. (In fact, radioactive isotopes allowed a neat refinement of paper chromatography: the radioactive spots on the paper, representing the presence of the tracer, would produce dark spots on a photographic film laid under it, so that the chromatogram would take its own picture — a technique called "autoradiography.")

After World War II, a University of California group headed by A. A. Benson and Melvin Calvin picked up the ball. They exposed microscopic one-celled plants ("chlorella") to carbon dioxide containing carbon 14 for short periods, in order to allow the photosynthesis to progress only through its earliest stages. Then they mashed the plant cells, separated their substances on a chromatogram, and made an autoradiograph.

493

They found that even when the cells had been exposed to the tagged carbon dioxide for only a minute and a half, the radioactive carbon atoms turned up in as many as 15 different substances in the cell. By cutting down the exposure time, they reduced the number of substances in which radiocarbon was incorporated, and eventually they decided that the first, or almost the first, compound in which the cell incorporated the carbon-dioxide carbon was "glyceryl phosphate." (At no time did they detect any formaldehyde, so the venerable formaldehyde theory passed quietly out of the picture.)

Glyceryl phosphate is a three-carbon compound. Evidently it must be formed by a roundabout route, for no one-carbon or two-carbon precursor could be found. Benson went on to locate two other phosphate-containing compounds that took up tagged carbon within a very short time. Both were varieties of sugars: "ribulose diphosphate" (a five-carbon compound) and "sedoheptulose phosphate" (a seven-carbon compound). The investigators identified enzymes that catalyzed reactions involving such sugars, studied those reactions, and worked out the travels of the carbon-dioxide molecule. The scheme that best fits all their data is the following.

First, carbon dioxide is added to the five-carbon ribulose diphosphate, making a six-carbon compound. This quickly splits in two, creating the three-carbon glyceryl phosphate. A series of reactions involving sedoheptulose phosphate and other compounds then puts two glyceryl phosphates together to form the six-carbon glucose phosphate. Meanwhile ribulose diphosphate is regenerated and is ready to take on another carbon-dioxide molecule. You can imagine six such cycles turning. At each turn, each cycle supplies one carbon atom (from the carbon dioxide), and out of these a molecule of glucose phosphate is built. Another turn of the six cycles produces another molecule of glucose phosphate, and so on.

This is the reverse of the citric-acid cycle, from an energy standpoint. Whereas the citric-acid cycle converts the fragments of carbohydrate breakdown to carbon dioxide, the ribulose-diphosphate cycle builds up carbohydrates from carbon dioxide. The citric-acid cycle delivers energy to the organism; the ribulose-diphosphate cycle, conversely, has to consume energy.

Here the earlier results of Ruben and Kamen fit in. The energy of sunlight is used, thanks to the catalytic action of chlorophyll, to split a molecule of water into hydrogen and oxygen, a process called "photolysis" (from Greek words meaning "loosening by light"). This is the way that the radiant energy of sunlight is converted into chemical energy, for the hydrogen and oxygen molecules contain more chemical energy than did the water molecule from which they came.

In other circumstances it takes a great deal of energy to break up water molecules into hydrogen — for instance, heating the water to something like 2,000 degrees or sending a strong electric current through it. But chlorophyll does the trick easily at ordinary temperatures. All it needs is the relatively weak energy of visible light. The plant uses the light-energy that it absorbs with an efficiency of at least 30 per cent; some investigators believe its efficiency may approach 100 per cent under ideal conditions. If man could harness energy as efficiently as the plants do, he would have much less to worry about with regard to his supplies of food and energy.

After the water molecules have been split, half of the hydrogen atoms find their way into the ribulose-diphosphate cycle, and half of the oxygen atoms are liberated into the air. The rest of the hydrogens and oxygens recombine into water. In doing so, they release the excess of energy that was given to them when sunlight split the water molecules, and this energy is transferred to high-energy phosphate compounds such as ATP. The energy stored in these compounds is then used to power the ribulose-diphosphate cycle.

Such is the reaction that makes life on our planet possible. Our reaction can only be: long life and more power to chlorophyll!

CHAPTER

12

THE CELL

CHROMOSOMES

IT IS AN ODD PARADOX that until recent times man knew very little about his own body. In fact, it was only some 300 years ago that he learned about the circulation of the blood, and only within the last 50 years or so has he discovered the functions of many of the organs.

Prehistoric man, from cutting up animals for cooking and embalming his own dead in preparation for afterlife, was aware of the existence of the large organs, such as the brain, liver, heart, lungs, stomach, intestines, and kidneys. The ancient Greeks went so far as to dissect animals and an occasional human cadaver with the deliberate purpose of learning something about "anatomy" (from Greek words meaning "to cut up"). Ancient anatomy reached its peak with Galen, a Greek physician who practiced in Rome in the latter half of the second century. Galen worked up theories of bodily functions which were accepted as gospel for 1,500 years afterward. But his notions about the human body were full of curious errors. This is understandable, for the ancients obtained most of their information from dissecting animals. Inhibitions of one kind or another made men uneasy about dissecting the human body.

In their denunciations of the pagan Greeks, early Christian writers accused them of having practiced heartless vivisections on human beings. But this comes under the heading of polemical literature; not only is it doubtful that the Greeks did human vivisections but obviously they did not even dissect enough dead bodies to learn much about the human anatomy. In any case, the Church's disapproval of dissection virtually put a stop to anatomical studies throughout the Middle Ages. To be sure, there were a few clandestine researches. In the fifteenth century Leonardo da Vinci did some dissections from which he derived theories of physiology more advanced than Galen's. But Leonardo, though he was a genius in science as well as in art, had little influence on scientific thought in his time. Either from neurotic disinclination or from sober caution, he did not publish any of his scientific work but kept it hidden in coded notebooks. It was left for later generations to discover his scientific achievements when his notebooks were finally published.

The French physician Jean Fernel was the first modern to take up dissection as an important part of a physician's duties. He published a book on the subject in 1542. However, his work was almost completely overshadowed by a much greater work published in the following year. This was the famous *De Humani Corporis Fabrica* ("Concerning the Structure of the Human Body") of Andreas Vesalius, a Belgian who did most of his work in Italy. On the theory that the proper study of mankind was man, Vesalius dissected the appropriate subject and corrected many of Galen's errors. The drawings of the human anatomy in his book (which are reputed to have been made by the artist Titian) are so beautiful and accurate that they are still republished today and will always stand as classics. And Vesalius can be called the father of modern anatomy. His

Fabrica was as revolutionary in its way as Copernicus's *De Revolutionibus Orbium Coelestium,* published in the very same year.

Just as the revolution initiated by Copernicus was brought to fruition by Galileo, so the one initiated by Vesalius came to a head in the crucial discoveries of William Harvey. Harvey was an English physician and experimentalist, of the same generation as Galileo and William Gilbert, the experimenter with magnetism. His particular interest was that vital body juice — the blood. What did it do in the body, anyway?

It was known that there were two sets of blood vessels: the veins and the arteries. (Praxagoras of Cos, a Greek physician of the third century B.C., had given the latter the name "artery" from Greek words meaning "I carry air," because these vessels were found to be empty in dead bodies. Galen had later shown that in life they carried blood.) It was also known that the heartbeat drove the blood in some sort of motion, for when an artery was cut, the blood gushed out in pulses that synchronized with the heartbeat.

Galen had proposed that the blood see-sawed to and fro in the blood vessels, traveling first in one direction through the body and then in the other. This theory required him to explain why the back-and-forth movement of the blood was not blocked by the wall between the two halves of the heart; Galen answered simply that the wall was riddled with invisibly small holes which let the blood through.

Harvey took a closer look at the heart. He found that each half was divided into two chambers, separated by a one-way valve that allowed blood to flow from the upper chamber ("auricle") to the lower ("ventricle") but not vice versa. In other words, blood entering one of the auricles could be pumped into its corresponding ventricle and from there into blood vessels issuing from it, but there could be no flow in the opposite direction.

Harvey then performed some simple but beautifully clear-cut experiments to determine the direction of flow in the blood vessels. He would tie off an artery or a vein in a living animal to see on which side of this blockage the pressure within the blood vessel would

499

build up. He found that when he stopped the flow in an artery, the vessel always bulged on the side between the heart and the block. This meant that the blood in arteries must flow in the direction away from the heart. When he tied a vein, the bulge was always on the other side of the block; therefore the blood flow in veins must be toward the heart.

Harvey went on to apply quantitative measurements to the blood flow (the first time anyone had applied mathematics to a biological problem). His measurements showed that the heart pumped out blood at such a rate that each half-hour its output equaled the total amount of blood contained in the body. It did not seem reasonable to suppose that the body could manufacture new blood, or consume the old, at any such rate. The logical conclusion, therefore, was that the blood must be recycled through the body. Since it flowed away from the heart in the arteries and toward the heart in the veins, Harvey decided that the blood was pumped by the heart into the arteries, then passed from them into the veins, then flowed back to the heart, then was pumped into the arteries again, and so on. In other words, it circulated continuously in one direction through the heart-and-blood-vessel system.

Earlier anatomists, including Leonardo da Vinci, had hinted at such an idea, but Harvey was the first to state and investigate the theory in detail. He set forth his reasoning and experiments in a small, badly printed book entitled *De Motus Cordis* ("Concerning the Motion of the Heart"), which was published in 1628 and has stood ever since as one of the great classics of science.

The main question left unanswered by Harvey's work was: how did the blood pass from the arteries into the veins? Harvey said there must be connecting vessels of some sort, though they were too small to be seen. This was reminiscent of Galen's theory about small holes in the heart wall, but whereas Galen's holes in the heart were never found and do not exist, Harvey's connecting vessels were confirmed as soon as a microscope became available. In 1661, just four years after Harvey's death, an Italian physician named Marcello Malpighi examined the lung tissues of a frog with a primitive microscope, and,

Unfortunately, further study of the cell nucleus and the mechanism of division was thwarted for a long time by the fact that the cell was more or less transparent, so that its substructures could not be seen. Then the situation was improved by the discovery that certain dyes would stain parts of the cell and not others. A dye called "hematoxylin" (obtained from logwood) stained the cell nucleus black and brought it out prominently against the background of the cell. After Perkin and other chemists began to produce synthetic dyes, biologists found themselves with a variety of dyes from which to choose.

In 1879 the German biologist Walther Flemming found that with certain red dyes he could stain a particular material in the cell nucleus which was distributed through it as small granules. He called this material "chromatin" (from the Greek word for "color"). By examining this material, Flemming was able to follow some of the changes in the process of cell division. To be sure, the stain killed the cell, but in a slice of tissue he would catch various cells at different stages of cell division. They served as still pictures which he put together to form a kind of "moving picture" of the progress of cell division.

In 1882 Flemming published an important book in which he described the process in detail. At the start of cell division, the chromatin material gathered itself together in the form of threads. The thin membrane enclosing the cell nucleus seemed to dissolve, and at the same time a tiny object just outside it divided in two. Flemming called this object the "aster," from a Greek word for "star," because radiating threads gave it a starlike appearance. After dividing, the two parts of the aster traveled to opposite sides of the cell. Its trailing threads apparently entangled the threads of chromatin, which had meanwhile lined up in the center of the cell, and the aster pulled half the chromatin threads to one side of the cell, half to the other. As a result, the cell pinched in at the middle and split into two cells. A cell nucleus developed in each, and the chromatin material that the nuclear membrane enclosed broke up into granules again.

Flemming called the process of cell division "mitosis," from the

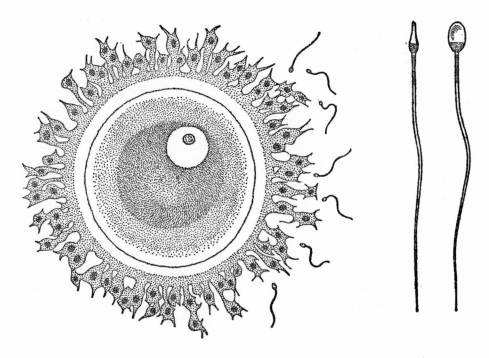

HUMAN EGG AND SPERM CELLS.

German physiologist Karl Ernst von Baer had identified the ovum, or egg cell, of mammals. Biologists came to realize that the union of an egg and a spermatozoon formed a fertilized ovum from which the animal eventually developed by repeated divisions and re-divisions.

The big question was: how did cells divide? The answer lay in a small globule of comparatively dense material within the cell first reported by the Scottish botanist Robert Brown in 1831 and named the "nucleus." (To distinguish it from the nucleus of the atom, I will refer to it from now on as the "cell nucleus.")

If a one-celled organism was divided into two parts, one of which contained the intact cell nucleus, the part containing the cell nucleus was able to grow and divide, but the other part could not. (Later it was also learned that the red blood cells of mammals, lacking nuclei, are short-lived and have no capacity for either growth or division. For that reason, they are not considered true cells and are usually called "corpuscles.")

503

sure enough, there were tiny blood vessels connecting the arteries with the veins. Malpighi named them "capillaries," from a Latin word meaning "hair-like."

THE COMING OF THE MICROSCOPE introduced biologists to a more basic level of organization of living things. In 1665 the English scientist Robert Hooke, using his newly invented "compound microscope" (which gave greater magnification than one with a single lens), discovered that cork, the bark of a tree, was built of extremely tiny compartments, like a superfine sponge. He called these holes "cells," likening them to small rooms such as the cells in a monastery. Other microscopists then found similar "cells," but full of fluid, in living tissue.

Over the next century and a half it gradually dawned on biologists that all living matter was made up of cells, and that each cell was an independent unit of life. Some forms of life — certain microorganisms — consisted of only a single cell; the larger organisms were composed of many cooperating cells. One of the earliest to propose this view was the French physiologist René Joachim Henri Dutrochet. His report, published in 1824, went unnoticed, however, and the cell theory gained prominence only after Matthias Jakob Schleiden and Theodor Schwann of Germany independently formulated it in 1838 and 1839.

The cell theory is to biology about what the atomic theory is to chemistry and physics. Its importance in the dynamics of life was established when, around 1860, the German pathologist Rudolf Virchow asserted, in a succinct Latin phrase, that all cells arose from cells. He showed that the cells in diseased tissue were produced by the division of originally normal cells.

By that time it had become clear that every living organism, even the largest, began life as a single cell. One of the earliest microscopists, Johann Ham, an assistant of Leeuwenhoek, had discovered in seminal fluid tiny bodies which were later named "spermatozoa" (from Greek words meaning "animal seed"). Much later, in 1827, the

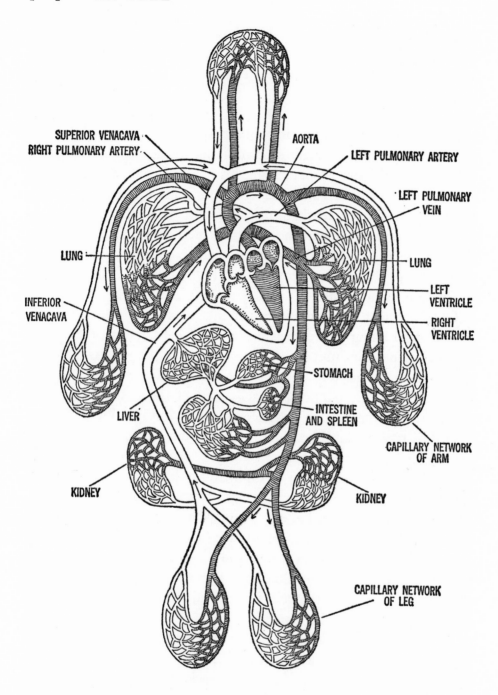

SUPERIOR VENACAVA
RIGHT PULMONARY ARTERY

AORTA

LEFT PULMONARY ARTERY

LEFT PULMONARY VEIN

LUNG

LUNG

LEFT VENTRICLE

INFERIOR VENACAVA

RIGHT VENTRICLE

STOMACH

INTESTINE AND SPLEEN

LIVER

CAPILLARY NETWORK OF ARM

KIDNEY

KIDNEY

CAPILLARY NETWORK OF LEG

THE CIRCULATORY SYSTEM.

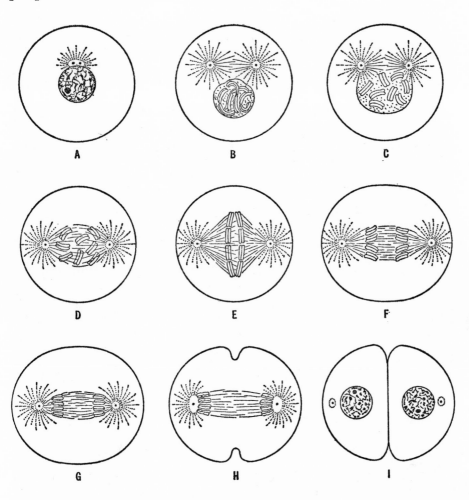

DIVISION OF A CELL BY MITOSIS.

Greek word for "thread," because of the prominent part played in it by the chromatin threads. In 1888 the German anatomist Wilhelm von Waldeyer gave the chromatin thread the name "chromosome" (from the Greek for "colored body"), and that name has stuck. It should be mentioned, though, that chromosomes, despite their name, are colorless in their unstained natural state.

Continued observation of stained cells showed that the cells of each species of plant or animal had a fixed and characteristic number

5 0 5

of chromosomes. Before a cell divides in two during mitosis, the number of chromosomes is doubled, so that each of the two daughter cells after the division has the same number as the original mother cell.

The Belgian embryologist Eduard van Beneden discovered in 1885 that the chromosomes did *not* double in number when egg and sperm cells were being formed. Consequently each egg and each sperm cell had only half the number of chromosomes that ordinary cells of the organism possessed. (The cell division that produces sperm and egg cells therefore is called "meiosis," from a Greek word meaning "to make less.") When an egg and a sperm cell combined, however, the combination (the fertilized ovum) had a complete set of chromosomes, half contributed by the mother through the egg cell and half by the father through the sperm cell. This complete set was passed on by ordinary mitosis to all the cells that made up the body of the organism developing from the fertilized egg.

GENES

MEANWHILE AN AUSTRIAN MONK named Gregor Johann Mendel, who was too occupied with the affairs of his monastery to pay attention to the biologists' excitement about cell division, had quietly done some experiments in his garden which were destined eventually to make sense out of chromosomes. Abbé Mendel was an amateur botanist, and he became particularly interested in the results of cross-breeding pea plants of varying characteristics. He would cross plants with different seed colors (green or yellow), or smooth-seeded peas with wrinkle-seeded ones, or long-stemmed plants with short-stemmed ones, and then would follow the results in the offspring of the succeeding generations. Mendel kept a careful statistical record of his results, and his conclusions can be summarized essentially as follows:

1. Each characteristic was governed by "factors" which (in the

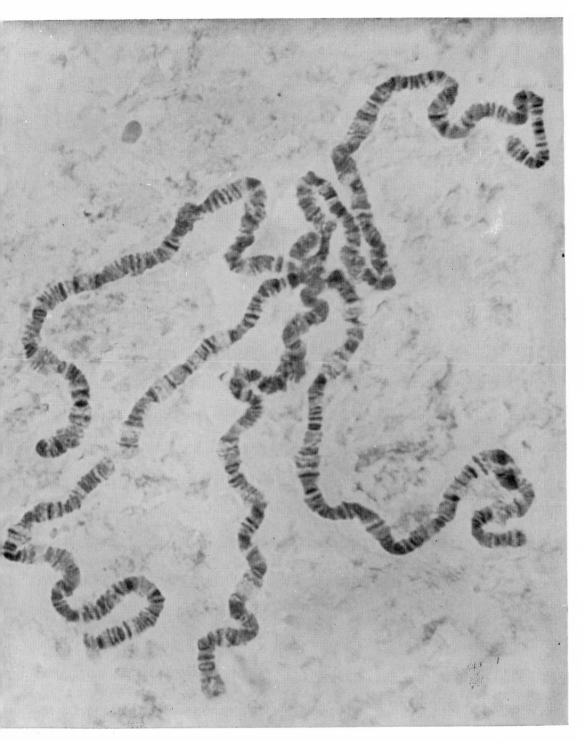

NORMAL CHROMOSOMES *of Drosophila, the fruit fly.*

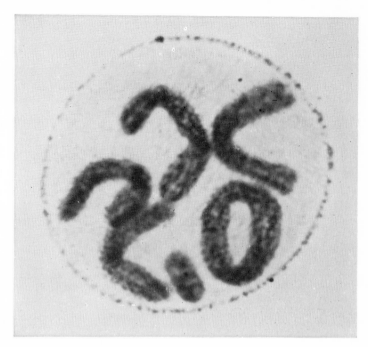

CHROMOSOMES DAMAGED
BY RADIATION. *Some are
broken, and one is coiled
into a ring.*

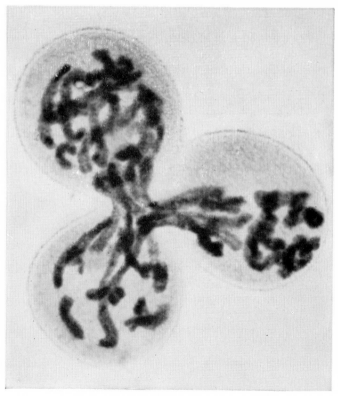

RADIATION DAMAGE *caused
these chromosomes to di-
vide into three groups instead of the normal two.*

MUTATIONS IN FRUIT FLIES, *shown here in the form of shriveled wings. The mutations were produced by exposure of the male parent to radiation.*

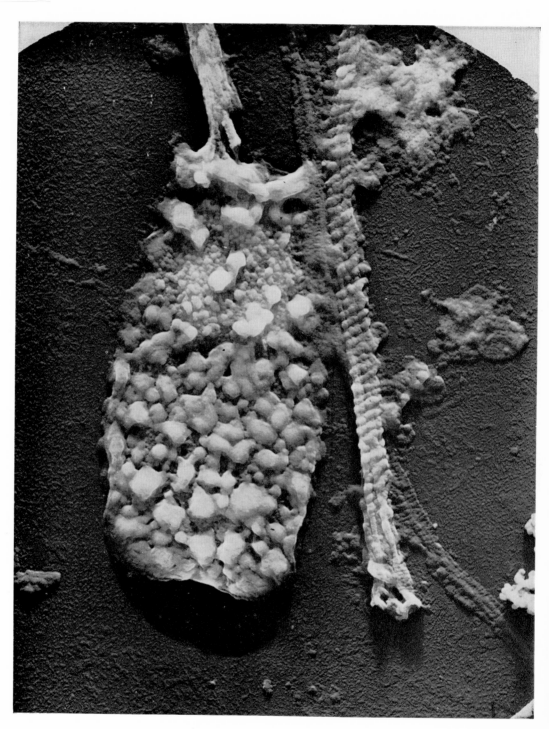

SPERM CELL *of a bull*.

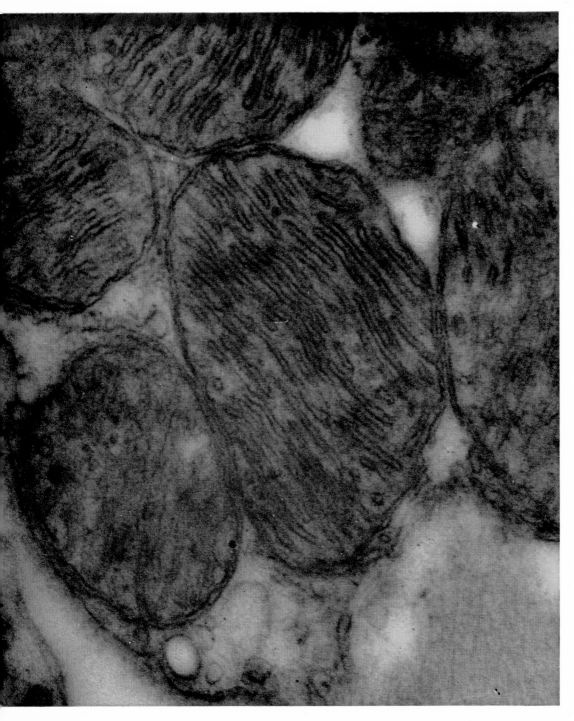

HEART CELL *in the right ventricle of a rat, magnified more than 100,000 times by the electron microscope.*

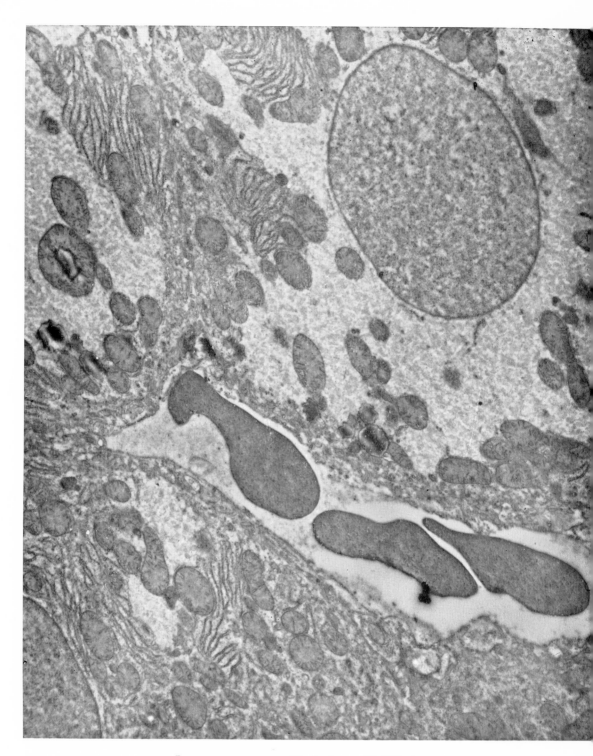

LIVER CELL, *magnified about 10,000 times.*

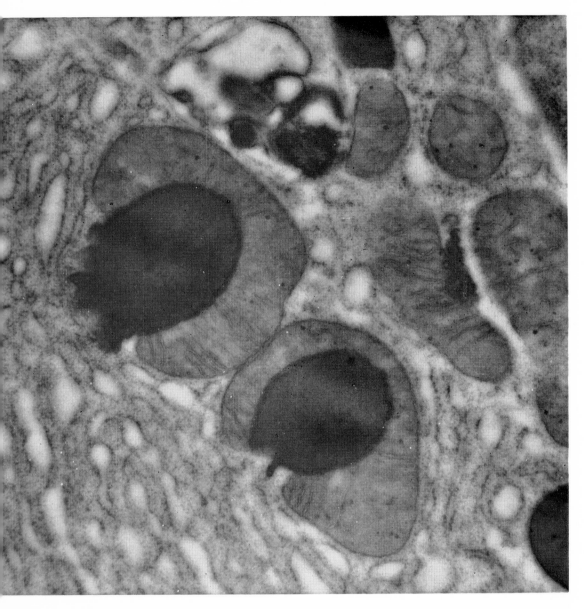

MITOCHONDRIA, *sometimes called "powerhouses of the cell," because they carry out energy-yielding chemical reactions. The mitochondria are the black bodies in the center of the picture.*

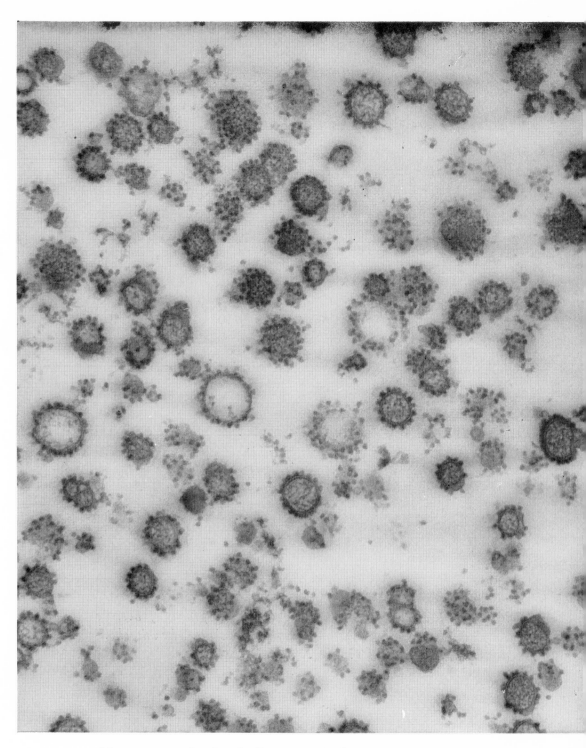

MICROSOMES, *the tiny bodies found in the cytoplasm of cells. These were separated from pancreas cells by a centrifuge and magnified about 100,000 times under the electron microscope.*

cases that Mendel studied) could exist in one of two forms. One version of the factor for seed color, for instance, would cause the seeds to be green; the other form would make them yellow. (For convenience, let us use the present-day terms. The factors are now called "genes," from a Greek word meaning "to give birth to," and the different forms of a gene controlling a given characteristic are called "alleles." Thus the seed-color gene possessed two alleles, one for green seeds, the other for yellow seeds.)

2. Every plant had a pair of genes for each characteristic, one contributed by each parent. The plant transmitted one of its pair to a germ cell, so that when the germ cells of two plants united by pollination, the offspring had two genes for the characteristic once more. The two genes might be either identical or alleles.

3. When the two parent plants contributed alleles of a particular gene to the offspring, one allele might overwhelm the effect of the other. For instance, if a plant producing yellow seeds was crossed with one producing green seeds, all the members of the next generation would produce yellow seeds. The yellow allele of the seed-color gene was "dominant," the green allele "recessive."

4. Nevertheless, the recessive allele was not destroyed. The green allele, in the case just cited, was still present, even though it produced no detectable effect. If two plants containing mixed genes (*i.e.,* each with one yellow and one green allele) were crossed, some of the offspring might have two green alleles in the fertilized ovum; in that case those particular offspring would produce green seeds, and the offspring of such parents in turn would also produce green seeds. Mendel pointed out that there were four possible ways of combining alleles from a pair of hybrid parents, each possessing one yellow and one green allele. A yellow allele from the first parent might combine with a yellow allele from the second; a yellow allele from the first might combine with a green allele from the second; a green allele from the first might combine with a yellow allele from the second; and a green allele from the first might combine with a green allele from the second. Of the four combinations, only the last would result in a plant that would produce green seeds. Assuming that all

507

four combinations were equally probable, one-fourth of the plants of the new generation should produce green seeds. Mendel found that this was indeed so.

5. Mendel also found that characteristics of different kinds — for instance, seed color and flower color — were inherited independently of each other. That is, red flowers were as apt to go with yellow seeds as with green seeds. The same was true of white flowers.

Mendel performed these experiments in the early 1860's, wrote them up carefully, and sent a copy of his paper to Karl Wilhelm von Nägeli, a Swiss botanist of great reputation. Von Nägeli's reaction was negative. Von Nägeli had, apparently, a predilection for all-encompassing theories (his own theoretical work was semi-mystical and turgid in expression), and he saw little merit in the mere counting of pea-plants as a way to truth. Besides, Mendel was an unknown amateur.

It seems that Mendel allowed himself to be discouraged by von Nägeli's comments, for he turned to his monastery duties, grew fat (too fat to bend over in the garden), and abandoned his researches. He did, however, publish his paper in 1866 in a provincial Austrian journal, where it attracted no further attention for a generation.

But other scientists were slowly moving toward the same conclusions to which (unknown to them) Mendel had already come. One of the routes by which they arrived at an interest in genetics was the study of "mutations," that is, of freak animals, or monsters, which had always been regarded as bad omens. (The word "monster" came from a Latin word meaning "warning.") In 1791 a Massachusetts farmer named Seth Wright took a more practical view of a sport that turned up in his flock of sheep. A lamb was born with abnormally short legs, and it occurred to the shrewd Yankee that short-legged sheep could not escape over the low stone walls around his farm. He therefore deliberately bred a line of short-legged sheep from his not unfortunate accident.

This practical demonstration stimulated others to look for useful mutations. By the end of the nineteenth century the American horticulturist Luther Burbank was making a successful career of breeding new varieties of plants which were improvements over the old in one respect or another.

Meanwhile botanists tried to find an explanation of mutation. And in what is perhaps the most startling coincidence in the history of science, no fewer than three men independently, and in the very same year, came to precisely the same conclusions that Mendel had reached a generation earlier. They were Hugo de Vries of Holland, Karl Erich Correns of Germany, and Erich von Tschermak, of Austria. None of them knew of each other's or Mendel's work. All three were ready to publish in 1900. All three, in a final check of previous publications in the field, came across Mendel's paper, to their own vast surprise. All three did publish in 1900, each citing Mendel's paper, giving Mendel full credit for the discovery, and advancing his own work only as confirmation.

A number of biologists immediately saw a connection between Mendel's genes and the chromosomes that could be seen under the microscope. The first to draw a parallel was an American cytologist named W. S. Sutton. He pointed out that chromosomes, like genes, came in pairs, one of which was inherited from the father and one from the mother. The only trouble with this analogy was that the number of chromosomes in the cells of any organism was far smaller than the number of inherited characteristics. Man, for instance has only 23 pairs of chromosomes. (For many years biologists thought that the human cell had 24 pairs, but careful inspection with a new type of microscope in 1957 showed that there were 23. Anyone who has ever looked at a photograph of chromosomes in a dividing human cell can understand the miscount: they look like a tangle of short spaghetti strands or of stubby worms.) Since the number of characteristics inherited by human beings certainly runs into many thousands, biologists had to conclude that chromosomes were not genes. Each must be a collection of genes.

In short order, biologists discovered an excellent tool for studying specific genes. It was not a physical instrument but a new kind of laboratory animal. In 1906 the Columbia University zoologist Thomas Hunt Morgan conceived the idea of using fruit flies (*Dro-*

sophila melanogaster) for research in genetics. (The term "genetics" was invented about this time by the British biologist William Bateson.)

Fruit flies had considerable advantages over pea plants (or any ordinary laboratory animal) for studying the inheritance of genes. They bred quickly and prolifically, could easily be raised by the hundreds on very little food, had scores of inheritable characteristics which could be observed readily, and had a comparatively simple chromosomal setup — only four pairs of chromosomes per cell.

With the fruit fly Morgan and his coworkers discovered an important fact about the mechanism of inheritance of sex. They found that the female fruit fly has four perfectly matched pairs of chromosomes so that all the egg cells, receiving one of each pair, are identical as far as chromosome makeup is concerned. However, in the male one of the four pairs consists of a normal chromosome, called the "x-chromosome," and a stunted one, which was named the "y-chromosome." Therefore when sperm cells are formed, half have an x-chromosome and half a y-chromosome. When a sperm cell with the x-chromosome fertilizes an egg cell, the fertilized egg, with four matched pairs, naturally becomes a female. On the other hand, a sperm cell with a y-chromosome produces a male. Since both alternatives are equally probable, the number of males and females in the typical species of living things is roughly equal. (In some creatures, notably various birds, it is the female that has a y-chromosome.)

This chromosomal difference explains why some disorders or mutations show up only in the male. If a defective gene occurs on one of a pair of x-chromosomes, the other member of the pair is still likely to be normal and can salvage the situation. But in the male, a defect on the x-chromosome paired with the y-chromosome generally cannot be compensated for, because the latter carries very few genes. Therefore the defect shows up.

Research on fruit flies showed that traits were not necessarily inherited independently, as Mendel had thought. It happened that the seven characteristics of pea plants that he had studied were governed

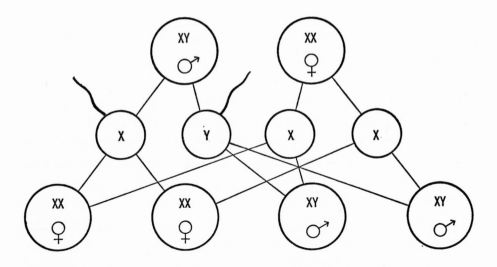

COMBINATIONS OF X AND Y CHROMOSOMES.

by genes on separate chromosomes. Morgan found that where two genes governing two different characteristics were located on the same chromosome, those characteristics were generally inherited together (just as a passenger in the front seat of a car and one in the back seat travel together).

This genetic linkage is not, however, unchangeable. Just as a passenger can change cars, so a piece of one chromosome occasionally switches to another, swapping places with a piece from the other. Such "crossing over" may occur during the division of a cell. As a result, linked traits are separated and reshuffled in a new linkage. For instance, there is a variety of fruit fly with scarlet eyes and curly wings. When it is mated with a white-eyed, miniature-winged fruit fly, the offspring will generally be either red-eyed and curly-winged or white-eyed and miniature-winged. But the mating may sometimes produce a white-eyed, curly-winged fly or a red-eyed, miniature-winged one as a result of crossing over. The new form will persist in succeeding generations unless another crossing over takes place.

Now picture a chromosome with a gene for red eyes at one end and a gene for curly wings at the other end. Let us say that in the

5 1 1

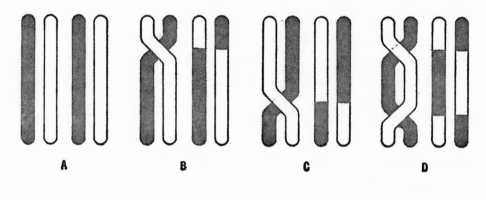

A   B   C   D

NO CROSSOVER   :SINGLE CROSSOVER   SINGLE CROSSOVER   DOUBLE CROSSOVER

CROSSING OVER IN CHROMOSOMES.

middle of the chromosome's length there are two adjacent genes governing two other characteristics. Obviously the probability of a break occurring at that particular point, separating those two genes, is smaller than the probability of a break coming at one of the many points along the length of the chromosome which would separate the genes at the opposite ends. By noting the frequency of separation of given pairs of linked characteristics by crossing over, Morgan and his coworkers were able to deduce the relative locations of the genes in question, and in this way they worked out chromosome "maps" of gene locations for the fruit fly.

For his work on the genetics of fruit flies, Morgan received the Nobel Prize in medicine and physiology in 1933.

Every once in a while, with a frequency which can be calculated, a sudden change occurs in a gene. The mutation shows itself by some new and unexpected physical characteristic, such as the short legs of Farmer Wright's lamb. Mutations in Nature are very rare. In 1926 the geneticist Hermann Joseph Muller, who had been a member of Morgan's research team, discovered a way to increase the rate of mutations artificially in fruit flies so that the inheritance of such changes could be studied more easily. He found that X-rays would do the trick; presumably they damaged the genes. The study of mutations made possible by Muller's discovery won him the Nobel Prize in medicine and physiology in 1946.

As it happens, Muller's researches have given rise to some rather disquieting thoughts concerning the future of the human species. While mutations are an important driving force in evolution, occasionally producing an improvement that enables a species to cope with its environment better, the beneficial mutation is very much the exception. Most mutations — at least 99 per cent of them — are detrimental, some even lethal. Eventually even those that are only slightly harmful die out, because their bearers do not get along as well and leave fewer descendants than healthy individuals do. But in the meantime a mutation may cause illness and suffering for many generations. Furthermore, new mutations keep cropping up continually, and every species carries a constant load of defective genes.

Muller and other geneticists are particularly concerned about the growing load carried by the human species. Two modern developments seem to be adding steadily to this load. First, the advances in medicine and social care tend to compensate for the handicaps of people with detrimental mutations, at least as far as the ability to reproduce is concerned. Eye-glasses are available to individuals with defective vision; insulin keeps alive sufferers from diabetes (a hereditary disease), and so on. Thus they pass on their defective genes to future generations. The alternatives — allowing defective individuals to die young or sterilizing or imprisoning them — are of course, unthinkable, except where the handicap is sufficiently great to make the individual less than human, as in idiocy or homicidal paranoia. Undoubtedly the human species can still bear its load of negatively mutated genes, despite its humanitarian impulses.

But there is less excuse for the second modern hazard — namely, adding to the load by unnecessary exposure to radiation. Genetic research shows incontrovertibly that for the population as a whole even a slight increase in general exposure to radiation means a corresponding slight increase in the mutation rate. And since 1895 mankind has been exposed to types and intensities of radiation of which previous generations knew nothing. Solar radiation, the natural radio-activity of the soil, and cosmic rays have always been with us. Now, however, we use X-rays in medicine and dentistry with abandon; we concentrate radioactive material; we form artificially radioactive isotopes of terrifying radiant potency; we even explode nuclear bombs. All of this increases the background radiation.

No one, of course, suggests that research in nuclear physics be abandoned, or that X-rays never be used by the doctor and dentist. There is, however, a strong recommendation that the danger be recognized and that exposure to radiation be minimized; that, for instance, X-rays be used with discrimination and care and that the sexual organs be routinely shielded during all such use. Another suggested precaution is that each individual keep a record of his total accumulated exposure to X-rays, so that he will have some idea of whether he is in danger of exceeding a reasonable limit.

Of course, the geneticists could not be sure that the principles established by experiments on plants and insects necessarily applied to man. After all, man was neither a pea plant nor a fruit fly. But direct studies of certain characteristics in man showed that human genetics did follow the same rules. The best-known example is the inheritance of blood types.

Blood transfusion is a very old practice, and early physicians occasionally even tried to transfuse animal blood into persons weakened by loss of blood. But transfusions even of human blood often turned out badly, so that laws were sometimes passed forbidding transfusion. In the 1890's the Austrian pathologist Karl Landsteiner finally discovered that human blood came in different types, some of which were incompatible with each other. He found that sometimes when blood from one person was mixed with a sample of serum (the blood fluid remaining after the red cells and a clotting factor are removed) from another person, the red cells of the first person's whole blood would clump together. Obviously such a mixture would be very bad if it occurred in a transfusion, and it might even kill the patient if the clumped cells blocked the blood circulation in key vessels. Landsteiner also found, however, that some bloods could be mixed without causing any deleterious clumping.

By 1902 Landsteiner was able to announce that there were four types of human blood, which he called A, B, AB, and O. Any given individual had blood of just one of these types. Of course, a particular type could be transfused without danger from one person to another having the same type. In addition, O blood could safely be transfused to a person possessing any of the other three types, and either A blood or B blood could be given to an AB patient. But redcell clumping ("agglutination") would result when AB blood was transfused to an A or B individual, or when A and B were mixed, or when an O individual received a transfusion of any blood other than O. (Nowadays, because of possible serum reactions, in good practice patients are given only blood of their own type.)

In 1930 Landsteiner (who by then had become a United States citizen) received the Nobel Prize in medicine and physiology.

Geneticists have established that these blood types (and all the others since discovered, including the Rh variations) are inherited in a strictly Mendelian manner. It seems that there are three gene alleles, responsible respectively for A, B, and O blood. If both parents have O-type blood, all the children of that union will have O-type blood. If one parent is O-type and the other A-type, all the children may show A-type blood, for the A allele is dominant over the O. The B allele likewise is dominant over the O allele. The B allele and A allele, however, show no dominance with respect to each other, and an individual possessing both alleles has AB-type blood.

The Mendelian rules work out so strictly that blood groups can be (and are) used to test paternity. If an O-type mother has a B-type child, the child's father must be B-type, for that B allele must have come from somewhere. If the woman's husband happens to be A or O, it is clear that she has been unfaithful (or there has been a baby mixup at the hospital). If an O-type woman with a B-type child accuses an A or O man of being the parent, she is either mistaken or lying. On the other hand, while blood type can sometimes prove a negative, it can never prove a positive. If the woman's husband, or the man accused, is indeed a B-type, the case remains unproved. Any B-type man, or any AB-type man, could have been the father.

The applicability of the Mendelian rules of inheritance to human beings has also been borne out by the existence of sex-linked traits. Color blindness and hemophilia (a hereditary failure of the blood to clot) are found almost exclusively in males, and they are inherited in precisely the manner that sex-linked characteristics are inherited in the fruit fly.

Human genetics is an enormously complicated subject which is not likely to be completely or neatly worked out in the foreseeable future. Because man breeds neither as frequently nor as prolifically as the fruit fly; because his matings cannot be subjected to laboratory control for experimental purposes; because he has many more chromosomes and many more inherited characteristics than the fruit fly; because the human characteristics in which we are most interested, such as creative genius, intelligence, and moral strength, are extremely complex, involving the interplay of numerous genes plus environmental influences — for all these reasons, geneticists cannot deal with human genetics with the same confidence with which they study fruit-fly genetics.

JUST HOW DOES A GENE bring the physical characteristic for which it is responsible into being? What is the mechanism whereby it gives rise to yellow seeds in pea plants, or curled wings in fruit flies, or blue eyes in human beings?

Biologists are now certain that genes exert their effects by way of enzymes. One of the clearest cases in point involves the color of eyes, hair, and skin. The color (blue or brown, yellow or black, pink or brown or shades in between) is determined by the amount of pigment, called "melanin" (from the Greek word for "black"), that is present in the eye pupil, the hair or the skin. Now melanin is formed from an amino acid, tyrosine, by way of a number of steps, most of which have now been worked out. A number of enzymes are involved, and the amount of melanin formed will depend upon the quantity of these enzymes. For instance, one of the enzymes, which catalyzes the first two steps, is tyrosinase. Presumably some particular gene controls the production of tyrosinase by the cells. In that way, it will control the coloring of the skin, hair, and eyes. And since the gene is transmitted from generation to generation, children will naturally resemble their parents in coloring. If a mutation happens to produce a defective gene that cannot form tyrosinase, there will be no melanin, and the individual will be an "albino." The absence of a single enzyme (and hence the deficiency of a single gene) will thus suffice to bring about a major change in personal characteristics.

Granted that an organism's characteristics are controlled by its enzyme makeup, which in turn is controlled by genes, the next question is: how do the genes work? Unfortunately, even the fruit fly is much too complex an organism to trace out the matter in detail. But in 1941 the American biologists George W. Beadle and Edward L. Tatum began such a study with a simple organism which they found admirably suited to this purpose. It is the common pink bread mold (scientific name, *Neurospora crassa*).

Neurospora is not very demanding in its diet. It will grow very well on sugar plus inorganic compounds that supply nitrogen, sulfur, and various minerals. Aside from sugar, the only organic substance that has to be supplied to it is a vitamin called "biotin."

At a certain stage in its life cycle, the mold produces eight spores, all identical in genetic constitution. Each spore contains seven chromosomes; as in the sex cell of a higher organism, its chromosomes come singly, not in pairs. Consequently if one of its chromosomes is changed, the effect can be observed, because there is no normal partner present to mask the effect. Beadle and Tatum therefore were able to create mutations in Neurospora by exposing the mold to X-rays and then could follow the specific effects in the behavior of the spores.

If, after the mold had received a dose of radiation, the spores still thrived on the usual medium of nutrients, clearly no mutation had taken place, at least as far as the organism's nutritional requirements for growth were concerned. If the spores would not grow on the usual medium, the experimenters proceeded to determine whether they were alive or dead, by feeding them a complete medium containing all the vitamins, amino acids, and other items they might possibly need. If the spores grew on this, the conclusion was that the X-rays had produced a mutation which had changed Neurospora's nutritional requirements. Apparently it now needed at least one new item in its diet. To find out what that was, the experimenters tried the spores on one diet after another, each time with some items of the complete medium missing. They might omit all the amino acids, or all the various vitamins, or all but one or two amino acids or one or two vitamins. In this way they narrowed down the requirements until they identified just what it was that the spore now needed that it had not needed in its diet before the mutation.

It turned out sometimes that the mutated spore required the amino acid arginine. The normal, "wild strain" had been able to manufacture its own arginine from sugar and ammonium salts. Now, thanks to the genetic change, it could no longer synthesize arginine, and unless this amino acid was supplied in its diet, it could not make protein and therefore could not grow.

The clearest way to account for such a situation was to suppose that the X-rays had disrupted a gene responsible for the formation of an enzyme necessary for manufacturing arginine. For lack of the normal gene, Neurospora could no longer make the enzyme. No enzyme, no arginine.

Beadle and his coworkers went on to use this sort of information to study the relation of genes to the chemistry of metabolism. There was a way to show, for instance, that more than one gene was involved in the making of arginine. For simplicity's sake, let us say there are two — gene A and gene B — responsible for the formation of two different enzymes, both of which are necessary for the synthesis of arginine. Then a mutation of either gene A or gene B will rob Neurospora of the ability to make the amino acid. Suppose we irradiate two batches of Neurospora and produce an arginine-less strain in each one. If we are lucky, one mutant may have a defective A gene and a normal B gene, the other a normal A and defective B. To see if that has happened, let us cross the two mutants at the sexual stage of their life cycle. If the two strains do indeed differ in this way, the recombination of chromosomes may produce some spores whose A and B genes are both normal. In other words, from two mutants that are incapable of making arginine, we will get some off-spring that *can* make it. Sure enough, exactly that sort of thing happened when the experiments were performed.

It was possible to explore the metabolism of Neurospora in finer detail than this. For instance, here were three different mutant strains incapable of making arginine on an ordinary medium. One would grow only if it was supplied with arginine itself. The second would grow if it received either arginine or a very similar compound called citrulline. The third could grow on arginine or citrulline or still another similar compound called ornithine.

What conclusion would you draw from all this? Well, we can guess that these three substances are steps in a sequence of which arginine is the final product. Each requires an enzyme. First ornithine is formed from some simpler compound with the help of an enzyme, then another enzyme converts ornithine to citrulline, and finally a third enzyme converts citrulline to arginine. (Actually chemical analysis shows that each of the three is slightly more complex than the one before.) Now a Neurospora mutant that lacks the enzyme for making ornithine but possesses the other enzymes can get along if it is supplied with ornithine, for from it the spore can make citrulline and then the essential arginine. Of course, it can also grow on citrulline, from which it can make arginine, and on arginine itself. By the same token, we can reason that the second mutant strain lacks the enzyme needed to convert ornithine to citrulline. This strain therefore must be provided with citrulline, from which it can make arginine, or with arginine itself. Finally, we can conclude that the mutant that will grow only on arginine has lost the enzyme (and gene) responsible for converting citrulline to arginine.

519

By analyzing the behavior of the various mutant strains they were able to isolate, Beadle and his coworkers founded the science of "chemical genetics." They worked out the course of synthesis of many important compounds by organisms. Beadle proposed what has become known as the "one-gene-one-enzyme theory" — that is, that every gene governs the formation of a single enzyme. For their pioneering work, Beadle and Tatum shared in the Nobel Prize in medicine and physiology in 1958.

BEADLE'S DISCOVERIES put biochemists on the *qui vive* for evidence of gene-controlled changes in proteins, particularly in human mutants, of course. A case turned up, unexpectedly, in connection with the disease called "sickle-cell anemia."

This disease had first been reported in 1910 by a Chicago physician named James B. Herrick. Examining a sample of blood from a Negro teenage patient under the microscope, he found that the red cells, normally round, had odd, bent shapes, many of them resembling the crescent shape of a sickle. Other physicians began to notice the same peculiar phenomenon, almost always in Negro patients. Eventually investigators decided that sickle-cell anemia was a hereditary disease. It followed the Mendelian laws of inheritance. Apparently there is a sickle-cell gene which, when inherited in double dose from both parents, produces these distorted red cells. Such cells are unable to carry oxygen properly and are exceptionally short-lived, so there is a shortage of red cells in the blood. Those who inherit the double dose tend to die of the disease in childhood. On the other hand, when a person has only one sickle-cell gene, from one of his parents, the disease does not appear. Sickling of his red cells shows up only when the person is deprived of oxygen to an unusual degree, as at high altitudes. Such people are considered to have the "sickle-cell trait" but not the disease.

It was found that about 9 per cent of the Negroes in America have the trait, and 0.25 per cent have the disease. In some localities in Central Africa as much as a quarter of the Negro population shows the trait. Apparently the sickle-cell gene arose as a mutation in Africa and has been inherited ever since by individuals of African descent. If the disease is fatal, why hasn't the defective gene died out? Studies in Africa during the 1950's turned up the answer. It seems that people with the sickle-cell trait tend to have greater immunity to malaria than normal individuals do. The sickle cells are somehow inhospitable to the malarial parasite. It is estimated that in areas infested with malaria, children with the trait have a 25 per cent better chance of surviving to child-bearing age than those without the trait have. So possessing a single dose of the sickle-cell gene (but not the anemia-causing double dose) confers an advantage. The two opposing tendencies — promotion of the defective gene by the protective effect of the single dose and elimination of the gene by its fatal effect in double dose — tend to produce an equilibrium which maintains the gene at a certain level in the population.

In regions where malaria is not an acute problem, the gene does tend to die out. In America the incidence of sickle-cell genes among Negroes may have started as high as 25 per cent. Even allowing for a reduction to an estimated 15 per cent by admixture with non-Negro individuals, the present incidence of only 9 per cent shows that the gene is dwindling away. In all probability it will continue to do so. If Africa is freed of malaria, it will presumably dwindle there, too.

Now the biochemical significance of the sickle-cell gene suddenly came into prominence in 1949 when Linus Pauling and his coworkers at Caltech (where Beadle also was working) showed that the gene affected the hemoglobin of the red blood cells. Persons with a double dose of the sickle-cell gene were unable to make normal hemoglobin. Pauling proved this by means of the technique called "electrophoresis," a method that uses an electric current to separate proteins by virtue of differences in the net electric charge on the various protein molecules. (The electrophoretic technique was developed by the Swedish chemist Arne Wilhelm Kaurin Tiselius, who received the Nobel Prize in chemistry in 1948 for this valuable contribution.) Pauling, by electrophoretic analysis, found that patients with sickle-cell anemia had an abnormal hemoglobin (named "hemoglobin S") which could be separated from normal hemoglobin. The normal kind was given the name hemoglobin A (for "adult") to distinguish it from a hemoglobin in fetuses, called hemoglobin F.

Since 1949 biochemists have discovered a number of other abnormal hemoglobins besides the sickle-cell one, and they are lettered from hemoglobin C to hemoglobin M. Apparently the gene responsible for the manufacture of hemoglobin has been mutated into many defective alleles, each giving rise to a hemoglobin that is inferior for carrying out the functions of the molecule in ordinary circumstances but perhaps helpful in some unusual condition. Thus, just as hemoglobin S in a single dose improves resistance to malaria, so hemoglobin C in a single dose improves the ability of the body to get along on marginal quantities of iron.

Since the various abnormal hemoglobins differ in electric charge, they must differ somehow in the arrangement of amino acids in the peptide chain, for the amino-acid makeup is responsible for the charge pattern of the molecule. The differences must be very small, because the abnormal hemoglobins all function as hemoglobin after a fashion. The hope of locating the difference in a huge molecule of some 600 amino acids was correspondingly small. Nevertheless, the British biochemist Vernon M. Ingram and coworkers tackled the problem of the chemistry of the abnormal hemoglobins.

They first broke hemoglobin A, hemoglobin S, and hemoglobin C down into peptides of various sizes by digesting them with a protein-splitting enzyme. Then they separated the fragments of each hemoglobin by "paper electrophoresis" — that is, using the electric current to convey the molecules along a moistened piece of filter paper instead of through a solution. (We can think of this as a kind of electrified paper chromatography.) When the investigators had done this with each of the three hemoglobins, they found that the only difference among them was that a single peptide turned up in a different place in each case.

They proceeded to break down and analyze this peptide. Eventually they learned that it was composed of nine amino acids and that

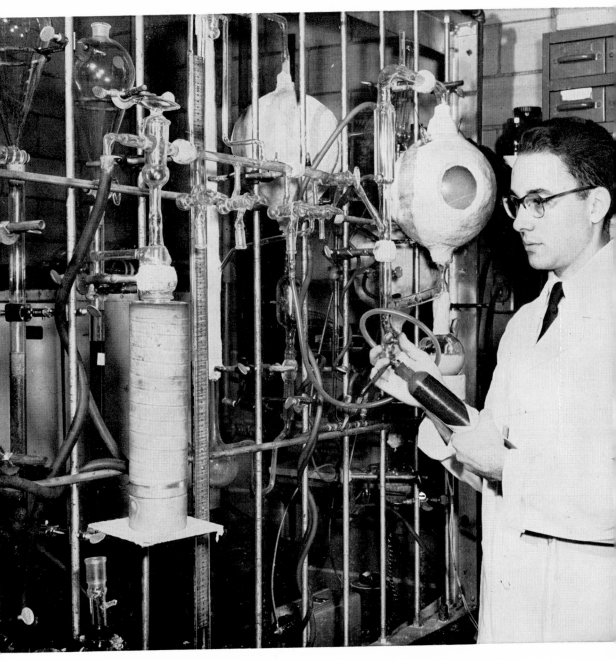

STANLEY MILLER'S HISTORIC EXPERIMENT *creating amino acids in the laboratory.*

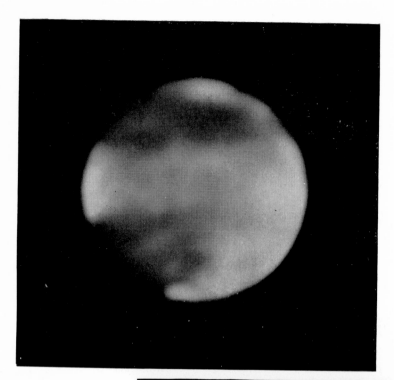

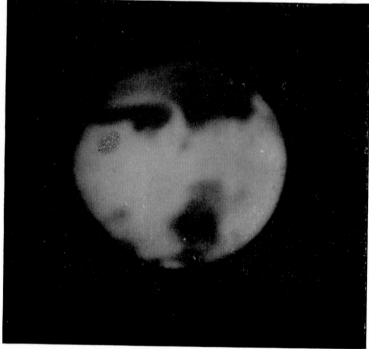

THE PLANET MARS, *photographed in blue* (top) *and red* (bottom) *light by the 200-inch telescope on Palomar Mountain. The pictures show the planet's ice caps and dark areas which may represent vegetation.*

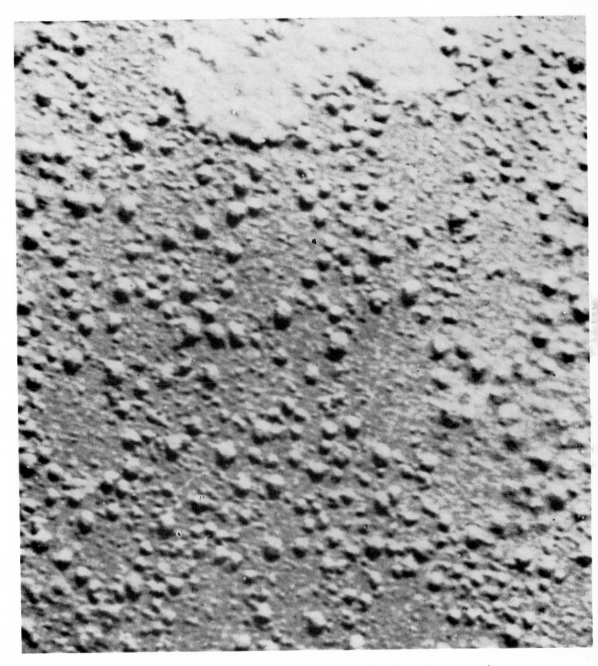

DNA-protein complex *photographed with the electron micro-scope. The spherical bodies, isolated from the germ cells of a sea animal and magnified 77,500 times, are believed to consist of DNA in combination with protein.*

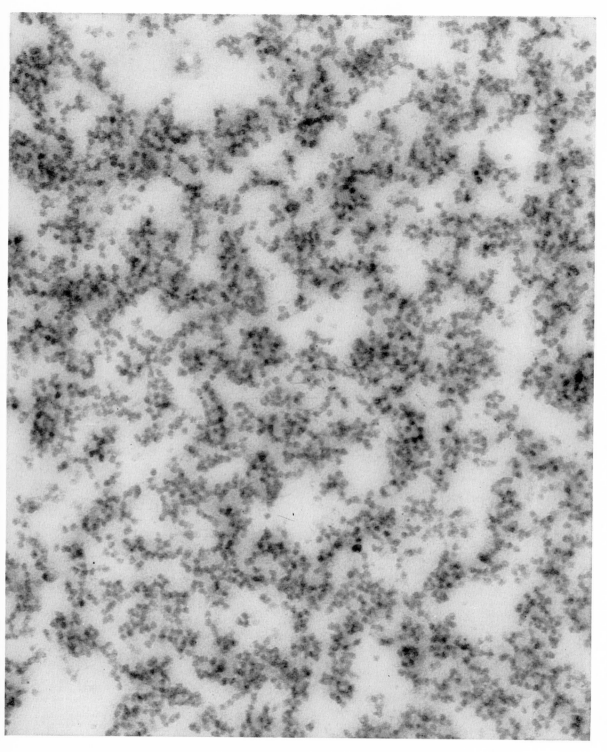

RIBONUCLEOPROTEIN PARTICLES, *obtained from microsomes of liver cells in a guinea pig. These particles are believed to be the main sites of the synthesis of proteins in the cell.*

the arrangement of these nine was exactly the same in all three hemo-globins except at one position. The respective arrangements were:

Hemoglobin A: His-Val-Leu-Leu-Thr-Pro-Glu-Glu-Lys
Hemoglobin S: His-Val-Leu-Leu-Thr-Pro-Val-Glu-Lys
Hemoglobin C: His-Val-Leu-Leu-Thr-Pro-Lys-Glu-Lys

As far as could be told, the only difference among the three hemo-globins lay in that single amino acid in the seventh position in the peptide: it was glutamic acid in hemoglobin A, valine in hemoglobin S, and lysine in hemoglobin C. Since glutamic acid gives rise to a negative charge, lysine to a positive charge, and valine to no charge at all, it is not surprising that the three proteins behave differently in electrophoresis. Their charge pattern is different.

But why should so slight a change in the molecule result in so drastic a change in the red cell? Well, the normal red cell is one-third hemoglobin A. The hemoglobin A molecules are packed so tightly in the cell that they just barely have room for free movement. In short, they are on the point of precipitating out of solution. Part of the influence that determines whether a protein is to precipitate out or not is the nature of its charge. If all the proteins have the same net charge, they repel one another and keep from precipitating. The greater the charge (*i.e.*, the repulsion), the less likely the proteins are to precipitate. Now in hemoglobin S the intermolecular repul-sion may be slightly less than in hemoglobin A, and hemoglobin S is correspondingly less soluble and more likely to precipitate. When a sickle-cell gene is paired with a normal gene, the latter may form enough hemoglobin A to keep the hemoglobin S in solution, though it is a near squeak. But when both of the genes are sickle-cell mutants, they will produce only hemoglobin S. This molecule cannot remain in solution. It precipitates out into crystals, and they distort and weaken the red cell.

This theory would explain why the change of just one amino acid

523

in a molecule made up of nearly 600 is sufficient to produce a serious disease and the near-certainty of an early death.

Albinism and sickle-cell anemia are not the only human defects that have been traced to the absence of a single enzyme or the mutation of a single gene. There is phenylketonuria, a hereditary defect of metabolism which often causes mental retardation. It results from the lack of an enzyme needed to convert the amino acid phenylalanine to tyrosine. There is galactosemia, a disorder causing eye cataracts and damage to the brain and liver, which has been traced to the absence of an enzyme required to convert a galactose phosphate to a glucose phosphate. There is a defect, involving the lack of one or another of the enzymes that control the breakdown of glycogen and its conversion to glucose, which results in abnormal accumulations of glycogen in the liver and elsewhere and usually leads to early death.

Such diseases are generally governed by a recessive allele of the gene that produces the enzyme involved. When only one of a pair of genes is defective, the normal one can carry on, and the individual is usually capable of leading a normal life (as in the case of a possessor of the sickle-cell trait). Trouble generally comes only when two parents happen to have the same unfortunate gene and have the further bad luck of combining those two in a fertilized egg. Their child then is the victim of a kind of Russian roulette. Probably all of us carry our load of abnormal, defective, even dangerous genes, usually masked by normal genes. You can understand why the human geneticists are so concerned about radiation or anything else that may add to the load.

NUCLEIC ACIDS

THE REALLY REMARKABLE THING about heredity is not these spectacular, comparatively rare aberrations but the fact that by and large inheritance runs so strictly true to form. Generation after generation, millennium after millennium, the genes go on reproducing themselves in exactly the same form and generating exactly the same enzymes, with only an occasional accidental variation of the blueprint. They rarely fail by so much as the introduction of a single wrong amino acid in a large protein molecule. How do they manage to make pure copies of themselves over and over again with such astounding faithfulness?

A gene is built of two major components. Perhaps half of it is protein; but the other part is not. To this non-protein portion we must now direct our attention.

In 1869 a Swiss biochemist named Friedrich Miescher, while breaking down the protein of cells with pepsin, discovered that the pepsin did not break up the cell nucleus. The nucleus shrank some, but it remained intact. By chemical analysis Miescher then found that the cell nucleus consisted largely of a phosphorus-containing substance which did not at all resemble protein in its properties. He called the substance "nuclein." It was later renamed "nucleic acid," because the substance was found to be strongly acid.

Miescher devoted himself to a study of this new material and eventually discovered that sperm cells (which have very little material outside the cell nucleus) were particularly rich in nucleic acid. Meanwhile the German chemist Felix Hoppe-Seyler, in whose laboratories Miescher had made his first discovery, isolated nucleic acid from yeast cells. This seemed different in properties from Miescher's material, so Miescher's variety was named "thymus nucleic acid" (because it could be obtained with particular ease from the thymus gland of animals), and Hoppe-Seyler's, naturally, was called "yeast nucleic acid." Since thymus nucleic acid was at first derived only from animal cells and yeast nucleic acid only from plant cells, it was thought for a while that this might represent a general chemical distinction between animals and plants.

The German biochemist Albrecht Kossel was the first to make a systematic investigation of the structure of the nucleic-acid molecule. By careful hydrolysis, he isolated from it a series of nitrogen-containing compounds which he named "adenine," "guanine," "cytosine," and "thymine." Their formulas are now known to be:

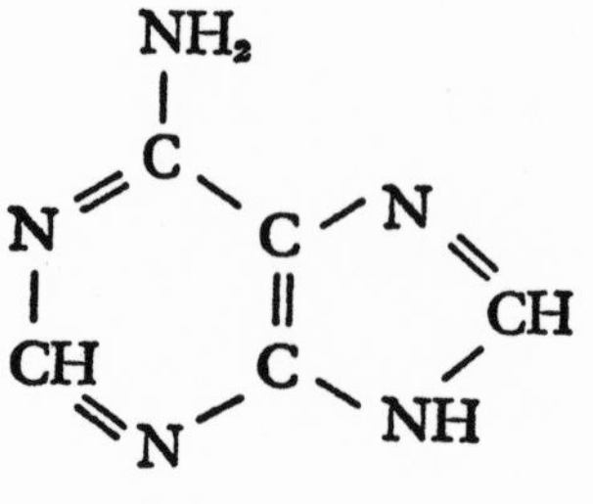

adenine

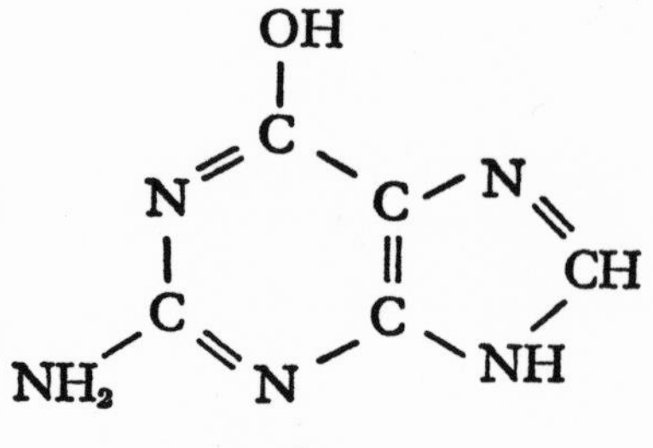

guanine

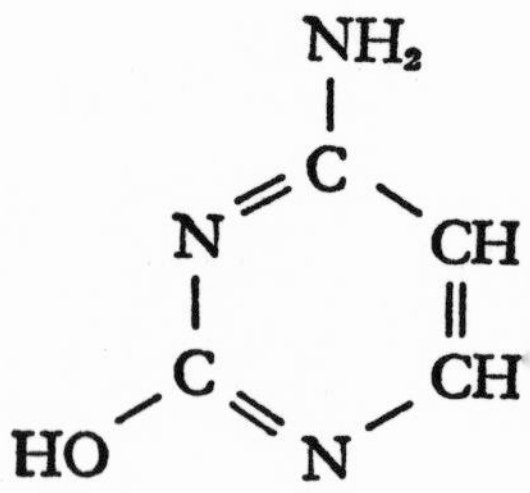

cytosine

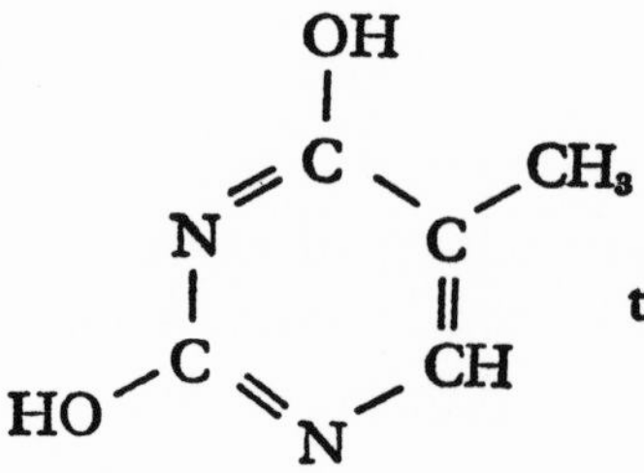

thymine

The double-ring formation in the first two compounds is called the "purine ring," and the single ring in the other two is the "pyrimidine ring." Therefore adenine and guanine are referred to as purines and cytosine and thymine are pyrimidines.

For these researches, which started an extraordinarily fruitful train of discoveries, Kossel received the Nobel Prize in medicine and physiology in 1910.

In 1911 the Russian-born American biochemist Phoebus Aaron Theodore Levene carried the investigation a stage farther. He showed that the nucleic acids contained five-carbon sugar molecules. (This was, at the time, an unusual finding. The best-known sugars, such as glucose, contain six carbons.) Levene followed this by showing that the two varieties of nucleic acid differed in the nature of the five-carbon sugar. Yeast nucleic acid contained "ribose," while thymus nucleic acid contained a sugar very much like ribose except for the absence of one oxygen atom, so this sugar was called "deoxyribose." Their formulas are:

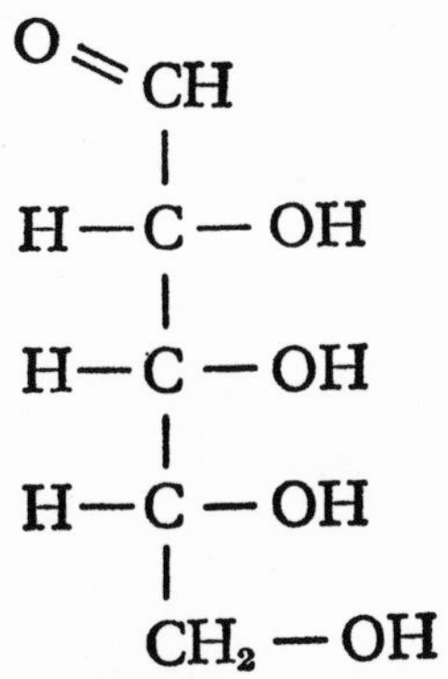

$$O{=}CH$$
$$H-C-OH$$
$$H-C-OH$$
$$H-C-OH$$
$$CH_2-OH$$

ribose

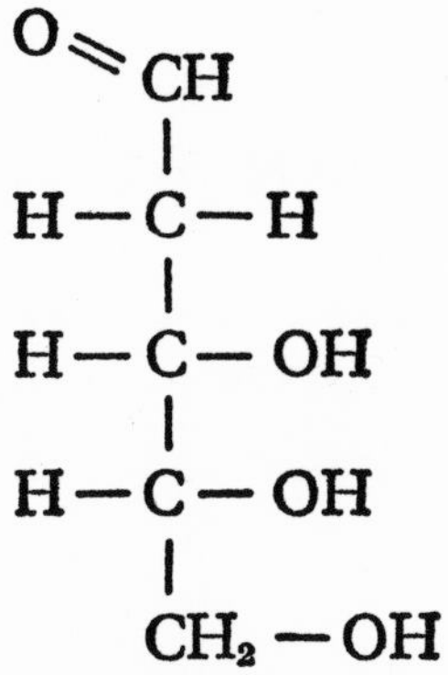

$$O{=}CH$$
$$H-C-H$$
$$H-C-OH$$
$$H-C-OH$$
$$CH_2-OH$$

deoxyribose

In consequence the two varieties of nucleic acid came to be called "ribonucleic acid" (RNA) and "deoxyribonucleic acid" (DNA).

Besides the difference in their sugars, the two nucleic acids also differ in one of the pyrimidines. RNA has "uracil" in place of thymine. Uracil is very like thymine, however, as you can see from the formula:

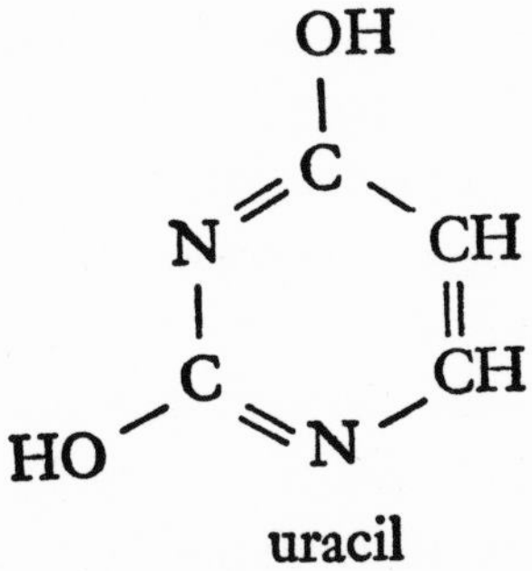

uracil

By 1934 Levene was able to show that the nucleic acids could be broken down to fragments which contained a purine or a pyrimidine, either the ribose or the deoxyribose sugar, and a phosphate group. This combination is called a "nucleotide." Levene proposed that the nucleic-acid molecule was built up of nucleotides as a protein is built up of amino acids. His quantitative studies suggested to him that the molecule consisted of just four nucleotide units, one containing adenine, one guanine, one cytosine, and one either thymine (in DNA) or uracil (in RNA). It turned out, however, that what Levene had isolated were not nucleic-acid molecules but pieces of them, and by the middle 1950's biochemists found that the molecular weights of nucleic acids ran as high as six million. Nucleic acids now appear to be comparable with proteins in molecular size.

BY THE USE OF CELL-STAINING TECHNIQUES, investigators began to pin down the location of nucleic acids in the cell. The German chemist Robert Feulgen, employing a red dye that stained DNA but not RNA, found that DNA was located in the cell nucleus, specifically in the chromosomes. He detected it not only in animal cells but also in plant cells. What's more, by staining RNA he showed that this nucleic acid, too, occurred in both plant and animal cells. In short, the nucleic acids were universal materials existing in all living cells.

The Swedish biochemist Torbjörn Caspersson proceeded to prove that DNA occurred only in the chromosomes and RNA mainly in the "cytoplasm," the material outside the cell nucleus. He did this by removing one of the nucleic acids (by means of an enzyme which reduced it to soluble fragments that could be washed out of the cell) and concentrating on the other. He would photograph the cell in ultraviolet light; since a nucleic acid absorbs ultraviolet much more strongly than other cell materials do, the location of the DNA or the RNA — whichever he had left in the cell — showed up clearly. DNA showed up only in the chromosomes. RNA made its appearance mainly in certain particles called "mitochondria" in the cytoplasm. Some RNA also showed up in the "nucleolus," a structure within the nucleus. (In 1948 the Rockefeller Institute biochemist A. E. Mirsky showed that small quantities of RNA are present even in the chromosomes.)

Caspersson's pictures disclosed that the DNA lay in localized bands in the chromosomes. Was it possible that DNA molecules were none other than the genes, which up to this time had had a rather vague and formless existence?

Through the 1940's biochemists pursued this lead with growing excitement. They found it particularly significant that the amount of DNA in the cells of an organism was always rigidly constant, except that the sperm and egg cells had only half this amount, which would be expected, since they had only half the chromosome supply of normal cells. The amount of RNA and of the protein in chromosomes might vary all over the lot, but the quantity of DNA remained fixed. This certainly seemed to indicate a close connection between DNA and genes.

There were, of course, a number of things that argued against the idea. For instance, what about the protein in chromosomes? Proteins of various kinds were associated with the nucleic acid, forming a combination called "nucleoprotein." Considering the complexity of proteins, and their great and specific importance in other capacities in the body, should not the protein be the important part of the molecule? It would seem that the nucleic acid might well be no more than an adjunct — at most a working portion of the molecule, like the heme in hemoglobin.

But the proteins (known as protamine and histone) most commonly found in isolated nucleoprotein turned out to be rather simple as proteins went. Meanwhile DNA was steadily being found to be more and more complex. The tail was beginning to wag the dog.

At this point three biochemists at the Rockefeller Institute brought in some remarkable evidence in favor of the genetic importance of DNA. It involved the pneumococcus, the well-known pneumonia microbe. Bacteriologists had long studied two different strains of pneumococci grown in the laboratory — one with a smooth coat made of a complex carbohydrate, the other lacking this coat and therefore rough in appearance. Apparently the rough strain lacked some enzyme needed to make the carbohydrate capsule. But an English bacteriologist named Fred Griffith had discovered that if killed bacteria of the smooth variety were mixed with live ones of the rough strain and then injected into a mouse, the tissues of the infected mouse would eventually contain live pneumococci of the smooth variety! How could this happen? The dead pneumococci had certainly not been brought to life. Something must have transformed the rough pneumococci so that they were now capable of making the smooth coat. What was that something? Evidently it was a factor of some kind contributed by the dead bacteria of the smooth strain.

In 1944 the three Rockefeller Institute biochemists, Oswald T. Avery, Colin M. Macleod and Maclyn McCarty, identified the transforming principle. It was DNA. When they isolated pure DNA from the smooth strain and gave it to rough pneumococci, that alone sufficed to transform the rough strain to a smooth.

Investigators went on to isolate other transforming principles, involving other bacteria and other properties, and in every case the principle turned out to be a variety of DNA. The only plausible conclusion was that DNA could act like a gene. In fact, various lines of research, particularly with viruses (see Chapter 13), showed that the protein associated with DNA is almost superfluous from a genetic point of view: DNA can produce genetic effects all by itself.

If DNA is the key to heredity, it must have a complex structure, because it has to carry an elaborate pattern, or code of instructions, for the synthesis of specific enzymes. Assuming that it is made up of the four kinds of nucleotides, they cannot be strung in a regular arrangement, such as 1, 2, 3, 4, 1, 2, 3, 4, 1, 2, 3, 4, ... Such a molecule would be far too simple to carry a blueprint for enzymes. And in fact the American biochemist Erwin Chargaff and his coworkers found definite evidence in 1948 that the composition of nucleic acids was more complicated than had been thought. Their analysis showed that the various purines and pyrimidines were not present in equal amount, that the proportions varied in different nucleic acids, and that the molecule contained other pyrimidines besides cytosine and thymine or uracil.

In 1952 two British biochemists, R. Markham and J. D. Smith, managed to determine the order of nucleotides in some sections of a nucleic-acid molecule, much after the manner in which protein chemists had determined the order of amino acids in the protein molecule. They found no regularity. The different purines and pyrimidines were distributed as randomly along the nucleotide backbone as the amino acids were along the peptide backbone.

Yet some regularities began to emerge. Nucleic acids scattered X-rays in diffraction patterns, a good sign of the existence of structural regularities in the molecule. The British biochemist M. H. F. Wilkins and his coworkers calculated that these regularities repeated themselves at intervals considerably greater than the distance from nucleotide to nucleotide. The logical conclusion was that the nucleic-acid molecule took the form of a helix, with the coils of the helix forming the repetitive unit noted by the X-rays.

In the early 1950's two biologists at Cambridge University, J. D. Watson and F. H. C. Crick, putting all the information together, came up with a model of the nucleic-acid molecule. They pictured it as a double helix — two nucleotide chains winding like a double-railed spiral staircase up the same vertical axis. How might the purines and pyrimidines be arrayed along these parallel chains? Well, to make a good, uniform fit, a double-ring purine on one helix should face a single-ring pyrimidine on the other (see the diagrams on the next page). The purine and the pyrimidine would be linked together by hydrogen bonds, which would thus serve to hold the two helices together. Watson and Crick showed that hydrogen bonds would form most easily if an adenine (purine) on one chain faced a thymine (pyrimidine) on the other; similarly a guanine should pair up with a cytosine. (Chemists had found, in fact, that when nucleic acids were broken down, the amount of adenine equaled that of thymine, and guanine and cytosine also were present in equal quantities.)

The Watson-Crick model of nucleic acids fits in nicely with the very similar Pauling-Corey helical structure of proteins. It is now generally accepted to be basically correct. About the only jarring note has been the discovery of what seems to be a single-helix DNA

5 3 1

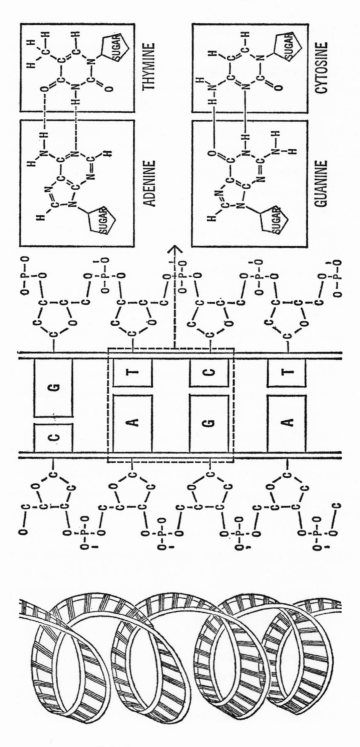

MODEL OF THE NUCLEIC-ACID MOLECULE. *The drawing at the left shows the double helix; in the center a portion of it is shown in detail (omitting the hydrogen atoms); at the right is a detail of the nucleotide combinations.*

in one strain of virus by the American biophysicist Robert I. Sinsheimer. But the authors of the model believe that this can be explained in a way that does not upset their picture.

It now becomes possible to explain just how a chromosome may duplicate itself in the process of cell division. Consider the chromosome as a string of DNA molecules. The molecules can first divide by a separation of the two helices making up the double helix; the two chains unwind themselves from each other, so to speak. Now each chain is a half-molecule which can bring about the synthesis of its own missing complement. Where it has a thymine, it attaches an adenine; where it has a cytosine, it attaches a guanine; and so on. All the raw materials for making the units, and the necessary enzymes, are on hand in the cell. The half-molecule simply plays the role of a "template," or mold, for putting the units together in the proper order. The units eventually will fall into the appropriate places and stay there because that is the most stable arrangement.

To summarize, then, each half-molecule guides the formation of its own complement, held to itself by hydrogen bonds. In this way it rebuilds the complete, double-helix DNA molecule, and the two half-molecules into which the original molecule divided thus form two molecules where only one existed before. Such a process, carried out by all the DNA's down the length of a chromosome, will create two chromosomes which are exactly alike and perfect copies of the original mother chromosome. Occasionally something may go wrong: the impact of a subatomic particle or of energetic radiation, or the intervention of certain chemicals, may introduce an imperfection somewhere or other in the new chromosome. The result is a mutation.

Evidence in favor of this mechanism of replication has been piling up. Tracer studies, employing heavy nitrogen to label chromosomes and following the fate of the labeled material during cell division, have tended to bear out the theory. Besides this, some of the important enzymes involved in replication have been identified.

In 1955 the Spanish-born American biochemist Severo Ochoa isolated from a bacterium (*Aztobacter vinelandii*) an enzyme which proved capable of catalyzing the formation of RNA from nucleotides. In 1956 a former pupil of Ochoa's, Arthur Kornberg, isolated another enzyme (from the bacterium *Escherichia coli*) which could catalyze the formation of DNA from nucleotides. Ochoa proceeded to synthesize RNA-like molecules from nucleotides, and Kornberg did the same for DNA. (The two men shared the Nobel Prize in medicine and physiology in 1959). Kornberg also showed that his enzyme, given a bit of natural DNA to serve as a template, could catalyze the formation of a molecule which seemed to be identical with natural DNA. This is the best evidence yet in favor of the Watson-Crick mechanism of replication.

How does a nucleic acid bring about the synthesis of a specific enzyme — that is to say, a protein? To form a protein it has to direct the placement of amino acids in a certain specific order in a molecule made up of hundreds or thousands of units. For each position it must choose the correct amino acid from some 19 different amino acids. If there were 19 corresponding units in the DNA molecule, it would be easy. But DNA is made up of only four different building blocks — the four nucleotides. Thinking about this, the astronomer George Gamow suggested that the nucleotides, in various combinations, might be used as a code (just as the dot and dash of the Morse Code can be combined in various ways to represent the letters of the alphabet, numerals, and so on). Gamow pointed out that from four nucleotides, 20 different combinations of three could be formed. Following up this possibility, Gamow (and also Crick himself) worked up codes whereby combinations of nucleotides, taken three at a time, would correspond to the 19 different amino acids. Each grouping of three nucleotides in the DNA chain would select a specific amino acid, and thus the sequence of nucleotide groups in a particular DNA molecule would serve as a pattern for the placement of amino acids in a protein chain.

The American biochemist Mahlon B. Hoagland went on to bring RNA into the picture. He suggested that DNA acts as a template for the formation of a corresponding RNA molecule, and that it is the RNA that superintends the construction of the protein. In sup-

534

port of this idea, a number of biochemists have reported that the cells found to be most active in synthesizing protein are also richest in RNA.

Hoagland and his group discovered that some of the RNA in the cytoplasm of a cell is in the form of small, soluble fragments. These small molecules show a strong tendency to attach amino acids. Hoagland calls them "transfer RNA," and he suggests that each variety is so constructed that it will attach one particular amino acid and no other. The transfer RNA molecules, with amino acids attached, may then assemble on a nucleic-acid template (perhaps a large RNA molecule in the mitochondria) which places them, together with the attached amino acids, in a specific order. After the amino acids have combined to form a protein, they detach themselves from the transfer RNA molecules. These in turn drop off the template and are ready for another cycle.

Nothing more exciting and attractive than this interplay of cell nucleus and cytoplasm, of DNA and RNA, of nucleic acid and protein, has yet been suggested to account for the continuity of life.

THE ORIGIN OF LIFE

ONCE WE GET DOWN to the nucleic-acid molecules, we are as close to the basis of life as we can get. Here, surely, is the prime substance of life itself. Without DNA, living organisms could not reproduce, and life as we know it could not have started. All the substances of living matter — enzymes and all the others, whose production is catalyzed by enzymes — depend in the last analysis on DNA. How, then, did it all start?

This is a question that science has always hesitated to ask, because the origin of life has been bound up with religious beliefs even more strongly than has the origin of the earth and the Universe. It is still dealt with only hesitantly and apologetically. But in recent years a book entitled *The Origin of Life,* by the Russian biochemist A. I.

Oparin, has brought the subject very much to the fore. The book was published in the Soviet Union in 1924 and in English translation in 1936. In it the problem of life's origin for the first time was dealt with in detail from a completely materialistic point of view. Since the Soviet Union is not bound by the religious scruples to which the Western nations feel bound, this, perhaps, is not surprising.

Most of man's early cultures developed myths telling of the creation of the first human beings (and sometimes of other forms of life as well) by gods or demons. However, the formation of life itself was rarely thought of as being entirely a divine prerogative. At least the lower forms of life might arise spontaneously from non-living material without supernatural intervention. Insects and worms might, for instance, arise from decaying meat, frogs from mud, mice from rotting wheat. This idea was based on actual observation, for decaying meat, to take the most obvious example, did indeed suddenly give rise to maggots. It was only natural to assume that the maggots were formed from the meat.

Aristotle believed in the existence of "spontaneous generation." So did the great theologians of the Middle Ages, such as Thomas Aquinas. So did William Harvey and Isaac Newton. After all, the evidence of one's own eyes was hard to refute.

The first to put this belief to the test of experimentation was the Italian physician Francesco Redi. In 1668 he decided to check on whether maggots really formed out of decaying meat. He put pieces of meat in a series of jars and then covered some of them with fine gauze and left others uncovered. Maggots developed only in the meat in the uncovered jars, to which flies had had free access. Redi concluded that the maggots had arisen from microscopically small eggs laid on the meat by the flies. Without flies and their eggs, he insisted, meat could never produce maggots, however long it decayed and putrefied.

Experimenters who followed Redi confirmed this, and the belief that visible organisms arose from dead matter died. But when microbes were discovered, shortly after Redi's time, many scientists decided that these forms of life at least must come from dead matter.

536

Even in gauze-covered jars, meat would soon begin to swarm with microorganisms. For two centuries after Redi's experiments, belief in the possibility of the spontaneous generation of microorganisms remained very much alive.

It was another Italian, the naturalist Lazzaro Spallanzani, who first cast serious doubt on this notion. In 1765 he set out two sets of vessels containing a broth. One he left open to the air. The other, which he had boiled to kill any organisms already present, he sealed up to keep out any organisms that might be floating in the air. The broth in the first vessels soon teemed with microorganisms, but the boiled and sealed-up broth remained sterile. This proved to Spallanzani's satisfaction that even microscopic life could not arise from inanimate matter.

The proponents of spontaneous generation were not convinced. They maintained that boiling destroyed some "vital principle," and that this was why no microscopic life developed in Spallanzani's boiled, sealed flasks. It remained for Pasteur to settle the question, seemingly once and for all. He devised a flask with a long swan neck in the shape of a horizontal S. With the opening unstoppered, air could percolate into the flask, but dust particles and microorganisms could not, for the curved neck would serve as a trap, like the drain trap under a sink. Pasteur put some broth in the flask, attached the S-shaped neck, boiled the broth until it steamed (to kill any microorganisms in the neck as well as in the broth), and waited for developments. The broth remained sterile. There was no vital principle in air. Pasteur's demonstration apparently laid the theory of spontaneous generation to rest permanently.

All this left a germ of embarrassment for scientists. How had life arisen, after all, if not through divine creation or through spontaneous generation?

Toward the end of the nineteenth century some theorists went to the other extreme and made life eternal. The most popular theory was advanced by Svante Arrhenius (the chemist who had developed the concept of ionization). In 1907 he published a book entitled *Worlds in the Making*, picturing a universe in which life had always

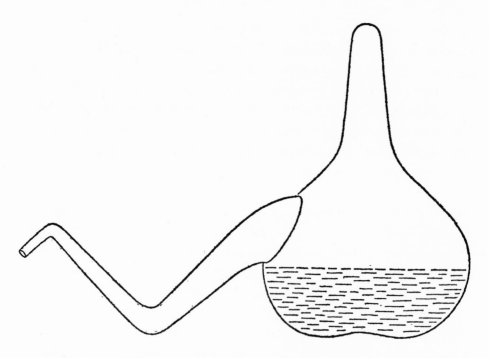

Pasteur's flask *for the experiment on spontaneous generation.*

existed and migrated across space, continually colonizing new planets. It traveled in the form of spores that escaped from the atmosphere of a planet by random movement and then were driven through space by the pressure of light from the sun. The spores traveled on and on through interstellar space, driven by light radiation this way and that, until they died or fell on some planet, where they would come to active life and compete with life forms already present or inoculate the planet with life if it was uninhabited but habitable.

At first blush, this theory looks attractive. Bacterial spores, protected by a thick coat, are very resistant to cold and dehydration and might conceivably last a long time in the vacuum of space. Also they are of just the proper size to be more affected by the outward pressure of a sun's radiation than by the inward pull of its gravity. But Arrhenius's suggestion fell before the onslaught of ultraviolet light.

In 1910 experimenters showed that ultraviolet quickly killed bacterial spores, and in interplanetary space the sun's ultraviolet rays are intense — not to speak of other destructive radiations, such as cosmic rays, solar X-rays and zones of charged particles like the Van Allen belts around the earth. Conceivably there may be spores somewhere that are resistant to radiation, but spores made of protein and nucleic acid, as we know them, certainly could not make the grade.

WE COME BACK, then, to the problem of accounting for the origin of life here on the earth, and we must look again at the idea of spontaneous generation. Could life have come into being spontaneously in the terrestrial environment that existed billions of years ago?

The earth's primeval atmosphere must have been drastically different from what it is now. As we saw in Chapter 3, it almost certainly contained no free oxygen. But if the earth was formed from the same raw materials as the sun, it probably did contain a good deal of hydrogen combined with other elements, for hydrogen, after all, makes up nine-tenths of all the matter in the Universe. The atmosphere probably consisted of hydrogenated gases, such as water vapor (H_2O), ammonia (NH_3), and methane (CH_4).

As the earth cooled, the water vapor would condense to form the oceans, leaving an atmosphere composed largely of ammonia and methane, as Urey contended in his book, *The Planets*, published in 1952. We know from spectroscopic data that the outer planets in the solar system have ammonia and methane in their atmospheres.

Some scientists disagree with this view. W. W. Rubey, of the United States Geological Survey, has suggested that the earth's primeval atmosphere was made up of carbon dioxide and nitrogen. Mars and Venus seem to have such atmospheres now, and the gases trapped in meteors are mostly carbon dioxide and nitrogen. But perhaps the two theories are not completely incompatible. It may be that the earth's original atmosphere was water vapor, ammonia, and methane, and that this changed to one composed of carbon dioxide

539

and nitrogen. Water vapor reaching the upper atmosphere would have been decomposed by the sun's ultraviolet rays to oxygen and hydrogen. The hydrogen would tend to escape into outer space, leaving free oxygen behind. This might have reacted with methane, forming water and carbon dioxide, and with ammonia, forming water and nitrogen:

$$2O_2 + CH_4 \rightarrow CO_2 + 2H_2O$$
$$3O_2 + 4NH_3 \rightarrow 2N_2 + 6H_2O$$

The water would join the oceans, leaving behind an atmosphere of carbon dioxide and nitrogen. Thus Urey's atmosphere would slowly change into Rubey's atmosphere.

Ammonia and carbon dioxide are soluble in water. Therefore, while this change in the atmosphere was taking place, the ocean may have been warm and rich in dissolved ammonia and carbon dioxide. The ultraviolet radiation from the sun at sea level probably was much more intense than it is today, for lack of a shielding layer of ozone, and the earth still had a great deal of radioactive material. Under such conditions, could organic matter have sprung into existence?

The strong ultraviolet radiation of the sun and the earth's still energetic radioactivity would have provided energy. The ammonia, carbon dioxide, and other compounds dissolved in the sea would have provided raw material.

Intrigued by this idea, American biochemists in 1951 began to experiment. Melvin Calvin of California (the investigator of photosynthesis) sent high-energy radiation through a mixture of water, carbon dioxide, and hydrogen. He found that energy-consuming chemical reactions did take place, and that simple molecules were built into more complex ones. Carbon dioxide and hydrogen combined to form first the one-carbon formaldehyde (CH_2O) and then the two-carbon acetic acid (CH_3COOH). When Calvin irradiated a solution of acetic acid in water, he got the four-carbon compound succinic acid ($HOOCCH_2CH_2COOH$).

In 1952 Stanley L. Miller, then a graduate student in Urey's laboratories, went a step farther. He circulated water, plus a Urey-type primeval atmosphere of ammonia, methane and hydrogen, past an electric discharge (to simulate the ultraviolet radiation of the sun). At the end of a week he analyzed his solution by paper chromatography and found that, in addition to the simple substances of the type Calvin had found, he also had glycine and alanine, the two simplest of the amino acids, plus some indication of one or two more complicated ones.

The results of these experiments certainly gave encouragement to the belief that on the primeval earth, with its warm ocean and its oxygen-free atmosphere, organic molecules of increasing complexity might have been built under the lash of solar and radioactive energies.

It is important to remember that acetic acid and glycine, two of the first compounds formed in these experiments, are the two materials from which the porphyrin ring is constructed by a living organism. They may well have combined to produce porphyrin in the dead ocean. That would have been a definite stepping stone toward life, for some of the most important enzymes possess porphyrins as their working groups. Then, too, chlorophyll, the key compound in photosynthesis, is a porphyrin.

Furthermore, an organism builds the purines and pyrimidines from formic-acid groups, carbon dioxide, and glycine. They, too, might have been synthesized in the ocean.

Any compound that formed in the lifeless ocean would tend to endure and accumulate. There were no organisms, either large or small, to consume them or cause them to decay. Moreover, in the primeval atmosphere there was no free oxygen to oxidize and break down the molecules. The only important factors tending to break down complex molecules would have been the very ultraviolet and radioactive energies that built them up. But ocean currents might have carried much of the material to a safe haven at mid-levels in the sea, away from the ultraviolet-irradiated surface and the radioactive bottom.

There seems to be no logical barrier to supposing that, with time,

541

higher and higher concentrations of the more complicated amino acids were formed, as well as simple sugars; that amino acids combined to form peptides; that purines, pyrimidines, sugar, and phosphate combined to form nucleotides; and that gradually, over the ages, proteins and nucleic acids were created. Then, eventually, must have come the key step — the formation, through chance combinations, of a nucleic acid molecule, capable of inducing replication. That moment marked the beginning of life.

Thus a period of "chemical evolution" preceded the evolution of life itself. If you are disturbed about the high improbability of anything so complicated as a replicating nucleoprotein — a living molecule — coming into existence strictly by chance, remember that it evolved by stages and over a tremendously long period. The earth, as a solid body, is certainly at least four billion years old. The oldest known fossils date back to not much more than 500 million years ago, and if we assume that it took three times that length of time for life to evolve into forms complex enough to leave fossils (a generous estimate), then life on the earth began about two billion years ago. That leaves two billion years for the preliminary chemical evolution. Much can happen in two billion years.

A SINGLE LIVING MOLECULE, it seems, might well have been sufficient to get life under way and give rise to the whole world of living things, as a single fertilized cell can give rise to an enormously complex organism. In the organic "soup" that constituted the ocean at that time, the first living molecule could have replicated billions and billions of molecules like itself in short order. Occasional mutations would create slightly changed forms of the molecule, and those that were in some way more efficient than the others would multiply at the expense of their neighbors and replace the old forms. If one group was more efficient in warm water and another group in cold water, two varieties would arise, each restricted to the environment it fitted best. In this fashion the course of "organic evolution" would be set in motion.

Even if several living molecules came into existence independently at the beginning, it is very likely that the most efficient one would have outbred the others, so that all life today may very well be descended from a single original molecule in any case. In spite of the great present diversity of living things, all have the same basic ground plan. Their cells all carry out metabolism in pretty much the same way. Furthermore, it seems particularly significant that the proteins of all living things are composed of *L*-amino acids rather than amino acids of the *D* type. It may be that the original nucleoprotein from which all life is descended happened to be built from *L*-amino acids by chance, and since *D* could not be associated with *L* in any stable chain, what began as chance persisted by replication into grand universality.

The prime need of all life-forms, of course, is energy to maintain the energy-consuming life processes. Present-day animal life obtains energy mainly by oxidizing carbohydrates and fats, an energy-liberating process. In the primeval world, there was no free oxygen to speak of, and other methods had to serve. Some of those still exist today and may have been the main sources in primeval times. The conversion of glucose to lactic acid by muscle or to alcohol by yeast requires no free oxygen. There are some bacteria that obtain energy by catalyzing inorganic conversions involving sulfur or iron compounds. These creatures live out their lives in the absence of oxygen; indeed, for some of them free oxygen is poisonous. They are known as "anaerobic" organisms (from Greek words meaning "living without air").

As long as the early living molecules could obtain energy only by breaking down organic matter, their numbers were perforce limited. The rate of formation of organic molecules in the ocean by the sun's ultraviolet light and the energy from radioactive matter was probably fairly slow. For a long time, therefore, the concentration of living molecules in the ocean must have been low. But the situation changed when the evolving life-forms reached the point where they could begin to manufacture their own organic material by photosynthesis. This process could build organic molecules much more

5 4 3

rapidly than ultraviolet radiation could. Furthermore, the life-forms could synthesize their food from ubiquitous materials such as water and carbon dioxide, instead of having to depend on blundering upon food in the thinning "soup" of the oceans.

Now the evolving life-forms would begin to acquire an enveloping membrane within which they stored the material they synthesized, and thus cells were born. The cells would take over the ocean and clear it of its organic molecules. They would begin to remove carbon dioxide from the atmosphere and replace it with oxygen. This would favor the development of enzymes capable of utilizing molecular oxygen. Any cell that developed such enzymes would have so much more energy at its disposal that it would quickly replace virtually all cells not equally endowed.

The cell nucleus today still lacks any enzymes capable of utilizing free oxygen. Consequently all the processes within the nucleus remain anaerobic. Perhaps the cell nucleus itself is the descendant of the first, simple cells, which grew up in an oxygen-free atmosphere. Around that nucleus the cytoplasm, which contains a rich supply of oxygen-utilizing enzymes, may have developed later as an adaptation to the change in the atmosphere.

Once the earth's atmosphere became rich in oxygen, the upper atmosphere acquired the ozone layer that blocks off most of the sun's ultraviolet radiation from the earth's surface. Moreover, by this time the earth's radioactivity had declined considerably. But these sources of energy were no longer needed for making organic material. Photosynthesis had taken over. And the decline in disruptive radiation allowed a new evolutionary spurt toward more delicate, more complex, and larger forms of life.

As photosynthesizing cells developed in numbers and complexity, there emerged a new type of cell which lacked the apparatus for photosynthesis but could live on the food provided by the plant cells. This marked the birth of the animal kingdom. Eventually organisms grew complex enough to begin to leave the fossil record (plant and animal) that we have today.

Meanwhile the earth environment had changed fundamentally,

from the standpoint of creation of new life. Life could no longer originate and develop from purely chemical evolution. For one thing, the forms of energy that had brought it into being in the first place — ultraviolet and radioactive energy — were effectively gone. For another, the well-established forms of life would quickly consume any organic molecules that arose spontaneously. For both these reasons there is virtually no chance of any new and independent breakthrough from non-life into life (barring some future intervention by man, if he learns to turn the trick). Spontaneous generation today is so highly improbable that it can be regarded as essentially impossible.

LIFE IN OTHER WORLDS

IF WE ACCEPT THE VIEW that life arose simply from the workings of physical and chemical laws, it follows that in all likelihood life is not confined to the earth. What are the possibilities of life elsewhere in the Universe?

The total number of stars in the known Universe is estimated to be at least 1,000,000,000,000,000,000,000 (a billion trillion). If all the stars developed by the same sort of process as the one that is believed to have created our own solar system (*i.e.*, the condensing of a large cloud of dust and gas), then it is likely that no star is solitary but each is part of a local system containing more than one body. We know that there are many double stars, revolving around a common center, and it is estimated that at least one out of three stars belongs to a system containing two or more stars. It is doubtful that such systems can have habitable planets, as we shall see. But that still leaves two-thirds of all the stars in a position to be circled by planets that might be habitable.

Unfortunately we have no means (so far) of detecting directly any planet beyond our solar system, even for the nearest stars. The closest astronomers have come to finding any evidence of a planet at all was the recent discovery that one of the stars in the 61 Cygni group has a wobbly motion indicating the presence of a small partner. From the amount of perturbation of the star's motion, it is calculated that the mass of the partner is roughly ten times that of Jupiter. That makes it definitely too small to be a star, so the body must be a giant planet.

What conditions must a planet fulfill to be habitable? Well, we can be pretty sure that a planet such as Jupiter, for instance, cannot support anything that we would recognize as our sort of life. To begin with, a planet capable of developing life in our sense must be close enough to its sun so that water is liquid rather than frozen, at least most of the time, and far enough away from the sun so that the water is below the boiling point. This means that only the planets within a certain "habitable zone" around each star are eligible. The larger and more luminous the star, the farther out the habitable zone is, and the broader it is. Around dim stars the habitable zone is so narrow that it is unlikely that any planet stays within the zone throughout its orbit.

A second condition is that the star must have a long lifetime — at least a billion years — to allow time for chemical evolution to produce life (unless a most improbable stroke of chance were to form a living molecule suddenly). That condition eliminates very large and luminous stars, because their lifetimes are considerably less than a billion years.

Thirdly, we probably have to rule out multiple stars, for their habitable zones may be so complicated in shape (in view of the different spheres of radiation from two or more suns) that any planet would move out of the zone during parts of its orbit. As it happens, the first possible-planet man has detected, the giant planet near the star in 61 Cygni, is associated with a multiple-star system.

Bearing these conditions in mind, and looking over the field, the University of California astronomer S. S. Huang has pitched on two stars as the only ones among our nearest neighbors that may have habitable zones in which an earthlike planet might circulate. The two stars are Epsilon Eridani (eleven light-years away) and Tau

Ceti (twelve light-years). Both are smaller than the sun and therefore have smaller, but not too small, habitable zones.

Huang estimates that perhaps one in 20 stars possesses planets on which life as we know it could develop. And, of course, the thinking and experiments of investigators such as Oparin, Calvin, Urey, and Miller suggest that on every planet where life can develop, life *will* develop. Thus there may be as many as five billion life-bearing planets in our Galaxy and 50 billion billion in the known Universe.

That is exciting enough, if true. Even more exciting is the probability that on at least some of those planets life may very well have evolved to what we would call "intelligent" forms. Even if this has happened in only one inhabited planet out of a million, there would still be 5,000 planets in our Galaxy bearing intelligent life and 50 million billion in the Universe.

Until recently this sort of possibility was considered seriously only in science-fiction stories. Those of my readers who happen to be aware that I have written a few science-fiction stories in my time and who may put down my remarks here to over-enthusiasm may be assured that today many astronomers accept the high probability of life, even intelligent life, on many planets.

In fact, United States scientists take the possibilities seriously enough to have set up an enterprise called Project Ozma (deriving its name from one of the *Oz* books for children) to listen for possible radio signals from other worlds. The idea is to look for some pattern in radio waves coming in from space. If they detect signals in an ordered pattern, as opposed to the random, formless broadcasts from radio stars or excited matter in space, it may be assumed that such signals will represent messages from some extraterrestrial intelligence. Of course, even if such messages were received, communication with the distant intelligence would still be a problem. The messages would have been many years on the way, and a reply also would take many years to reach the distant broadcasters, since the nearest potentially habitable planet is at least eleven light-years away.

At what wavelength might the intelligent beings of another world be broadcasting? Well, there is one universal wavelength with which

547

astronomers are well acquainted in their exploration of space — namely, the "song of hydrogen" at 1420 megacycles. This signal is emitted by a hydrogen atom when its electron jumps from a certain level to a certain other level. As a universal constant, it is a logical wavelength to choose in attempting to communicate with other intelligent beings across space.

IS ALL THIS STRICTLY SPECULATION and nothing more? Not quite. It is fair to say today that scientists are finding signs — very faint still but taken more and more seriously — of the possible existence of forms of life in our own solar system.

The sun's habitable zone, includes, at most, the orbits of the earth (with its moon), Venus, and Mars. Mercury is too hot for life as we know it, and all bodies beyond Mars are too cold.

We can eliminate the moon pretty definitely, because of its lack of detectable air or water. There has been some speculation that very primitive forms of life may exist here and there in deep crannies where traces of water and air might conceivably be present. The British astronomer V. A. Firsoff has argued in his book, *Strange World of the Moon*, that water may lie below the moon's surface, and that gases adsorbed on the dust-covered surface may give rise to a very shallow atmosphere that might support life of a sort. But all this is pure speculation. Nevertheless, scientists are sufficiently uncertain of the possibility of life taking hold on the moon, at least temporarily, to have taken pains to sterilize rocket payloads which might land on the moon. The Soviet Union reported that it had sterilized Lunik II, with which it scored a hit on the moon. The scientists are anxious to avoid planting any life on the moon before man gets there to observe it in its pristine state.

Venus is a somewhat better candidate for the existence of life. It is much like the earth in size and mass and has an atmosphere that is even thicker than ours. Its atmosphere seems to be mainly nitrogen and carbon dioxide. Venus has no detectable free oxygen, but this lack is not a fatal barrier to life. As I explained above, the earth very likely supported life for ages before it possessed free oxygen in its atmosphere (although, to be sure, that life was undoubtedly very primitive).

Until recently no sign of water vapor was found in Venus's air, and that *was* a fatal objection to the possibility of life there. But astronomers were uncomfortable about the failure to find water on Venus, because it left them with no completely satisfactory explanation of the planet's cloud cover. Then in 1959 Charles Moore of the Arthur D. Little Company laboratory went up in a balloon and at an altitude of 15 miles in the stratosphere, above most of the earth's interfering atmosphere, took pictures of Venus with a telescope. Its spectrum in the infrared showed that Venus's upper atmosphere contained as much water vapor as does the earth's.

This improves the possibilities. At least Venus is no longer automatically eliminated as a possible abode of life. However, there are still difficulties. Calculations indicate that the temperature on the surface of Venus is somewhat above the boiling point of water, because of the "hothouse effect" of the carbon dioxide in its atmosphere. And radio waves coming from Venus suggest that its surface temperature may be as high as 250° C. If so, Venus is out as an inhabited planet, at least for life as we know it.

But until we pierce the planet's cloud cover in some way, by an instrument-carrying space probe or, better still, by a manned landing, the question will remain open. We can only say that the odds against life on Venus are very great but not overwhelming.

Mars is without doubt a more hopeful possibility. It has a thin atmosphere of carbon dioxide and nitrogen, and it has enough water vapor to show thin ice caps (probably an inch or so thick at most) which form and melt with the seasons. (It is estimated that all the water on Mars would about fill Lake Erie.) The Martian temperatures are low, but not too low for life and probably no worse at any time than Antarctica. The temperature may even reach an occasional balmy 80° F. at Mars' equator during the height of the summer day.

The possibility of life on Mars has excited the world for nearly a

549

century. In 1877 the Italian astronomer Giovanni Virginio Schiaparelli detected fine, straight lines on the surface of the planet. He named them "canali." That is the Italian word for "channels," but it was mistranslated into English as "canals," whereupon people jumped to the conclusion that the lines were artificial waterways, perhaps built to bring water from the ice caps to other parts of the planet for irrigation. The American astronomer Percival Lowell vigorously championed this interpretation of the markings, and the Sunday supplements (and science-fiction stories) went to town on the "evidence" of intelligent life on Mars.

Actually, there is considerable doubt that the markings exist at all. Many astronomers have never seen them, despite earnest attempts; others have seen them only in flashes. Many believe that they may be optical illusions, arising from strained efforts to see something just at the limit of vision. In any case, no astronomer believes that Mars could support any form of advanced life.

Yet the evidence seems persuasive that something does grow on Mars. It hinges on Mars' famous green patches. They change with the seasons, expanding in the hemisphere that is experiencing summer and contracting in the hemisphere that is experiencing winter. The patches seem to advance with the melting of the ice cap.

Ingeborg Schmidt, an astronomer at Indiana University, questions whether the green areas of Mars really are green. She points out that their apparent greenness may be an optical illusion resting on the contrast with the reddish-orange color of most of Mars. According to her observations, the "green" areas are actually gray. But green or gray, it is still possible, as she admits, that the patches are a form of vegetation or other primitive life.

Laboratory experiments have shown that some microorganisms of the earth, though adapted to the earth's rather than Mars' conditions, can live and grow at temperatures and in an atmosphere which are believed to simulate the Martian environment. The strongest evidence in favor of simple plant life on Mars was advanced in 1959 by the astronomer William M. Sinton, working at the Lowell Observatory in Arizona. He found that the wavelengths of sunlight absorbed by the green areas of Mars were those that would be absorbed by organic compounds. There had been suggestions that the seasonal color changes on Mars were the result of the interaction of water and inorganic compounds in the soil, but Sinton's evidence indicates that the light reflected from the planet's green areas is not coming from mere soil or rocks.

Notwithstanding all this, there is no certainty about the presence of life on Mars, just as there is none about its absence on Venus. What can be said is that, whereas in the case of Venus the odds are all against life, they are all in favor of life in the case of Mars.

NATURALLY SCIENTISTS look forward with great anticipation to man's first landing on Mars. For science it will be the single most exciting event in the space-travelers' exploration of our solar system — far more exciting than the first landing on the moon. As Melvin Calvin has remarked, proof that there is life on Mars would change mankind's whole outlook toward the Universe.

In 1959 Calvin announced a finding which was, in its way, remarkable enough. Analyzing the makeup of some meteorites, he had detected a substance that seemed to resemble a pyrimidine! Meteorites may be fragments of an exploded planet, conceivably an inhabited one. But that is merely speculation, and not the main point of the discovery. Whether the pyrimidine-like substance came from a former planet, or was built up in the meteorite itself by the action of solar radiation on carbon dioxide and nitrogen trapped in the meteorite, as it flew through space through eons of time, this was the first approach to evidence in favor of chemical evolution actually proceeding in nature (rather than merely in the chemical glassware of the research chemist). It seems to be another possible sign, however faint, of the multiplicity of life in the Universe.

CHAPTER

13

THE MICRO-ORGANISMS

BACTERIA

BEFORE THE SEVENTEENTH CENTURY, the smallest known living creatures were tiny insects. It was taken for granted, of course, that no smaller organisms existed. Living beings might be made invisible by a supernatural agency (all cultures believed that in one way or another), but no one supposed that there were creatures in nature too small to be seen.

Had man suspected such a thing, he might have come much sooner to the deliberate use of magnifying devices. Even the Greeks and Romans knew that glass objects of certain shapes would focus sunlight on a point and would magnify objects seen through it. A hollow glass sphere filled with water would do so, for instance. Archimedes may have used such a "burning glass" to set afire the besieging Roman fleet at Syracuse in 212 B.C. (as he is said to have done). Ptolemy discussed the optics of burning glasses, and Arabic writers extended his observations.

It was Robert Grosseteste, an English bishop, philosopher, and keen amateur scientist, who, early in the thirteenth century, first suggested a peacetime use for this weapon. He pointed out that lenses (so named because they were shaped like lentils) might be useful in magnifying objects too small to see conveniently. His pupil, Roger Bacon, acted on this suggestion and devised spectacles to improve poor vision.

At first only convex lenses, to correct far-sightedness, were made. Concave lenses, to correct near-sightedness, were not developed until about 1400. The invention of printing brought more and more demand for spectacles, and by the sixteenth century spectacle-making was a skilled profession. It became a particular specialty in the Netherlands.

(Bifocals, serving both for far and near vision, were invented by Benjamin Franklin in 1760. In 1827 the British astronomer George Biddell Airy designed the first lenses to correct astigmatism, from which he suffered himself. And around 1888 a French physician introduced the idea of contact lenses, which may some day make ordinary spectacles more or less obsolete.)

To get back to the Dutch spectacle-makers. In 1608, so the story goes, an apprentice to a spectacle-maker named Hans Lippershey, whiling away an idle hour, amused himself by looking at objects through two lenses held one behind the other. He was amazed to find that when he held them a certain distance apart, far-off objects appeared close at hand. The apprentice promptly told his master about it, and Lippershey proceeded to build the first "telescope," placing the two lenses in a tube to hold them at the proper spacing. Prince Maurice of Nassau, commander of the Dutch forces in rebellion against Spain, saw the military value of the instrument and endeavored to keep it secret.

He reckoned without Galileo, however. Hearing rumors of the invention of a far-seeing glass, Galileo, knowing no more than that it was made with lenses, soon discovered the principle and built his own telescope; his was completed within six months after Lippershey's.

By rearranging the lenses of his telescope, Galileo found that he could magnify close objects, so that it was in effect a "microscope." Over the next decades several scientists built microscopes. An Italian naturalist named Francesco Stelluti studied insect anatomy with one; Malpighi discovered the capillaries; and Hooke discovered the cells in cork.

But the importance of the microscope was not really appreciated until Anton van Leeuwenhoek, a merchant in the city of Delft, took it up. Van Leeuwenhoek ground lenses as a hobby, and he concentrated on grinding perfect lenses for his microscopes. He used only a single lens, but with his small beauties he could see tiny objects more clearly than could anyone else in his day, for the compound microscopes were handicapped by having lenses ground in the usual slipshod fashion of the time. Some of van Leeuwenhoek's lenses could enlarge up to 200 times.

Van Leeuwenhoek looked at all sorts of objects quite indiscriminately, describing what he saw in lengthy detail in letters to the Royal Society in London. It was rather a triumph for the democracy of science that the tradesman was elected a fellow of the gentlemanly Royal Society. Before he died, the Queen of England and Peter the Great, Czar of all the Russias, visited the humble microscope-maker of Delft.

Through his lenses van Leeuwenhoek discovered sperm cells, red blood cells, and actually saw blood moving through capillaries in the tail of a tadpole. More important, he was the first to see living creatures too small to be seen by the unaided eye. He discovered these "animalcules" in stagnant water in 1675. He also resolved the tiny cells of yeast, and, at the limit of his lenses' magnifying power, he finally came upon "germs," which today we know as bacteria.

Microscopes improved only slowly, and it took a century and a half before objects the size of germs could be studied with ease. For instance, it wasn't until 1830 that the English optician Joseph Jackson Lister devised an "achromatic microscope," which eliminated the rings of color that limited the sharpness of the image. Lister found that red blood cells were biconcave disks — like tiny dough-nuts with dents instead of a hole.

The members of the new world of microscopic life gradually received names. Van Leeuwenhoek's "animalcules" actually were animals, feeding on small particles and moving about by means of small whips (flagellae) or hairlike cilia or advancing streams of protoplasm (pseudopods). These animals were given the name "protozoa" (Greek for "first animals"), and the German zoologist Karl Theodor Ernst Siebold identified them as single-celled creatures.

"Germs" were something else: much smaller than protozoa and much simpler. Although some could move about, most lay quiescent and merely grew and multiplied. Except for their lack of chlorophyll, they showed none of the properties associated with animals. For that reason they were usually classified among the fungi — plants that lack chlorophyll and live on organic matter. Nowadays most biologists tend to consider them as neither plant nor animal but put them in a class by themselves. "Germ" is a misleading name for them. The same term may apply to the living part of a seed (*e.g.*, the "wheat germ"), or to sex cells ("germ cells"), or to embryonic organs ("germ layers"), or, in fact, to any small object possessing the potentiality of life.

The Danish microscopist Otto Frederik Müller managed to see the little creatures well enough in 1773 to distinguish two types: "bacilli" (from a Latin word meaning "little rods") and "spirilli" (for their spiral shape). With the advent of achromatic microscopes, the Austrian surgeon Theodor Billroth saw still smaller varieties to which he applied the term "coccus" (from the Greek word for "berry"). It was the German botanist Ferdinand Julius Cohn who finally coined the name "bacterium" (also from a Latin word meaning "little rod").

Pasteur popularized the general term "microbe" ("small life") for all forms of microscopic life — plant, animal, and bacterial. But this word was soon adopted for the bacteria, just then coming into noto-

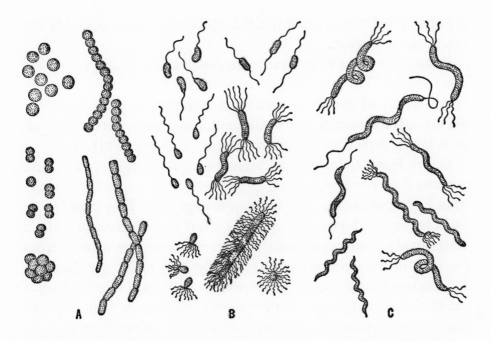

TYPES OF BACTERIA: *cocci* (A), *bacilli* (B), *and spirilli* (C). *Each type has a number of varieties.*

riety. Today the general term for microscopic forms of life is "microorganism."

IT WAS PASTEUR who first definitely connected microorganisms with disease, and, oddly enough, this came about through his efforts to save another French industry. In the 1860's the French silk industry was being ruined by a disease of the silkworms. Pasteur, having already rescued France's wine-makers, was put to work on this problem, too. Again making inspired use of the microscope, as he had in studying asymmetric crystals and varieties of yeast cells, Pasteur found microorganisms infecting the sick silkworms and the mulberry leaves on which they fed. He recommended that all infected worms and leaves be destroyed and a fresh start be made with the uninfected worms and leaves that remained. This drastic step was taken, and it worked.

Pasteur did more with these researches than merely to revive the silk industry. He generalized his conclusions and enunciated the "germ theory of disease" — without question one of the greatest single medical discoveries ever made (and it was made not by a physician, but by a chemist, as chemists delight in pointing out).

Before Pasteur, doctors had been able to do little more for their patients than recommend rest, good food, fresh air, and clean surroundings, and handle a few types of emergencies. They could lance boils, set broken bones, and prescribe a few specific remedies which were simply products of folk-wisdom: drugs such as quinine from the bark of the cinchona tree (originally chewed by the Peruvian Indians to cure themselves of malaria) and digitalis from the plant called foxglove (an old herb-women's remedy to stimulate the heart). Aside from these few treatments (and the smallpox vaccine, which I'll discuss later), many of the medicines and treatments dispensed by physicians tended to heighten the death rate rather than lower it.

It is not surprising that up to the nineteenth century even the most civilized countries were periodically swept by plagues, some of which had a profound effect on history. The plague in Athens that killed Pericles, at the time of the Peloponnesian War, was the first step in the ultimate ruin of Greece. Rome's downfall probably began with the plagues that fell upon the empire during the reign of Marcus Aurelius. The Black Death of the fourteenth century is estimated to have killed off a fourth of the population of Europe; this plague and gunpowder combined to destroy the social structure of the Middle Ages.

To be sure, plagues did not end when Pasteur discovered that infectious diseases were caused and spread by microorganisms. In India cholera is still endemic, and other underdeveloped countries suffer severely from epidemics. Disease has remained a major hazard of wartime. Virulent new organisms arise from time to time and sweep over the world; indeed, the influenza pandemic of 1918 probably killed a larger number of people than any other plague in the history of mankind. Nevertheless, Pasteur's discovery was a great turning point. The death rate in Europe and the United States began to fall markedly, and life expectancy steadily rose. Thanks to the scientific study of disease and its treatment, which began with Pasteur, men and women in the more advanced regions of the world can now expect to live an average of 70 years, whereas before Pasteur the average was only 40 years under the most favorable conditions and perhaps only 25 years under unfavorable conditions.

EVEN BEFORE PASTEUR advanced the germ theory in 1865, a Viennese physician named Ignaz Philipp Semmelweiss had made the first effective attack on bacteria, without, of course, knowing what he was fighting. He was working in the maternity ward of one of Vienna's hospitals, where 12 per cent or more of the new mothers died of something called "puerperal" fever (in plain English, "child-bed fever"). Semmelweiss noted uneasily that women who bore their babies at home with only the services of ignorant midwives practically never got puerperal fever. His suspicions were further aroused by the death of a doctor in the hospital with symptoms that strongly resembled those of puerperal fever, after the doctor had cut himself while dissecting a cadaver. Were the doctors and students who came in from the dissection wards somehow transmitting this disease to the women whose delivery they attended? Semmelweiss insisted that the doctors wash their hands in a solution of chlorinated lime. Within a year the death rate in the maternity wards fell from 12 per cent to 1.5 per cent.

But the veteran doctors were livid. Resentful of the implication that they had been murderers, and humiliated by all the hand-washing, they drove Semmelweiss out of the hospital. (In this they were helped by the fact that he was a Hungarian and Hungary was in revolt against the Austrian rulers.) Semmelweiss went to Budapest, where he reduced the maternal death rate, while in Vienna the hospitals reverted to death traps for another decade or so. But Semmelweiss himself died of puerperal fever from an accidental infection (at the age of 47) in 1865 — just too soon to see the scientific vindication of his suspicions about the transmission of disease. That was the year that Pasteur discovered microorganisms in the diseased silkworms, and an English surgeon named Joseph Lister (the son of the inventor of the achromatic microscope) independently introduced the chemical attack upon germs.

Lister resorted to the drastic substance phenol (carbolic acid). He used it first in dressings for a patient with a compound fracture. Up to that time, any serious wound almost invariably led to infection. Of course, Lister's phenol killed the tissues around the wound, but it did kill the bacteria. The patient made a remarkably untroubled recovery.

Lister followed up this success with the practice of spraying the operating room with phenol. It must have been hard on those who had to breathe it, but it began to save lives. As in Semmelweiss's case, there was opposition, but Pasteur's experiments had created a rationale for antisepsis, and Lister easily won the day.

Pasteur himself had somewhat harder going in France (unlike Lister, he lacked the union label of the M.D.), but he prevailed on surgeons to boil their instruments and steam their bandages. Sterilization with steam *à la* Pasteur replaced Lister's unpleasant phenol spray. Milder antiseptics, which could kill bacteria without unduly damaging tissue, were sought and found.

Meanwhile the German physician Robert Koch had begun to identify the specific bacteria responsible for various diseases. To obtain pure cultures of a single bacterium, he introduced the method of planting isolated samples on agar (a gelatin-like substance obtained from seaweed). If a single bacterium was deposited (with a fine needle) in a spot on this medium, a pure colony would grow around the spot. In this way individual bacteria would give rise to colonies which could then be cultured separately and tested to see what disease they would produce in an experimental animal. The technique not only made it possible to identify a given infection but also permitted experiments with various possible treatments to kill specific bacteria.

With his new techniques Koch isolated a bacillus that caused anthrax and another that caused tuberculosis. In 1905 he received the Nobel Prize in medicine and physiology.

ONCE BACTERIA HAD BEEN IDENTIFIED, the next task was to find drugs that would kill a bacterium without killing the patient as well. To such a search, the German physician and bacteriologist Paul Ehrlich, who had worked with Koch, now addressed himself. He thought of the task as looking for a "magic bullet" which would not harm the body but strike only the bacteria.

Ehrlich was interested in dyes that stained bacteria, and so he naturally turned to these as possible bactericides. A stain that reacted with bacteria more strongly than with other cells might well kill the bacteria even when it was injected into the blood in a concentration low enough not to harm the cells of the patient. By 1907 Ehrlich had discovered a dye, called "Trypan red," which would stain trypanosomes, the organisms responsible for the dreaded African sleeping sickness, transmitted via the tsetse fly. Trypan red, when injected in the blood in proper doses, could kill trypanosomes without killing the patient.

Ehrlich was not satisfied: he wanted a surer kill of the microorganisms. Assuming that the toxic part of the trypan-red molecule was the "azo" combination — that is, a pair of nitrogen atoms $(-N{=}N-)$ — he wondered what a similar combination of arsenic atoms $(-As{=}AS-)$ might accomplish. Arsenic is chemically similar to nitrogen but much more toxic. Ehrlich began to test arsenic compounds one after the other almost indiscriminately, numbering them methodically as he went. In 1909 a Japanese student of Ehrlich's, Sahachiro Hata, tested compound 606, which had failed against the trypanosomes, on the bacterium that caused syphilis. It proved deadly against this microbe (called a "spirochete" because it is spiral-shaped).

At once Ehrlich realized he had stumbled on something more important than a cure for trypanosomiasis, which after all was a limited disease confined to the tropics. Syphilis had been a hidden scourge of Europe for more than 400 years, ever since Columbus's time. (Columbus's men are supposed to have brought it back from the Caribbean Indians; in return, Europe donated smallpox to the Indians.) Not only was there no cure for syphilis, but prudishness had clothed the disease in a curtain of silence which let it spread unchecked.

Ehrlich devoted the rest of his life (he died in 1915) to the attempt to combat syphilis with compound 606, or, as he called it, "Salvarsan" — "safe arsenic." (Its chemical name is arsphenamine.) It could cure the disease, but its use was not without risk, and Ehrlich had to bully hospitals into using it correctly.

With Ehrlich, a new phase of chemotherapy came into being. This was the first synthetic drug, as opposed to the plant remedies such as quinine. Naturally the hope at once arose that every disease might be fought with a little tailored antidote all its own. But for a quarter of a century after Ehrlich's discovery the concocters of new drugs had little luck. About the only success of any sort was the synthesis by German chemists in the late 1920's of "plasmochin" and "atabrine," which could be used as substitutes for quinine against malaria. (They were very helpful to Western troops in jungle areas during World War II, when the Japanese held the sources of the world supply of quinine, which, like rubber, had moved from South America to Southeast Asia.)

In 1932 came a breakthrough. A German chemist named Gerhard Domagk had been injecting various dyes into infected mice. He tried a new red dye called "Prontosil" on mice infected with the deadly hemolytic streptococcus. The mice survived! Within three years Prontosil had gained worldwide renown as a drug that could stop the strep infection in man.

Oddly, Prontosil did not kill streptococci in the test-tube — only in the body. At the Pasteur Institute in Paris, J. Trefouëls and his coworkers decided that the body must change Prontosil into some other substance that took effect on the bacteria. They proceeded to break down Prontosil to the effective fragment, named "sulfanila-mide." This compound had been synthesized in 1908, reported per-functorily, and forgotten. Sulfanilamide's structure is:

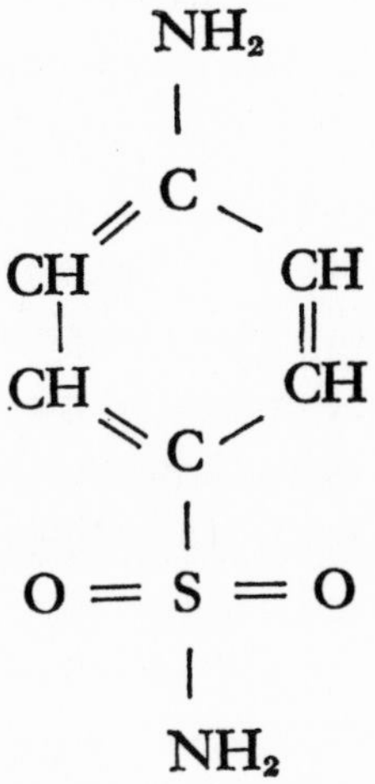

$$NH_2$$
$$|$$

$$\begin{array}{c} C \\ CH \qquad CH \\ CH \qquad CH \\ C \end{array}$$

$$|$$
$$O = S = O$$
$$|$$
$$NH_2$$

It was the first of the "wonder drugs." One after another bac-terium fell before it. Chemists found that by substituting various groups for one of the hydrogen atoms on the sulfur-containing group, they could obtain a series of compounds called "sulfapyri-dine," "sulfadiazine, "sulfathiazole," and so on, each of which had slightly different anti-bacterial properties. Physicians now could choose from a whole platoon of "sulfa drugs" for various infections. In the medically advanced countries, the death rates from bacterial diseases, notably pneumococcal pneumonia, dropped dramatically.

Domagk was awarded the Nobel Prize in medicine and physiol-ogy in 1939. When he wrote the usual letter of acceptance, he was promptly arrested by the Gestapo; the Nazi government, for pe-culiar reasons of its own, refused to have anything to do with the Nobel prizes. Domagk felt it the better part of valor to refuse the prize. After World War II, when he was at last free to accept the honor, Domagk went to Stockholm to receive it officially.

THE SULFA DRUGS had only a brief period of glory, for they were soon put in the shade by the discovery of a far more potent kind of anti-bacterial weapon — the antibiotics.

All living matter (including man) eventually returns to the soil to decay and decompose. With the dead matter and the wastes of living creatures go the germs of the many diseases that infect those creatures. Why is it, then, that the soil is usually so remarkably clean of infectious germs? Very few of them (the anthrax bacillus is one of the few) survive in the soil. A number of years ago bacteriologists began to suspect that the soil harbored microorganisms or substances that destroyed bacteria. One of those who conducted a deliberate search for such bactericides was René Jules Dubos of the Rockefeller Institute. In 1940 he isolated from a soil microorganism called *Bacillus brevis* two bacteria-killing substances which he named "gramicidin" and "tyrocidin." They turned out to be peptides containing *D*-amino acids — the mirror images of the ordinary *L*-amino acids that make up most natural proteins.

Gramicidin and tyrocidin were the first antibiotics produced as such. But an antibiotic which was to prove immeasurably more important had been discovered — and merely noted in a scientific paper — 12 years earlier.

The British bacteriologist Alexander Fleming found one morning that some cultures of staphylococcus (the common pus-forming bacterium), which he had left on a bench, were contaminated with something that had killed the bacteria. There were little clear circles where the staphylococci had been destroyed in the culture dishes. Fleming, being interested in antisepsis (he had discovered that an enzyme in tears, called "lysozome," had antiseptic properties), at once investigated to see what had killed the bacteria, and he discovered that it was a common bread mold, *Penicillium notatum*. Some substance produced by the mold was lethal to germs. Fleming dutifully published his results in 1929, but no one paid much attention at the time.

Ten years later the British biochemist Howard Walter Florey and his German-born associate Ernst Boris Chain became intrigued by the almost forgotten discovery and set out to try to isolate the anti-bacterial substance. By 1941 they had obtained an extract which proved effective clinically against a number of "gram-positive" bacteria (bacteria that retain a dye developed in 1884 by the Danish bacteriologist Hans Christian Joachim Gram).

Because wartime Britain was in no position to produce the drug, Florey went to the United States and helped to launch a program which developed methods of purifying "penicillin" and speeding up its production by the mold. By the war's end, large-scale production and use of penicillin was under way. Not only did penicillin pretty much supplant the sulfa drugs, but it became (and still is) one of the most important drugs in the entire practice of medicine. It is effective against a wide range of infections, including pneumonia, gonorrhea, syphilis, puerperal fever, scarlet fever, and meningitis. Furthermore, it has practically no toxicity or undesirable side-effects, except in penicillin-sensitive individuals.

In 1945 Fleming, Florey, and Chain shared the Nobel Prize in medicine and physiology.

Penicillin set off an almost unbelievably elaborate hunt for other antibiotics. (The word was coined in 1942 by the Rutgers University bacteriologist Selman A. Waksman.)

In 1943 Waksman isolated from a soil mold of the genus *Streptomyces* the antibiotic known as "streptomycin." Streptomycin hit the "gram-negative" bacteria (those that easily lose the Gram stain). Its greatest triumph was against the tubercle bacillus. But streptomycin, unlike penicillin, is rather toxic, and it must be used with caution.

For the discovery of streptomycin, Waksman received the Nobel Prize in medicine and physiology in 1952.

Another antibiotic, chloramphenicol, was isolated from molds of the genus *Streptomyces* in 1947. It attacks not only gram-positive and gram-negative bacteria but also certain smaller organisms, notably those causing typhus fever and psittacosis ("parrot fever"). But its toxicity calls for care in its use.

Then came a whole series of "broad-spectrum" antibiotics — Aureomycin, Terramycin, Achromycin, and so on. These are called "tetracyclines," because in each case the molecule is composed of four rings side by side. They are effective against a wide range of microorganisms and are particularly valuable because they are relatively non-toxic. One of their annoying side-effects is that, by disrupting the balance of useful bacteria in the digestive tract, they upset the natural course of intestinal events and sometimes cause diarrhea.

Next to penicillin (which is much less expensive), the tetracyclines are now the most commonly used prescription drugs for infection. And thanks to the antibiotics in general, the death rates for many of the infectious diseases have fallen to cheeringly low levels.

The chief disappointment in the use of antibiotics has been the speedy rise of resistant strains of bacteria. It is not that the bacteria "learn" to resist but that resistant mutants among them flourish and multiply when the "normal" strains are killed off. This danger is greatest in hospitals, where antibiotics are used constantly and where the patients naturally have below-normal resistance to infection. Certain new strains of staphylococci resist antibiotics with particular stubbornness. This "hospital staph" is now a serious worry in maternity wards, for instance.

Fortunately, where one antibiotic fails another may still attack a resistant strain. New antibiotics, and synthetic modifications of the old, may hold the line in the contest against mutations. The ideal thing would be to find an antibiotic to which no mutants are immune. Then there would be no survivors of that particular bacterium to multiply. A number of such candidates have been produced. They include new antibiotics, modified penicillins, modified tetracyclines, new sulfa drugs, new synthetics of types not previously used at all (*e.g.,* "nitrofuran"), and so on. Even a return to bacteria-killing sprays in hospitals is being tried out. There is, on the whole, every hope that the stubborn versatility of chemical science will manage to keep the upper hand over the stubborn versatility of the disease germs.

AS TO HOW THE CHEMOTHERAPEUTIC AGENTS WORK, the best guess seems to be that each drug inhibits some key enzyme in the microorganism in a competitive way. This is best established in the case of the sulfa drugs. They are very similar to "para-amino-benzoic acid," which has this structure:

$$
\begin{array}{c}
NH_2 \\
| \\
C \\
CH \quad\quad\quad CH \\
| \quad\quad\quad\quad || \\
CH \quad\quad\quad CH \\
C \\
| \\
C = O \\
| \\
OH
\end{array}
$$

Now para-aminobenzoic acid is necessary for the synthesis of "folic acid," a key substance in the metabolism of bacteria as well as other cells. A bacterium that picks up a sulfanilamide molecule instead of para-aminobenzoic acid can no longer produce folic acid, because the enzyme needed for the process is put out of action. Consequently the bacterium ceases to grow and multiply. The cells of the human patient, on the other hand, are not disturbed; they obtain folic acid from food and do not have to synthesize it. There are no enzymes in human cells to be inhibited by moderate concentrations of the sulfa drugs in this fashion.

Even where a bacterium and the human cell possess similar enzymes, there are other ways of attacking the bacterium selectively. The bacterial enzyme may be more sensitive to a given drug than the human enzyme is, so that a certain dose will kill the bacterium without seriously disturbing the human cells. Or a drug of the proper design may be able to penetrate the bacterial cell membrane but not the human cell membrane.

Do the antibiotics also work by competitive inhibition of enzymes? Here the answer is less clear. But there is good ground for believing that at least some of them do.

Gramicidin and tyrocidin, as I mentioned earlier, contain the "unnatural" *D*-amino acids. Perhaps these jam up the enzymes that form compounds from the natural *L*-amino acids. Another peptide antibiotic, bacitracin, contains ornithine; this may inhibit enzymes from making use of arginine, which ornithine resembles. There is a similar situation in streptomycin: its molecule contains an odd variety of sugar which may interfere with some enzyme acting on one of the normal sugars of living cells. Again, chloramphenicol resembles the amino acid phenylalanine; likewise, part of the penicillin molecule resembles the amino acid cysteine. In both of these cases the possibility of competitive inhibition is strong.

The clearest evidence of competitive action by an antibiotic turned up so far involves "puromycin," a substance produced by a *Streptomyces* mold. This compound has a structure much like that of nucleotides (the building units of nucleic acids), and Michael Yarmolinsky and his coworkers at Johns Hopkins University have shown that puromycin, competing with transfer-RNA, interferes with the synthesis of proteins. Unfortunately this form of interference makes it toxic to other cells besides bacteria, because it prevents their normal production of necessary proteins. Thus puromycin is too dangerous a drug to use.

VIRUSES

To MOST PEOPLE it may seem mystifying that the "wonder drugs" have had so much success against the bacterial diseases and so little success against the virus diseases. Since viruses, after all, can cause disease only if they reproduce themselves, why shouldn't it be possible to jam the virus's machinery just as we jam the bacterium's machinery? The answer is quite simple, and indeed obvious once you realize how a virus reproduces itself. As a complete parasite, incapable of multiplying anywhere except inside a living cell, the virus has very little, if any, metabolic machinery of its own. To make copies of itself, it depends entirely on materials supplied by the cell it invades. And it is therefore difficult to deprive it of those materials or jam the machinery without destroying the cell itself.

Biologists discovered the viruses only recently, after a series of encounters with increasingly simple forms of life. Perhaps as good a place as any to start this story is the discovery of the cause of malaria.

Until 1880, malaria, which year in and year out has probably killed more people in the world than any other infectious disease, was thought to be caused by the bad air (*mala aria* in Italian) of swampy regions. Then a French bacteriologist, Charles Louis Alphonse Laveran, discovered that the red blood cells of malaria-stricken individuals were infested with parasitic protozoa of the genus *Plasmodium*. (For this discovery, Laveran was awarded the Nobel Prize in medicine and physiology in 1907.)

In the early 1890's a British physician named Patrick Manson, who had conducted a missionary hospital in Hong Kong, pointed out that swampy regions harbored mosquitoes as well as dank air, and he suggested that mosquitoes might have something to do with the spread of malaria. A British physician in India, Ronald Ross, pursued this idea, and he was able to show that the malarial parasite did indeed pass part of its life cycle in mosquitoes (of the genus *Anopheles*). The mosquito picked up the parasite in sucking the blood of an infected person and then would pass it on to any person it bit.

For his work, bringing to light for the first time the transmission of a disease by an insect "vector," Ross received the Nobel Prize in medicine and physiology in 1902. It was a crucial discovery of modern medicine, for it showed that a disease might be stamped out by killing off the insect carrier. Drain the swamps that breed mos-

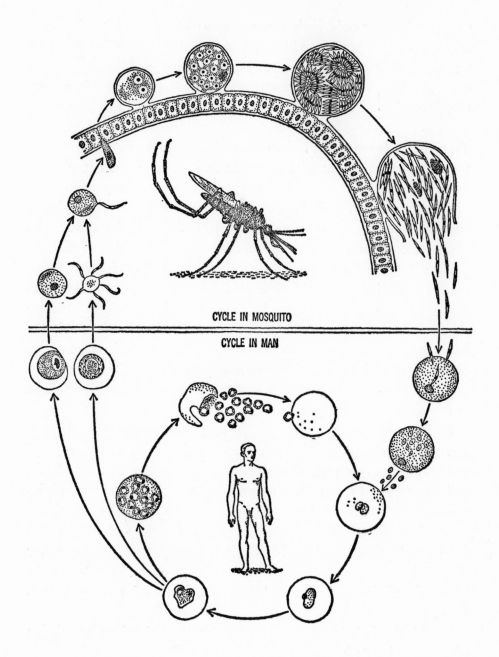

CYCLE IN MOSQUITO

CYCLE IN MAN

LIFE CYCLE OF THE MALARIAL MICROORGANISM.

LOUIS PASTEUR *working in his laboratory (1885).*

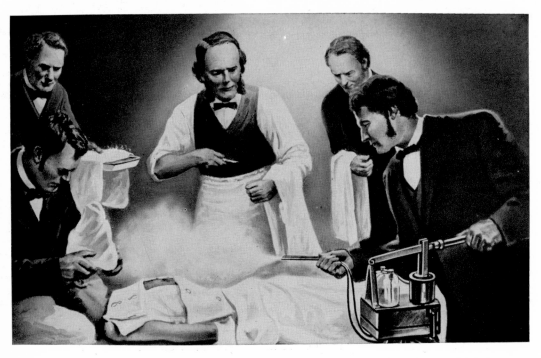

JOSEPH LISTER *directing an assistant who is spraying a surgical patient with carbolic acid as a disinfectant.*

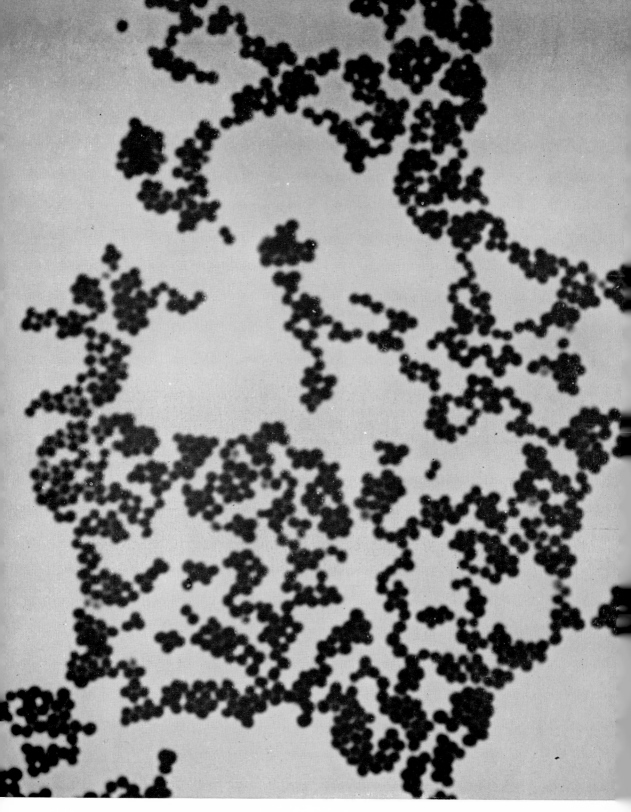

STAPHYLOCOCCUS BACTERIA, *magnified about 2,000 times. The picture clearly shows why they were named from the Greek word for "a bunch of grapes."*

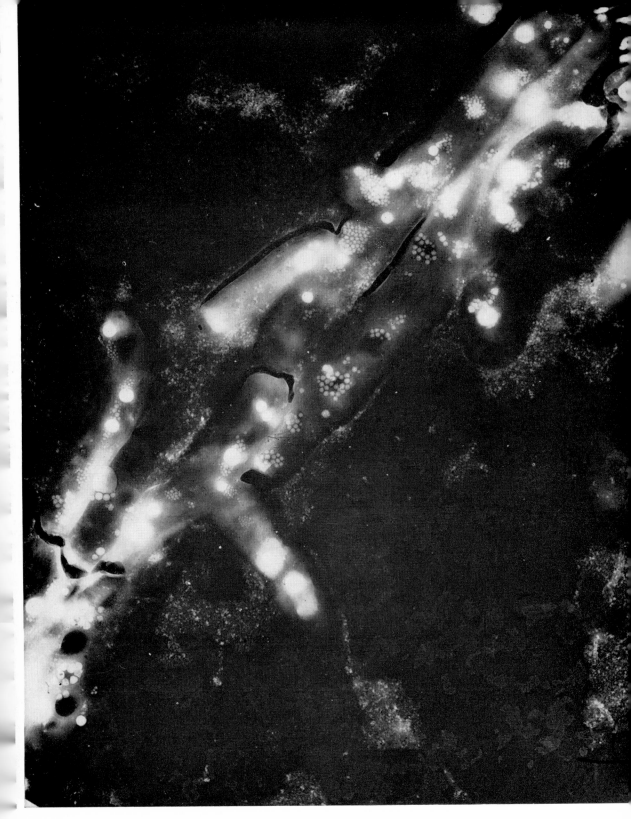

THE ROD-SHAPED BACILLUS *of tuberculosis, photographed with the electron microscope.*

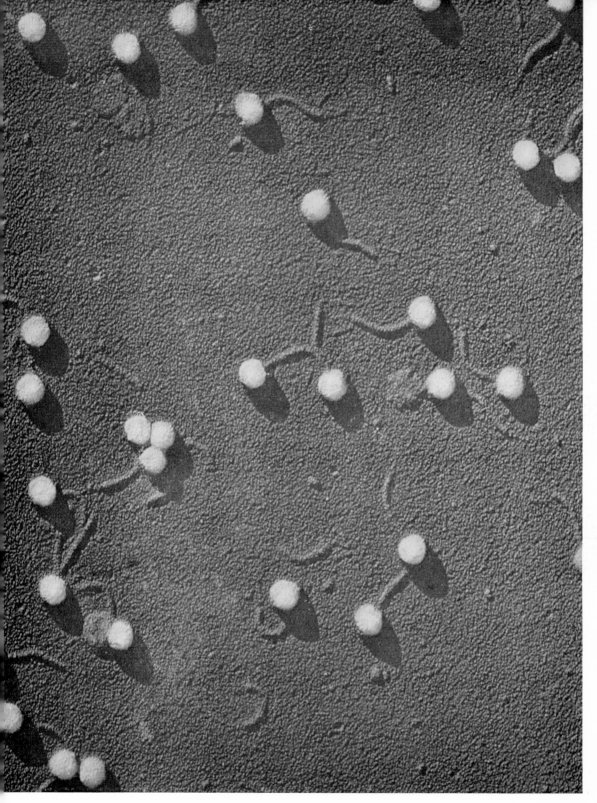

BACTERIOPHAGES. *The tails by which they attached themselves to bacteria can clearly be seen in this electron micrograph.*

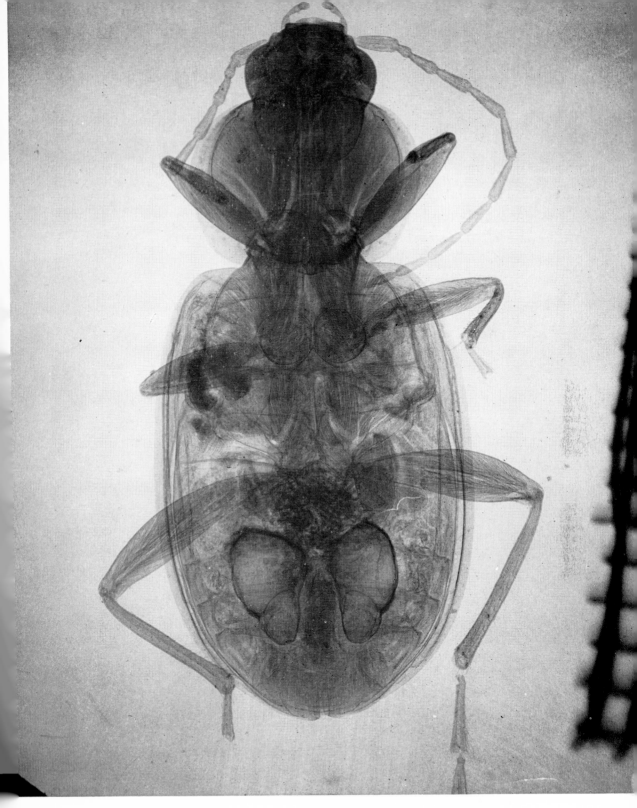

AN X-RAY MICROGRAPH of a beetle showing its internal organs and even muscles. The photograph was made in the Cavendish Physics Laboratory at the University of Cambridge.

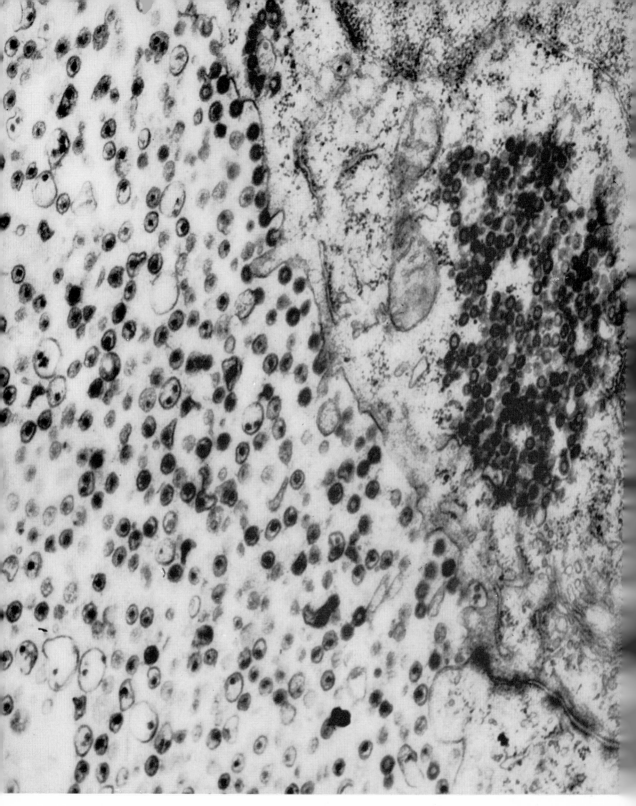

CANCER-PRODUCING PARTICLES, *the so-called "milk factor," which may consist of viruses, are shown here in a mouse breast tumor. They are the group of small, black bodies at the right of the picture. This electron micrograph magnifies them 50,000 times.*

quitoes; eliminate stagnant water; destroy the mosquitoes with insecticides, and you can stop the disease. Since World War II, large
areas of the world have been freed of malaria in just this way.

Malaria was the first infectious disease traced to a non-bacterial
microorganism (a protozoan in this case). Very shortly afterward,
another non-bacterial disease was tracked down to its cause. It was
the deadly yellow fever, which as late as 1898, during an epidemic
in Rio de Janeiro, killed nearly 95 per cent of those it struck. In
1899, when an epidemic of yellow fever broke out in Cuba, a United
States board of inquiry headed by the bacteriologist Walter Reed
went to Cuba to investigate the causes of the disease.

Reed suspected a mosquito vector, such as had just been exposed
as the transmitter of malaria. He first established that the disease
could not be transmitted by direct contact between the patients and
doctors or by way of the patients' clothing or bedding. Then some
of the doctors deliberately let themselves be bitten by mosquitoes
that had previously bitten a man sick with yellow fever. They got
the disease, and some of the courageous investigators died. But the
culprit was identified as the *Aedes aegypti* mosquito. The epidemic
in Cuba was checked, and yellow fever is no longer a serious disease
in the medically advanced parts of the world.

As a third case of a non-bacterial disease, there is typhus fever.
This infection is endemic in North Africa and was brought into
Europe via Spain during the long struggle of the Spaniards against
the Moors of North Africa. Commonly known as "plague," it is
very contagious and has devastated nations. In World War I the
Austrian armies were driven out of Serbia by typhus when the Ser-
bian army itself was unequal to the task. The ravages of typhus in
Poland and Russia during that war and its aftermath (some three million persons died of the disease) did as much as military action to
ruin those nations.

At the turn of the twentieth century the French bacteriologist
Charles Nicolle, then in charge of the Pasteur Institute in Tunis,
noticed that although typhus was rife in the city, no one caught it
in the hospital. The doctors and nurses were in daily contact with

typhus-ridden patients and the hospital was crowded, yet there was no spread of the disease there. Nicolle considered what happened when a patient came into the hospital, and it struck him that the most significant change was a thorough washing of the patient and removal of his lice-infested clothing. Nicolle decided that the body louse must be the vector of typhus. He proved the correctness of his guess by experiments. He received the Nobel Prize in medicine and physiology in 1928 for his discovery. Thanks to his finding, typhus was no scourge in World War II; soldiers and civilians alike were deloused by DDT. World War II, almost unique among history's wars, had the dubious merit of killing fewer people by disease than by guns and bombs.

Typhus, like yellow fever, is caused by an agent smaller than a bacterium, and we must now enter the strange and wonderful realm populated by sub-bacterial organisms.

To GET SOME IDEA of the dimensions of objects in this world, let's look at them in order of decreasing size. The human ovum is about 100 microns (100 millionths of a meter) in diameter, and it is just barely visible to the naked eye. The paramecium, a large protozoan which in bright light can be seen moving about in a drop of water, is about the same size. An ordinary human cell is only one-tenth as large (about ten microns in diameter), and it is quite invisible without a microscope. Smaller still is the red blood corpuscle — some seven microns in maximum diameter. The bacteria, starting with species as large as ordinary cells, drop down to a tinier level: the average rod-shaped bacterium is only two microns long, and the smallest bacteria are spheres perhaps no more than four-tenths of a micron in diameter. They can barely be seen in ordinary microscopes.

At this level, organisms apparently have reached the smallest possible volume into which all the metabolic machinery necessary for an independent life can be crowded. Any smaller organism cannot be a self-sufficient cell and must live as a parasite. It must shed most of the enzymatic machinery as excess baggage, so to speak. It is unable to grow or multiply on any artificial supply of food, however ample; hence it cannot be cultured, as bacteria can, in the test-tube. The only place it can grow is in a living cell, which supplies the enzymes that it lacks. Such a parasite grows and multiplies, naturally, at the expense of the host cell.

The first sub-bacteria were discovered by a young American pathologist named Howard Taylor Ricketts. In 1909 he was studying a disease called Rocky Mountain spotted fever, which is spread by ticks (blood-sucking arthropods, related to the spiders rather than to insects). Within the cells of infected hosts he found "inclusion bodies" that turned out to be very tiny organisms, now called "rickettsia" in his honor. Ricketts and others soon found that typhus also was a rickettsial disease. In the process of establishing a proof of this fact, Ricketts himself caught typhus, and he died in 1910 at the age of 39.

The rickettsia are still big enough to be attacked by antibiotics such as chloramphenicol and the tetracyclines. They range from about four-fifths of a micron to one-fifth of a micron in diameter. Apparently they possess enough metabolic machinery of their own to differ from the host cells in their reaction to drugs. Antibiotic therapy has therefore considerably reduced the danger of rickettsial diseases.

At the lowest end of the scale, finally, come the viruses. They overlap the rickettsia in size; in fact, there is no actual dividing line between rickettsia and viruses. But the smallest viruses are small indeed. The virus of yellow fever, for instance, is only one-fiftieth of a micron in diameter. The viruses are much too small to be detected in a cell or to be seen under any optical microscope.

A virus is stripped practically clean of metabolic machinery. It depends almost entirely upon the enzyme equipment of the host cell. Some of the largest viruses are affected by certain antibiotics, but against the run-of-the-mill viruses drugs are helpless.

The existence of viruses was suspected many decades before they were finally seen. Pasteur, in his studies of hydrophobia, could find no organism in the body that could reasonably be suspected of causing the disease. Rather than decide that his germ theory of disease was wrong, Pasteur suggested that the germ in this case was simply too small to be seen. He was right.

In 1892 a Russian bacteriologist, Dmitri Ivanovski, was studying "tobacco mosaic disease," a disease that gave the leaves of the tobacco plant a mottled appearance. He found that the juice of infected leaves could transmit the disease when placed on the leaves of healthy plants. In an effort to trap the germs, he passed the juice through porcelain filters with holes so fine that not even the smallest bacterium could pass through. Yet the filtered juice still infected tobacco plants. Ivanovski decided that his filters must be defective and were actually letting bacteria through.

A Dutch bacteriologist, Martinus Willem Beijerinck, repeated the experiment in 1897, and he came to the decision that the agent of the disease was small enough to pass through the filter. Since he could see nothing in the clear, infective fluid under any microscope, and was unable to grow anything from it in a test-tube culture, he thought the infective agent might be a small molecule, perhaps about the size of a sugar molecule. Beijerinck called the infective agent a "filtrable virus" (virus being a Latin word meaning "poison").

In the same year a German bacteriologist, Friedrich August Johannes Löffler, found that the agent causing hoof-and-mouth disease in cattle could also pass through a filter. And in 1901 Walter Reed, in the course of his yellow-fever researches, found that the infective agent of that disease also was a filtrable virus.

By 1931 some 40 diseases (including measles, mumps, chickenpox, smallpox, poliomyelitis, and hydrophobia) were known to be caused by viruses, but the nature of viruses was still a mystery. Then an English bacteriologist, William J. Elford, finally began to trap some in filters and to prove that at least they were material particles of some kind. He used fine collodion membranes, graded to keep out smaller and smaller particles, and he worked his way down to membranes fine enough to remove the infectious agent from a liquid. From the fineness of the membrane that could filter out the agent of a given disease, he was able to judge the size of that virus. He found that Beijerinck had been wrong: even the smallest virus was larger than most molecules. The largest viruses approached the rickettsia in size.

For some years afterward, biologists debated whether viruses were living or dead particles. Their ability to multiply and transmit disease certainly suggested that they were alive. But in 1935 the American biochemist Wendell Meredith Stanley produced a piece of evidence which seemed to speak forcefully in favor of "dead." He mashed up tobacco leaves heavily infected with the tobacco mosaic virus and set out to isolate the virus in as pure and concentrated a form as he could get, using protein-separation techniques for the purpose. Stanley succeeded beyond his expectations, for he obtained the virus in crystalline form! His preparation was just as crystalline as a crystallized molecule, yet the virus evidently was still intact; when he redissolved it in liquid, it was just as infectious as before.

For his crystallization of the virus, Stanley shared the 1946 Nobel Prize in chemistry with Sumner and Northrop, the crystallizers of enzymes (see Chapter 11).

The fact that viruses could be crystallized seemed to many, including Stanley himself, to be proof that they were merely dead protein. Nothing living had ever been crystallized, and life and crystallinity just seemed to be mutually contradictory. Life was flexible, changeable, dynamic; a crystal was rigid, fixed, strictly ordered.

Yet the fact remained that viruses were infective, that they could grow and multiply even after having been crystallized. And growth and reproduction had always been considered the essence of life.

The turning point came when two British biochemists, Frederick C. Bawden and Norman W. Pirie, showed that the tobacco mosaic virus contained ribonucleic acid! Not much, to be sure; the virus was 94 per cent protein and only 6 per cent RNA. But it was nonetheless definitely a nucleoprotein. Furthermore, all other viruses turned out to be nucleoprotein, containing RNA or DNA or both.

The difference between being nucleoprotein and being merely protein is practically the difference between being alive and dead. Viruses turned out to be composed of the same stuff as genes, and the genes are the very essence of life. The larger viruses give every appearance of being collections of genes, or chromosomes "on the loose." Viruses undergo mutation; they form new "strains," differing in infectivity and composition. We can picture viruses in the cell as raiders which, pushing aside the supervising genes, take over the chemistry of the cell in their own interests, often causing the death of the cell or of the entire host organism in the process.

If the genes carry the "living" properties of a cell, then viruses are living things. Of course, a lot depends on how one defines life. I, myself, think it fair to consider any nucleoprotein molecule that is capable of replication to be living. By that definition, viruses are as alive as elephants and human beings.

No amount of indirect evidence of the existence of viruses is as good as seeing one, of course. Apparently the first man to lay eyes on a virus was a Scottish physician named John Brown Buist. In 1887 he reported that in the fluid from a vaccination blister he had managed to make out some tiny dots under the microscope. Presumably they were the cowpox virus, the largest known virus.

To get a good look — or any look at all — at a typical virus, something better than an ordinary microscope was needed. The something better was finally invented in the late 1930's: the electron microscope, which could reach magnifications as high as 100,000 and resolve objects as small as a thousandth of a micron in diameter.

The electron microscope has its drawbacks. The object has to be placed in a vacuum, and the inevitable dehydration may change its shape. An object such as a cell must be sliced extremely thin. The image is only two-dimensional; furthermore, the electrons tend to go right through a biological material, so that it does not stand out against the background.

In 1944 the American astronomer and physicist Robley C. Williams and the electron microscopist Ralph W. G. Wyckoff jointly worked out an ingenious solution of these last difficulties. It occurred to Williams, as an astronomer, that just as the craters and mountains of the moon are brought into relief by shadows when the sun's light falls on them obliquely, so viruses might be seen in three dimensions in the electron microscope if they could somehow be made to cast shadows. The solution the experimenters hit upon was to blow vaporized metal obliquely across the virus particles set up on the stage of the microscope. The metal stream left a clear space—a "shadow" — behind each virus particle. The length of the shadow indicated the height of the blocking particle. And the metal, condensing as a thin film, also defined the virus particles sharply against the background.

The shadow pictures of various viruses then disclosed their shapes. The cowpox virus was found to be shaped something like a barrel. It turned out to be about one-quarter of a micron thick — about the size of the smallest rickettsia. The tobacco-mosaic virus proved to be a thin rod 0.28 micron long by 0.015 micron thick. The smallest viruses, such as those of poliomyelitis, yellow fever, and hoof-and-mouth disease, were tiny spheres ranging in diameter from 0.025 down to 0.020 micron. This is considerably smaller than the estimated size of a single human gene. The weight of these viruses is only about 100 times that of an average protein molecule.

In 1959 the Finnish cytologist Alvar P. Wilska designed an electron microscope using comparatively low-speed electrons. Because they are less penetrating than high-speed electrons, they can define some of the internal detail in the structure of viruses.

VIROLOGISTS HAVE ACTUALLY BEGUN to take viruses apart and put them together again. For instance, at the University of California Heinz Fraenkel-Conrat and Robley Williams found that gentle chemical treatment broke down the tobacco-mosaic virus into fragments consisting of peptide chains made up of about 150 amino acids apiece. When dissolved, these fragments tended to recombine into rods again. But the rod, a tight helix of protein, was hollow. The cavity was just big enough for a nucleic-acid molecule to fit inside snugly.

Fraenkel-Conrat separated the nucleic acid and protein portions of tobacco-mosaic viruses and tried to find out whether each portion alone could infect a cell. It developed that separately they could not, as far as he could tell. But when he mixed the protein and nucleic acid together again, about 1 per cent of the original infectiousness of the virus sample was restored!

What had happened? The separated virus protein and nucleic acid had seemed dead, to all intents and purposes; yet, mixed together again, some at least of the material seemed to come to life. The public press hailed Fraenkel-Conrat's experiment as the creation of a living organism from non-living matter. The stories were mistaken, as we shall see in a moment.

Apparently some recombination of protein and nucleic acid had taken place. Each, it seemed, had a role to play in infection. What were the respective roles of the protein and the nucleic acid, and which was more important?

Fraenkel-Conrat performed a neat experiment that answered the question. He mixed the protein part of one strain of the virus with the nucleic-acid portion of another strain. The two parts combined to form an infectious virus with a mixture of properties! In virulence (*i.e.*, the degree of its power to infect tobacco plants) it was the same as the strain of virus that had contributed the protein; in the particular disease produced (*i.e.*, the nature of the mosaic pattern on the leaf) it was identical with the strain of virus that had supplied the nucleic acid.

This finding fitted well with what virologists already suspected about the respective functions of the protein and the nucleic acid. It seems that when a virus attacks a cell, its protein shell, or coat, serves to attach itself to the cell and to break open an entrance into the cell. Its nucleic acid then invades the cell and engineers the production of virus particles.

After Fraenkel-Conrat's hybrid virus had infected a tobacco leaf, the new generation of virus that it bred in the leaf's cells turned out to be not a hybrid but just a replica of the strain that had contributed the nucleic acid. It copied that strain in degree of infectiousness as well as in the pattern of disease produced. In other words, the nucleic acid had dictated the construction of the new virus's protein coat.

It had produced the protein of its own strain, not that of the strain with which it had been combined in the hybrid.

This reinforced the evidence that the nucleic acid is the "live" part of a virus, or, for that matter, of any nucleoprotein. Actually, Fraenkel-Conrat found in further experiments that pure virus nucleic acid alone could produce a little infection in a tobacco leaf. Apparently once in a while the nucleic acid somehow managed to breach an entrance into a cell all by itself.

So putting virus nucleic acid and protein together to form a virus is not creating life from non-life; the life is already there, in the shape of the nucleic acid. The protein merely serves to help the nucleic acid go about the business of infection and reproduction more efficiently. We might compare the nucleic-acid fraction to a man and the protein fraction to an automobile. The combination makes easy work of traveling from one place to another. The automobile by itself could never make the trip. The man could make it on foot (and occasionally does), but the automobile is a big help.

The clearest and most detailed information about the mechanism by which viruses infect a cell has come from studies of the viruses called bacteriophages, first discovered by the English bacteriologist Frederick William Twort in 1915 and, independently, by the Canadian bacteriologist Félix Hubert d'Hérelle in 1917. Oddly enough, these viruses are germs that prey on germs — namely, bacteria. D'Hérelle gave them the name "bacteriophage," from Greek words meaning "bacteria-eater."

The bacteriophages are beautifully convenient things to study, because they can be cultured with their hosts in a test-tube. The process of infection and multiplication goes about as follows.

A typical bacteriophage (usually called "phage" by the workers with the beast) is shaped like a tiny tadpole, with a blunt head and a tail. Under the electron microscope investigators have been able to see that the phage first lays hold of the surface of a bacterium with its tail. The best guess as to how it does this is that the pattern of electric charge on the tip of the tail (determined by charged amino acids) just fits the charge pattern on certain portions of the bacterium's surface. The configurations of the opposite, and attracting, charges on the tail and on the bacterial surface match so neatly that they come together with something like the click of perfectly meshing gear teeth. Once the virus has attached itself to its victim by the tip of its tail, it cuts a tiny opening in the cell wall, perhaps by means of an enzyme that cleaves the molecules at that point. As far as the electron-microscope pictures show, nothing whatever is happening. The phage, or at least its visible shell, remains attached to the outside of the bacterium. Inside the bacterial cell there is no visible activity. But within 20 minutes the cell bursts open and up to 300 full-grown viruses pour out.

Evidently only the protein shell of the attacking virus stays outside the cell. The nucleic acid within the virus's shell must pour into the bacterium through the hole in its wall made by the protein. That the invading material is just nucleic acid, without any detectable admixture of protein, was proved by the American bacteriologist Alfred D. Hershey by means of radioactive tracers. He tagged phages with radioactive phosphorus and radioactive sulfur atoms (by growing them in bacteria that had incorporated these radioisotopes from their nutritive medium). Now phosphorus occurs both in proteins and in nucleic acids, but sulfur will turn up only in proteins, because there is no sulfur in a nucleic acid. Therefore if a phage labeled with both tracers invaded a bacterium and its progeny turned up with radiophosphorus but no radiosulfur, the experiment would indicate that the parent virus's nucleic acid had entered the cell but its protein had not. The absence of radiosulfur would suggest that all the protein in the virus progeny was supplied by the host bacterium. The experiment, in fact, turned out just this way: the new viruses contained radiophosphorus (contributed by the parent) but no radiosulfur.

Once more, the dominant role of nucleic acid in the living process was demonstrated. Apparently only the phage's nucleic acid went into the bacterium, and there it superintended the construction of new viruses — protein and all — from the material in the cell.

IMMUNITY

VIRUSES ARE MAN'S MOST FORMIDABLE LIVING ENEMY (except man himself). By virtue of their intimate association with the body's own cells, viruses have been all but invulnerable to attack by drugs or any other artificial weapon. And yet man has been able to hold his own against them, even under the most unfavorable conditions. The human organism is endowed with impressive natural defenses against disease.

Consider the Black Death, the great plague of the fourteenth century. It attacked a Europe living in appalling filth, without any modern conception of cleanliness and hygiene, without plumbing, without any form of reasonable medical treatment — a crowded and helpless population. To be sure, people could flee from the infected villages, but the fugitive sick only spread the epidemics faster and farther. Notwithstanding all this, three-fourths of the population successfully resisted the infections. Under the circumstances, the marvel is not that one out of four died; the marvel is that three out of four survived.

There is clearly such a thing as natural resistance to any given disease. Of a number of people exposed to a serious contagious disease, some will have a relatively mild case, some will be very sick, some will die. There is also such a thing as complete immunity — sometimes inborn, sometimes acquired. A single attack of measles, mumps or chickenpox, for instance, will usually make a person immune to that particular disease for the rest of his life.

All three of these diseases, as it happens, are caused by viruses. Yet they are comparatively minor infections, seldom fatal. Measles usually produces only mild symptoms, at least in a child. How does the body fight off these viruses, and then fortify itself so that the virus it has defeated never troubles it again? The answer to that question forms a thrilling episode in modern medical science, and for the beginning of the story we must go back to the conquest of smallpox.

Up to the end of the eighteenth century, smallpox was a particularly dreaded disease, not only because it was often fatal but also because those who recovered were permanently disfigured. A light case would leave the skin pitted; a severe attack could destroy all traces of beauty and almost of humanity. A very large proportion of the population bore the marks of smallpox on their faces. And those who had not yet caught it lived in fear of when it might strike.

In the seventeenth century people in Turkey began to infect themselves deliberately with mild forms of smallpox, with the hope of making themselves immune to severe attack. They would have themselves scratched with the serum from blisters of a person who had a mild case. Sometimes they developed only a light infection; sometimes they suffered the very disfigurement or death they had sought to avoid. It was risky business, but it is a measure of the horror of the disease that people were willing to risk the horror itself in order to escape from it.

In 1718 the famous beauty Lady Mary Wortley Montagu learned about this practice when she went to Turkey with her husband, sent there briefly as the British ambassador, and she had her own children inoculated. They escaped without harm. But the idea did not catch on in England, perhaps partly because Lady Montagu was considered a notorious eccentric.

Certain country folk in Gloucestershire had their own idea about how to avoid smallpox. They believed that a case of cowpox, a disease that attacked cows and sometimes people, would make a person immune to both cowpox and smallpox. This was wonderful, if true, for cowpox produced hardly any blisters and left hardly any marks. A Gloucestershire doctor, Edward Jenner, decided that there might be some truth in this folk "superstition." Milkmaids, he noticed, were particularly prone to catch cowpox and apparently also particularly prone not to be pockmarked by smallpox. (Perhaps the eighteenth-century vogue of romanticizing the beautiful milkmaid was based on the fact that milkmaids, having clear complexions, were indeed beautiful in a pock-marked world.)

Was it possible that cowpox and smallpox were so alike that a defense formed by the body against cowpox would also protect against smallpox? Very cautiously Dr. Jenner began to test this notion (probably experimenting on his own family first). In 1796 he decided to chance the supreme test. First he inoculated an eight-year-old boy named James Phipps with cowpox, using fluid from a cowpox blister on a milkmaid's hand. Two months later came the crucial and desperate part of the test. Jenner deliberately inoculated young James with smallpox itself.

The boy did not catch the disease. He was immune.

Jenner called the process "vaccination," from *vaccinia*, the Latin name for cowpox. Vaccination spread through Europe like wildfire. It is one of the rare cases of a revolution in medicine which was adopted easily and almost at once — a true measure of the deadly fear inspired by smallpox and the eagerness of the public to try anything that promised escape. Even the medical profession put up only weak opposition to vaccination — though its leaders did what they could. When Jenner was proposed for election to the Royal College of Physicians in London in 1813, he was refused admission, on the ground that he was not sufficiently up on Hippocrates and Galen.

Today smallpox has practically been wiped out in civilized countries, though its terrors as a disease are still as strong as ever. A report of a single case in any large city is sufficient to send virtually the entire population running to doctors' offices for renewed vaccination.

ATTEMPTS TO DISCOVER SIMILAR INOCULATIONS for other severe diseases got nowhere for more than a century and a half. It was Pasteur who made the next big step forward. He discovered, more or less by accident, that he could change a severe disease into a mild one by weakening the microbe that produced it.

Pasteur was working with a bacterium which caused cholera in chickens. He concentrated a preparation so virulent that a little injected under the skin of a chicken would kill it within a day. On one occasion he used a culture that had been standing for a week. This time the chickens became only slightly sick and recovered. Pasteur decided that the culture was spoiled and prepared a virulent new batch. But his fresh culture failed to kill the chickens that had recovered from the dose of "spoiled" bacteria. Clearly the infection with the weakened bacteria had equipped the chickens with a defense against the fully potent ones.

In a sense Pasteur had produced an artificial "cowpox" for this particular "smallpox." He recognized the philosophical debt he owed to Jenner by calling his procedure vaccination, too, although it had nothing to do with vaccinia. Since then, the term has been used quite generally to mean inoculations against any disease, and the preparation used for the purpose is called a "vaccine."

Pasteur developed other methods of weakening (or "attenuating") disease agents. For instance, he found that culturing anthrax bacteria at a high temperature produced a weakened strain which would immunize animals against the disease. Until then, anthrax had been so hopelessly fatal and contagious that as soon as one member of a herd came down with it, the whole herd had to be slaughtered and burned.

Pasteur's most famous victory, however, was over the virus disease called hydrophobia, or "rabies" (from a Latin word meaning "to rave," because the disease attacked the nervous system and produced symptoms akin to madness). A person bitten by a rabid dog would, after an incubation period of a month or two, be seized by violent symptoms and almost invariably die an agonizing death.

Pasteur could find no visible microbe as the agent of the disease (of course, he knew nothing of viruses), so he had to use living animals to cultivate it. He would inject the infectious fluid into the brain of a rabbit, let it incubate, mash up the rabbit's spinal cord, inject the extract into the brain of another rabbit, and so on. Pasteur attenuated his preparations by aging and testing them continuously until the extract could no longer cause the disease in a rabbit. He then injected the attenuated virus into a dog, which survived. After a time, he infected the dog with hydrophobia in full strength and found the animal immune.

In 1885 Pasteur got his chance to try the cure on a human being. A nine-year-old boy, Joseph Meister, who had been severely bitten by a rabid dog, was brought to him. With considerable hesitation and anxiety, Pasteur treated the boy with inoculations of successively less and less attenuated virus, hoping to build up resistance before the incubation period had elapsed. He succeeded. At least, the boy survived. (Meister became the gatekeeper of the Pasteur Institute, and in 1940 he committed suicide when the Nazi army in Paris ordered him to open Pasteur's crypt.)

In the 1890's a German army doctor named Emil von Behring, working in Koch's laboratory, tried another idea. Why take the risk of injecting the microbe itself, even in attenuated form, into a human being? Assuming that the disease agent caused the body to manufacture some defensive substance, would it not serve just as well to infect an animal with the agent, extract the defensive substance that it produced, and inject that substance into the human patient?

Von Behring found that this scheme did indeed work. The defensive substance turned up in the blood serum, and von Behring called it "antitoxin." He caused animals to produce antitoxins against tetanus and diphtheria. His first use of the diphtheria antitoxin on a child with the disease was so dramatically successful that the treatment was adopted immediately and proceeded to cut the death rate from diphtheria drastically.

Paul Ehrlich (who later was to discover the "magic bullet" for syphilis) worked with von Behring, and it was probably he who calculated the appropriate antitoxin dosages. Later he broke with von Behring (Ehrlich was an irascible individual who found it easy to break with anyone), and alone he went on to work out the rationale of serum therapy in detail. Von Behring received the Nobel Prize in medicine and physiology in 1901, the first year in which it was awarded. Ehrlich also was awarded the Nobel Prize, sharing it with a Russian biologist in 1908.

The immunity conferred by an antitoxin lasts only as long as the antitoxin remains in the blood. But chemists found that by treating the toxin of diphtheria or tetanus with formaldehyde or heat they were able to change its structure in such a way that the new substance (called "toxoid") could safely be injected in a human patient. The antitoxin then made by the patient himself lasts longer than that from an animal; furthermore, new doses of the toxoid can be injected when necessary to renew immunity.

Pasteur's laborious wrestle with the virus of rabies showed the difficulty of dealing with viruses. Bacteria can be cultured, manipulated, and attenuated on artificial media in the test-tube. Viruses cannot; they can be grown only in living tissue. In the case of smallpox, the living hosts for the experimental material (the cowpox virus) were cows and milkmaids. In the case of rabies, Pasteur used rabbits. But living animals are, at best, an awkward, expensive, and time-consuming type of medium for culturing microorganisms.

In the first quarter of this century the French biologist Alexis Carrel won considerable fame with a stunt which was to prove immensely valuable to medical research — keeping bits of tissue alive in the test-tube. Carrel had become interested in this sort of thing through his work as a surgeon. He had developed new methods of transplanting animals' blood vessels and organs, for which he received the Nobel Prize in medicine and physiology in 1912. Naturally, he had to keep the excised organ alive while he was getting ready to transplant it. He worked out a way to nourish it, which consisted in perfusing the tissue with blood and supplying various extracts and ions. As an incidental dividend, Carrel, with the help of Charles Augustus Lindbergh, developed a crude "mechanical heart" to pump the blood through the tissue. This was a forerunner of the artificial "hearts," "lungs," and "kidneys" that have now come into use in surgery.

Carrel's devices were good enough to keep a piece of embryonic chicken heart alive for 34 years — much longer than a chicken's lifetime. Carrel even tried to use his tissue cultures to grow viruses — and he succeeded in a way. The only trouble was that bacteria also grew in the tissues, and in order to keep the virus pure, such tedious aseptic precautions had to be taken that it was easier to use animals.

The chick-embryo idea, however, was in the right ball park, so to speak. Better than just a piece of tissue would be the whole thing — the chick embryo itself. A chick embryo is a self-contained organism, protected by the egg shell, equipped with its own natural defenses against bacteria, and cheap and easy to come by in quantity. And in 1931 the pathologist Ernest W. Goodpasture and his co-workers at Vanderbilt University succeeded in transplanting a virus into a chick embryo. For the first time, pure viruses could be cultured nearly as easily as bacteria.

The first great medical victory by means of the culture of viruses in fertile eggs came in 1937. At the Rockefeller Institute, bacteriologists were still hunting for further protection against the yellow-fever virus. It was impossible to eradicate the mosquito completely, after all, and infected monkeys maintained a constantly threatening reservoir of the disease in the tropics. Max Theiler at the Institute set out to produce an attenuated yellow-fever virus. He passed the virus through 200 mice and 100 chick embryos until he had a mutant which caused only mild symptoms yet gave rise to complete immunity against yellow fever. For this achievement Theiler received the 1951 Nobel Prize in medicine and physiology.

When all is said and done, nothing can beat culture in glassware for speed, control of the conditions, and efficiency. In the late 1940's John F. Enders, Thomas H. Weller, and Frederick C. Robbins at the Harvard Medical School went back to Carrel's approach. (He had died in 1944 and was not to see their success.) This time they had a new and powerful weapon against bacteria contaminating the tissue culture — the antibiotics. They added penicillin and streptomycin to the supply of blood that kept the tissues alive, and they found that they could grow viruses without trouble. On impulse, they tried the poliomyelitis virus. To their delight, it flourished in this medium. It was the breakthrough that was to conquer polio, and the three men received the Nobel Prize in medicine and physiology in 1954.

The poliomyelitis virus could now be bred in the test-tube, instead of solely in monkeys (which are expensive and temperamental laboratory subjects). Large-scale experimentation with the virus became possible. Thanks to the tissue-culture technique, Jonas E. Salk of the University of Pittsburgh was able to experiment with chemical treatment of the virus, to learn that polio viruses killed by formaldehyde could still produce immune reactions in the body, and to develop his now-famous Salk vaccine.

Polio's sizable death rate, its dreaded paralysis, its partiality for children, and particularly the interest attracted to the disease by its eminent victim, Franklin D. Roosevelt, made its conquest one of the most celebrated victories over a disease in all human history. Probably no medical announcement ever received such a Hollywood-premiere-type reception as did the report of the evaluating committee that found the Salk vaccine effective. Of course, the event merited such a celebration more than do most of the performances that arouse people to throw ticker tape and trample one another. But science does not thrive on furore or wild publicity. The rush to respond to the public pressure for the vaccine apparently resulted in a few defective, disease-producing samples of the vaccine slipping through, and the subsequent counterfurore set back the vaccination program against the disease. Nevertheless, the taming of polio was a victory of research which will lead to other victories against viruses.

WHAT DOES A VACCINE DO, EXACTLY? The answer to this question may some day give us the chemical key to immunity.

For more than half a century biologists have known the body's main defenses against infection as "antibodies." (Of course, there are also the white blood cells called "phagocytes," which devour bacteria. This was discovered in 1883 by the Russian biologist Ilya Ilitch Mechnikov, who later succeeded Pasteur as the head of the Pasteur Institute in Paris and shared the 1908 Nobel Prize in medicine and physiology with Ehrlich. But phagocytes are no help against viruses and seem not to be involved in the immunity process we are considering.) A virus, or indeed almost any foreign substance entering into the body's chemistry, is called an "antigen." The antibody is a substance manufactured by the body to fight the specific antigen. It puts the antigen out of action by combining with it.

Long before the chemists actually ran down an antibody, they were pretty sure the antibodies must be proteins. For one thing, the best-known antigens were proteins, and presumably it would take a protein to catch a protein. Only a protein could have the subtlety of structure necessary to single out and combine with a particular antigen.

Early in the 1920's Landsteiner (the discoverer of blood groups) carried out a series of experiments which clearly showed that anti-bodies were very specific indeed. The substances he used to generate antibodies were not antigens but much simpler compounds whose structure was well known. They were arsenic-containing compounds called "arsanilic acids." In combination with a simple protein such as the albumin of egg-white, an arsanilic acid acted as an antigen: when injected into an animal, it gave rise to an antibody in the blood serum. Furthermore, this antibody was specific for the arsanilic acid; the blood serum of the animal would clump only the arsanilic-albumin combination, not albumin alone. Indeed, sometimes the antibody could be made to react with just an arsanilic acid, not combined with albumin. Landsteiner also showed that very small changes in the structure of the arsanilic acid would be reflected in the antibody. An antibody evoked by one variety of arsanilic acid would not react with a slightly altered variety.

Landsteiner coined the name "haptens" (from a Greek word meaning "to bind") for compounds, such as the arsanilic acids, that can give rise to antibodies when they are combined with protein. Presumably each natural antigen has a specific region in its molecule which acts as a hapten. On that theory, a germ or virus that can serve as a vaccine is one that has had its structure changed sufficiently to reduce its ability to damage cells but still has its hapten group intact, so that it can cause the formation of a specific antibody.

It would be interesting to learn the chemical nature of the natural haptens. If that could be determined, it might be possible to use a hapten, perhaps in combination with some harmless protein, to serve as a vaccine giving rise to antibodies for a specific antigen. That would avoid the necessity of resorting to toxins or attenuated viruses, which always carries some small risk.

Just how an antigen evokes an antibody has not been determined. Ehrlich believed that the body normally contains a small supply of all the antibodies it may need, and when an invading antigen reacts with the appropriate antibody, this stimulates the body to produce an extra supply of that particular antibody. Some immunologists still adhere to that theory or to modifications of it. Yet it seems highly unlikely that the body is prepared with specific antibodies for all the possible antigens, including unnatural substances such as the arsanilic acids.

The alternate suggestion is that the body has some generalized protein molecule which can be molded to fit any antigen. The antigen, then, acts as a template to shape the specific antibody formed in response to it. Pauling proposed such a theory in 1940. He suggested that the specific antibodies are varying versions of the same basic molecule, merely folded in different ways. In other words, the antibody is molded to fit its antigen as a glove fits the hand.

The very specificity of antibodies is a disadvantage, in a way. Suppose a virus mutates so that its protein has a slightly different structure. The old antibody for the virus often will not fit the new structure. It follows that immunity against one strain of virus is no safeguard against another strain. The virus of influenza and of the common cold are particularly prone to minor mutations, and that is one reason why we are plagued by frequent recurrences of these diseases. Influenza, in particular, will occasionally develop a mutant of extraordinary virulence, which may then sweep a surprised and non-immune world. This happened in 1918 and, with much less fatal result, in the "Asian flu" pandemic of 1957.

A still more annoying effect of the body's oversharp efficiency in forming antibodies is its tendency to produce them even against a harmless protein that happens to enter the body. The body then becomes "sensitized" to that protein, and it may react violently to any later incursion of the originally innocent protein. The reaction may take the form of itching, tears, production of mucus in the nose and throat, asthma, and so on. Such "allergic reactions" are evoked by the pollen of certain plants (causing hay-fever), by certain foods, by the fur or dandruff of animals, etc.

In a sense, every human being is more or less allergic to every other human being. A transplant, or graft, from one individual to another will not take, because the receiver's body treats the transplanted tissue as foreign protein and manufactures antibodies against it. The only person-to-person graft that will work is from one identical twin to the other. Since their identical heredity gives them exactly the same proteins, they can exchange tissues or even a whole organ, such as a kidney. Several dramatic operations of this nature have been successfully performed in recent years. There have been a few apparently successful grafts from one animal to another, and in one case between non-identical twins, but in each case drastic radiation treatments had to be given to impair the body's ability to produce antibodies.

In the 1940's researchers found that allergic reactions are brought about by the liberation of small quantities of a substance called "histamine" into the blood stream. This led to the successful search for neutralizing "anti-histamines," which can relieve the allergic symptoms but of course do not remove the allergy. (Noting that sniffling and other allergic symptoms were much like those of the common cold, pharmaceutical firms decided that what worked for one ought to work for the other, and in 1949 and 1950 they flooded the country with anti-histamine tablets. The tablets turned out to do little or nothing for colds, and their vogue diminished.)

In 1937, thanks to the protein-isolating techniques of electrophoresis, biologists finally tracked down the physical location of antibodies in the blood. The antibodies were located in the blood fraction called "gamma-globulin."

Physicians have long been aware that some children are unable to form antibodies and therefore are easy prey to infection. In 1951 doctors at the Walter Reed Hospital in Washington made an electrophoretic analysis of the plasma of an eight-year-old boy suffering from a serious septicemia ("blood-poisoning"), and to their astonishment they discovered that his blood had no gamma-globulin at all. Other cases were quickly discovered. Investigators established that this lack is due to an inborn defect of metabolism which deprives the person of the ability to make gamma-globulin; it is called "agammaglobulinemia." Such persons cannot develop immunity to bacteria. They can now be kept alive, however, by antibiotics. Surprisingly enough, they *are* able to become immune to virus infections, such as measles and chickenpox, after having the disease once. Apparently antibodies are not the body's only defense against viruses.

CANCER

As THE DANGER OF INFECTIOUS DISEASES DIMINISHES, the incidence of other types of disease increases. Many people who a century ago would have died young of tuberculosis or diphtheria or pneumonia or typhus now live long enough to die of heart disease or cancer. That is one reason why heart disease and cancer have become respectively the number one and the number two killers in the Western world. Cancer, in fact, has succeeded plague and smallpox as a great fear of man. It is a nightmare hanging over all of us, ready to strike anyone without warning or mercy.

Cancer is actually a group of many different diseases, affecting various parts of the body in various fashions. But the primary disorder is always the same: disorganization and uncontrolled growth of the affected tissues. The name cancer (the Latin word for "crab") comes from the fact that Hippocrates and Galen fancied the disease spreading its ravages through diseased veins like the crooked, outstretched claws of a crab.

"Tumor" (from the Latin word meaning "grow") is by no means synonymous with cancer; it applies to harmless growths such as warts and moles ("benign tumors") as well as to cancers ("malignant tumors"). The cancers are variously named according to the tissues affected. Cancers of the skin or the intestinal linings (the most common malignancies) are called "carcinomas" (from the Greek word for "crab"); cancers of the connective tissues are "sarcomas;" of the liver, "hepatoma;" of glands generally, "adenomas;" of the white blood cells, "leukemia," and so on.

Rudolf Virchow of Germany, the first to study cancer tissue under the microscope, believed that cancer was caused by the irritations and shocks of the outer environment. This is a natural thought, for it is just those parts of the body most exposed to the outer world that are most subject to cancer. But when the germ theory of disease became popular, pathologists began to look for some microbe as the cause of cancer. Virchow, a staunch opponent of the germ theory of disease, stubbornly insisted on the irritation theory. (He quit pathology for archaeology and politics when it turned out that the germ theory of disease was going to win out. Few scientists in history have gone down with the ship of mistaken beliefs in quite so drastic a fashion.)

If Virchow was stubborn for the wrong reason, he may have been so in the right cause. There has been increasing evidence that some environments are particularly conducive to cancer. In the eighteenth century chimney sweeps were found to be more prone to cancer of the scrotum than other people were. After the coal-tar dyes were developed, workers in the dye industries showed an above-average incidence of cancers of the skin or bladder. It seemed that something in soot and in the aniline dyes must be capable of causing cancer. Then in 1915 two Japanese scientists, K. Yamagiwa and K. Ichikawa, discovered that a certain coal-tar fraction could produce cancer in rabbits when it was applied to the rabbits' ears for long periods. In 1930 two British chemists induced cancer in animals with a synthetic chemical called "dibenzanthracene" (a hydrocarbon with a molecule made up of five benzene rings). This does not occur in coal-tar, but three years later it was discovered that "benzpyrene" (also containing five benzene rings but in a different arrangement), a chemical that *does* occur in coal-tar, can cause cancer.

Quite a number of "carcinogens" (cancer-producers) have now

been identified. Many are hydrocarbons made up of numerous benzene rings, like the first two discovered. Some are molecules related to the aniline dyes. In fact, one of the chief concerns about using artificial dyes in foods is the possibility that in the long run such dyes may be carcinogenic.

Many biologists believe that man has introduced a number of new cancer-producing factors into his environment within the last two or three centuries. There is the increased use of coal; there is the burning of oil on a large scale, particularly in gasoline engines; there is the growing use of synthetic chemicals in food, cosmetics, and so on. The most dramatic of the suspects, of course, is cigarette-smoking, which, statistically at least, seems to be accompanied by a relatively high rate of incidence of lung cancer.

ONE ENVIRONMENTAL FACTOR that is certainly carcinogenic is energetic radiation, and man has been exposed to such radiation in increasing measure since 1895.

On November 5, 1895, the German physicist Wilhelm Konrad Roentgen performed an experiment to study the luminescence produced by cathode rays. The better to see the effect, he darkened the room. His cathode-ray tube was enclosed in a black cardboard box. When he turned on the cathode-ray tube, he was startled to catch a flash of light from something across the room. The flash came from a sheet of paper coated with barium platinocyanide, a luminescent chemical. Was it possible that radiation from the closed box had made it glow? Roentgen turned off his cathode-ray tube, and the glow stopped. He turned it on again — the glow returned. He took the paper into the next room, and it still glowed. Clearly the cathode-ray tube was producing some form of radiation which could penetrate cardboard and walls.

Roentgen, having no idea what kind of radiation this might be, called it simply "X-rays." Other scientists tried to change the name to "Roentgen rays," but this was so hard for anyone but Germans to pronounce that "X-rays" stuck.

594

The X-rays revolutionized physics. They captured the imagination of physicists, started a typhoon of experiments, led within a few months to the discovery of radioactivity, and opened up the inner world of the atom. When the award of Nobel Prizes began in 1901, Roentgen was the first to receive the prize in physics.

The hard X-radiation also started something else — exposure of human beings to intensities of energetic radiation such as man had never experienced before. Four days after the news of Roentgen's discovery reached the United States, X-rays were used to locate a bullet in a patient's leg. They were a wonderful means of exploring the interior of the body. X-rays pass easily through the soft tissues (consisting chiefly of elements of low atomic weight) and tend to be stopped by elements of higher atomic weight, such as make up the bones (composed largely of phosphorus and calcium). On a photographic plate placed behind the body, bone shows up as a cloudy white, in contrast to the black areas where X-rays have come through in greater intensity because they have been much less absorbed by the soft tissues. A lead bullet shows up as pure white; it stops the X-rays completely.

X-rays are obviously useful for showing bone fractures, calcified joints, cavities in the teeth, foreign objects in the body, and so on. But it is also a simple matter to outline the soft tissues by introducing an insoluble salt of a heavy element. Barium sulfate, when swallowed, will outline the stomach or intestines. An iodine compound injected into the blood will travel to the kidneys and the ureter and outline those organs, for iodine has a high atomic weight and therefore is opaque to X-rays.

Even before X-rays were discovered, a Danish physician, Niels Ryberg Finsen, had found that high-energy radiation could kill microorganisms; he used ultraviolet light to destroy the bacteria causing lupus vulgaris, a skin disease. (For this he was awarded the Nobel Prize in physiology and medicine in 1903.) The X-rays turned out to be far more deadly. They could kill the fungus of ringworm. They could damage or destroy human cells, and were eventually used to kill cancer cells beyond reach of the surgeon's knife.

What was also discovered — the hard way — was that high-energy radiation could *cause* cancer. Several of the early workers with X-rays and radioactive materials died of cancer. As a matter of fact, both Marie Curie and her daughter, Irène Joliot-Curie, died of leukemia, and it is easy to believe that radiation was a contributing cause in both cases. In 1928 a British investigator, G. M. Findlay, found that even ultraviolet radiation was energetic enough to cause skin cancer in mice.

It is certainly reasonable to suspect that man's increasing exposure to energetic radiation (in the form of medical X-rays, and so on) may be responsible for part of the increased incidence of cancer. And the future will tell whether the accumulation in our bones of traces of strontium 90 from fallout will increase the incidence of bone cancer and leukemia.

WHAT CAN ALL THE VARIOUS CARCINOGENS — chemicals, radiation, and so on — possibly have in common? One reasonable thought is that all of them may cause genetic mutations, and that cancer may be the result of mutations in body cells.

Suppose that some gene is changed so that it no longer can produce a key enzyme needed in the process that controls the growth of cells. When a cell with such a defective gene divides, it will pass on the defect. With the control mechanism not functioning, further division of these cells may continue indefinitely, without regard to the needs of the body as a whole or even to the needs of the tissue involved (for example, the specialization of cells in an organ). The tissue is disorganized. It is, so to speak, a case of anarchy in the body.

That energetic radiation can produce mutations is well established. What about the chemical carcinogens? Well, mutation by chemicals also has been demonstrated. The "nitrogen mustards" are a good example. These compounds, like the "mustard gas" of World War I, produce burns and blisters on the skin resembling those caused by X-rays. They can also damage the chromosomes and increase the mutation rate. Moreover, a number of other chemicals have been found to imitate energetic radiation in the same way.

The chemicals that can induce mutations are called "mutagens." Not all mutagens have been shown to be carcinogens, and not all carcinogens have been shown to be mutagens. But there are enough cases of compounds that are both carcinogenic and mutagenic to arouse suspicion that the coincidence is not accidental.

Meanwhile, the notion that microorganisms may have something to do with cancer is far from dead. With the discovery of viruses, this suggestion of the Pasteur era was revived. The first investigator to look into the virus possibility was Peyton Rous of the Rockefeller Institute. In 1909 he ground up a chicken tumor, filtered it, and injected the clear filtrate into other chickens. Some of them developed tumors. The finer the filter, the fewer the tumors. This certainly looked as if particles of some kind were responsible for the initiation of tumors, and it seemed that these particles were the size of viruses.

The "tumor viruses" have had a rocky history. At first, the tumors pinned down to viruses turned out to be uniformly benign; for instance, viruses were shown to cause such things as rabbits' papillomas (similar to warts). In 1936 John J. Bittner, working in the famous mouse-breeding laboratory at Bar Harbor, Me., came on something more exciting. Maud Slye of the same laboratory had bred strains of mice which seemed to have an inborn resistance to cancer and other strains which seemed cancer-prone. The mice of some strains rarely developed cancer; those of other strains almost invariably did, after reaching maturity. Bittner tried the experiment of switching mothers on the new-born mice so that they would suckle at the opposite strain. He discovered that when baby mice of a "cancer-resistant" strain suckled at mothers of a "cancer-prone" strain, they usually developed cancer. On the other hand, supposedly cancer-prone baby mice that were fed by cancer-resistant mothers did not develop cancer. Bittner concluded that the cancer cause, whatever it was, was not inborn but was transmitted in the mothers' milk. He called it the "milk factor."

Naturally Bittner's milk factor was suspected to be a virus. Eventually the Columbia University biochemist Samuel Graff identified the factor as a particle containing nucleic acids. Other tumor viruses, causing certain types of mouse tumors and animal leukemias, have been found, and all of them contain nucleic acids. No viruses have been detected in connection with human cancers, but research on human cancer is obviously limited.

Now the mutation and virus theories of cancer begin to converge. Perhaps the seeming contradiction between the two notions is not a contradiction after all. Viruses and genes have a very important thing in common: the key to the behavior of both lies in their nucleic acids. Indeed, in 1959 G. A. di Mayorca and coworkers at the Sloan-Kettering Institute and the National Institutes of Health isolated DNA from a mouse-tumor virus and found that the DNA alone could induce cancers in mice just as effectively as the virus did.

Thus the difference between the mutation theory and the virus theory boils down to whether the cancer-causing nucleic acid arises by a mutation in a gene within the cell or is introduced by a virus invasion from outside the cell. These ideas are not mutually exclusive; cancer may come about in both ways.

WHAT GOES WRONG in the metabolic machinery when cells grow unrestrainedly? This question has as yet received no answer. But strong suspicion rests on some of the hormones, especially the sex hormones.

For one thing, the sex hormones are known to stimulate rapid, localized growth in the body (as in the breasts of an adolescent girl). For another, the tissues of sexual organs — the breasts, cervix, and ovaries in a woman, the testes and prostate in a man — are particularly prone to cancer. Strongest of all is the chemical evidence. In 1933 the German biochemist Heinrich Wieland (who had won the Nobel Prize in chemistry in 1927 for his work with bile acids) managed to convert a bile acid into a complex hydrocarbon called "methylcholanthrene," a powerful carcinogen. Now methylcholanthrene (like the bile acids) has the four-ring structure of a steroid, and it so happens that all the sex hormones are steroids. Could a mis-shapen sex-hormone molecule act as a carcinogen? Or might even a correctly shaped hormone be mistaken for a carcinogen, so to speak, by a distorted gene pattern in a cell, and so stimulate un-controlled growth? It is anyone's guess, but these are interesting speculations.

Curiously enough, changing the supply of sex hormones some-times checks cancerous growth. For instance, castration, to reduce the body's manufacture of male sex hormone, or the administration of neutralizing female sex hormone, has a mitigating effect on cancer of the prostate. As a treatment, this is scarcely something to shout about, and it is a measure of the desperation of cancer that such de-vices are resorted to.

The main line of attack against cancer still is surgery. And its limitations are still what they have always been: sometimes the cancer cannot be cut out without killing the patient; often the knife frees bits of malignant tissue (since the disorganized cancer tissue has a tendency to fragment), which are then carried by the blood stream to other parts of the body where they take root and grow.

The use of energetic radiation to kill the cancer tissue also has its drawbacks. Artificial radioactivity has added new weapons to the traditional X-rays and radium. One of them is cobalt 60, which yields high-energy gamma rays and is much less expensive than radium; another is a solution of radioactive iodine (the "atomic cocktail"), which concentrates in the thyroid gland and thus attacks a thyroid cancer. But the body's tolerance of radiation is limited, and there is always the danger that the radiation will start more cancers than it stops.

Still, surgery and radiation are the best we have, and they have saved, or at least prolonged, many a life. They will perforce be man's main reliance against cancer until biologists find what they are seeking: a "magic bullet" which, without harming normal cells, will search out the cancer cells and either destroy them or stop their wild division in its tracks.

599

A great deal of work is going on along two principal routes. One is to find out everything possible about how cells divide. The other is to learn in the greatest possible detail exactly how cells conduct metabolism, with the hope of finding some decisive difference between cancer cells and normal cells. Differences have been found, but they are pretty minor — so far.

Meanwhile a stupendous sifting of chemicals by trial and error is being carried out. For a time the nitrogen mustards looked hopeful, on the theory that they would mimic radiation in killing cancer cells. Some of the drugs of this type do seem to help against certain types of cancer, at least to the extent of prolonging life, but they are obviously only a stopgap.

More hope lies in the direction of the nucleic acids themselves. There must be some difference between the nucleic acids in cancer cells and those in normal cells. The object, then, is to find a way to interfere with the chemical workings of one and not the other. Then again, perhaps the disorganized cancer cells are less efficient than normal cells in manufacturing nucleic acids. If so, throwing a few grains of sand into the machinery might cripple the less efficient cancer cells without seriously disturbing the more efficient normal cells.

For instance, one substance that is vital to the production of nucleic acid is folic acid. It plays a major role in the formation of the purines and pyrimidines, the building blocks for nucleic acid. Now a compound resembling folic acid might, by competitive inhibition, slow things up just enough to prevent cancer cells from making nucleic acid while allowing normal cells to produce it at an adequate rate. And, of course, without nucleic acid the cancer cells could not multiply. There are, in fact, "folic-acid antagonists" of this sort. One of them, called "amethopterin," has shown some effect against leukemia.

There is a still more direct attack. Why not inject competitive substitutes for the purines and pyrimidines themselves? The most hopeful candidate is "6-mercaptopurine." This compound is just like adenine except that it has an —SH group in place of adenine's —NH₂.

The worldwide research attack upon cancer is keen, resourceful, and, in comparison with other biological research, handsomely financed. But a cure will not be found easily, for the secret of cancer is as subtle as the secret of life itself.

CHAPTER

14

THE BODY

FOOD

Perhaps the first great advance in medical science was the recognition by physicians that good health called for a simple, balanced diet. The Greek philosophers recommended moderation in eating and drinking, not only for philosophical reasons but also because those who followed this rule were more comfortable and lived longer. That was a good start, but biologists eventually learned that moderation alone was not enough. Even if one has the good fortune to avoid eating too little and the good sense to avoid eating too much, he will still do poorly if his diet happens to be shy of certain essential ingredients, as is actually the case for large numbers of people in some parts of the world.

The human body is rather specialized (as organisms go) in its dietary needs. A plant can live on just carbon dioxide, water, and certain inorganic ions. Some of the microorganisms likewise get along without any organic food; they are called "autotrophic" ("self-growing"), which means that they can grow in environments in which there is no other living thing. The bread mold, Neurospora, begins to get a little more complicated: in addition to inorganic substances it has to have sugar and the vitamin biotin. And as the forms of life become more and more complex, they seem to become more and more dependent on their diet to supply the organic building blocks necessary for building living tissue. The reason is simply that they have lost some of the enzymes that primitive organisms possess. A green plant has a complete supply of enzymes for making all the necessary amino acids, proteins, fats, and carbohydrates from inorganic materials. Neurospora has all the enzymes except one or more of those needed to make sugar and biotin. By the time we get to man, we find that he lacks the enzymes required to make many of the amino acids, the vitamins, and various other necessities, and he must get these ready-made in his food.

This may seem a kind of degeneration — a growing dependence on the environment which puts the organism at a disadvantage. Not so. If the environment supplies the building blocks, why carry the elaborate enzymatic machinery needed to make them? By dispensing with this machinery, the cell can use its energy and space for more refined and specialized purposes.

It was the english physician William Prout (the same Prout who was a century ahead of his time in suggesting that all the elements were built from hydrogen) who first suggested that the organic foods could be divided into three types of substances, later named carbohydrates, fats, and proteins.

The chemists and biologists of the nineteenth century, notably Justus von Liebig of Germany, gradually worked out the nutritive properties of these foods. Protein, they found, is the most essential, and the organism could get along on it alone. The body cannot make protein from carbohydrate and fat, because those substances have no nitrogen, but it could make the necessary carbohydrates and fats from the materials supplied by protein. Since protein is comparatively scarce in the environment, however, it would be wasteful to live on an all-protein diet—like stoking the fire with furniture when firewood is available.

Under favorable circumstances the human body's daily requirement of proteins, by the way, is surprisingly low. The Food and Nutrition Board of the National Research Council in its 1953 chart of recommendations suggested that the minimum for adults is one gram of protein per kilogram of body weight per day, which amounts to a little more than two ounces for the average grown man. About two quarts of milk can supply that amount. Children and pregnant or nursing mothers need somewhat more protein.

Of course, a lot depends on what proteins you choose. Nineteenth-century experimenters tried to find out whether the population could get along, in times of famine, on gelatin—a protein material obtained by heating bones, tendons, and other otherwise inedible parts of animals. But the French physiologist François Magendie demonstrated that dogs lost weight and died when gelatin was their sole source of protein. This does not mean there is anything wrong with gelatin as a food, but it simply doesn't supply all the necessary building blocks when it is the only protein in the diet. The key to the usefulness of a protein lies in the efficiency with which the body can use the nitrogen it supplies. In 1854 the English agriculturalists John Bennet Lawes and Joseph Henry Gilbert fed pigs protein in two forms — lentil meal and barley meal. They found that the pigs retained much more of the nitrogen in barley than of that in lentils. These were the first "nitrogen balance" experiments.

A growing organism gradually accumulates nitrogen from the food it ingests ("positive nitrogen balance"). If it is starving or suffering a wasting disease, and gelatin is the sole source of protein, the body continues to starve or waste away, from a nitrogen-balance standpoint (a situation called "negative nitrogen balance"). It keeps losing more nitrogen than it takes in, regardless of how much gelatin it is fed.

Why so? The nineteenth-century chemists eventually discovered that gelatin is an unusually simple protein. It lacks tryptophan and other amino acids present in most proteins. Without these building blocks, the body cannot build the proteins it needs for its own substance. Therefore, unless it gets other protein in its food as well, the amino acids that do occur in the gelatin are useless and have to be excreted. It is as if house-builders found themselves with plenty of lumber but no nails. Not only could they not build the house, but the lumber would just be in the way and eventually would have to be disposed of. Attempts were made in the 1890's to make gelatin a more efficient article of diet by adding some of those amino acids in which it was deficient, but without success. Better luck was obtained with proteins not as drastically limited as gelatin.

In 1906 the English biochemists Frederick Gowland Hopkins and E. G. Willcock fed mice a diet in which the only protein was "zein," found in corn. They knew that this protein had very little of the amino acid tryptophan. The mice died in about 14 days. The experimenters then tried mice on zein plus tryptophan. This time the mice survived twice as long. It was the first hard evidence that amino acids, rather than protein, might be the essential components of the diet. (Although the mice still died prematurely, this was probably due mainly to a lack of certain vitamins not known at the time.)

In the 1930's the American nutritionist William C. Rose got to the bottom of the amino-acid problem. By that time the major vitamins were known, so he could supply the animals with those needs and focus on the amino acids. Rose fed rats a mixture of amino acids instead of protein. The rats did not live long on this diet. But when he fed rats on the milk protein casein, they did well. Apparently there was something in casein—some undiscovered amino acid, in all probability — which was not present in the amino-acid mixture he was using. Rose broke down the casein and tried adding various of its molecular fragments to his amino-acid mixture. In this way he tracked down the amino acid "threonine," the last of the major amino acids to be discovered. When he added the threonine from casein to his amino-acid mixture, the rats grew satisfactorily, without any intact protein in the diet.

Rose proceeded to remove the amino acids from their diet one at a time. By this method he eventually identified ten amino acids as indispensable items in the diet of the rat: lysine, tryptophan, histidine, phenylalanine, leucine, isoleucine, threonine, methionine, valine, and arginine. If supplied with ample quantities of these, the rat could manufacture all it needed of the others, such as glycine, proline, aspartic acid, alanine, and so on.

In the 1940's Rose turned his attention to man's requirements of amino acids. He persuaded graduate students to submit to controlled diets in which a mixture of amino acids was the only source of nitrogen. By 1949 he was able to announce that the adult male required only eight amino acids in the diet: phenylalanine, leucine, isoleucine, methionine, valine, lysine, tryptophan, and threonine. Since arginine and histidine, indispensable to the rat, are dispensable in the human diet, it would seem that in this respect man is less specialized than the rat, or, indeed, than any other mammal that has been tested in detail.

Potentially a person could get along on the eight dietarily essential amino acids; given enough of these, he could make not only all the other amino acids he needs but also all the carbohydrates and fats. Actually a diet made up only of amino acids would be much too expensive, to say nothing of the flatness and monotony. But it is enormously helpful to have a complete blueprint of our amino-acid needs so that we can reinforce natural proteins when necessary for maximum efficiency in absorbing and utilizing nitrogen.

VITAMINS

Food fads and superstitions unhappily still delude too many people — and spawn too many cure-everything best sellers — even in these enlightened times. Nevertheless there are certain cases in which specific foods will definitely cure a disease. In every instance these are deficiency diseases—special cases that arise only when the person is deprived of a normal, balanced diet.

The ancient world was well acquainted with scurvy, a disease in which the capillaries become increasingly fragile, gums bleed and teeth loosen, wounds heal with difficulty if at all, and the patient grows weak and eventually dies. It was particularly prevalent in besieged cities and on long ocean voyages. (Magellan's crew suffered more from scurvy than from general undernourishment.) Ships on long voyages, lacking refrigeration, had to carry non-spoilable food, which meant hardtack and salt pork. Nevertheless, physicians for many centuries failed to connect scurvy with diet.

In 1536, while the French explorer Jacques Cartier was wintering in Canada, 110 of his men were stricken with scurvy. The native Indians knew and suggested a remedy: drinking water in which pine needles had been soaked. Cartier's men in desperation followed this seemingly childish suggestion. It cured them of their scurvy.

Two centuries later the Scottish physician James Lind took note of several incidents of this kind and experimented with fresh fruits and vegetables as a cure. Trying his treatments on scurvy-ridden sailors, he found that oranges and lemons brought about improvement most quickly. By 1795 the brass hats of the British Navy were sufficiently impressed by Lind's experiments (and by the fact that a scurvy-ridden flotilla could lose a naval engagement with scarcely a fight) to order daily rations of lime juice for British sailors. (They have been called "limeys" ever since, and the Thames area in London where the crates of limes were stored is still called "Limehouse.") Thanks to the lime juice, scurvy disappeared from the British Navy.

In spite of occasional dietary victories of this kind (which no one could explain), nineteenth-century biologists refused to believe that a disease could be cured by diet, particularly after Pasteur's germ theory of disease came into its own. In 1896, however, a Dutch physician named Christiaan Eijkman convinced them.

Eijkman was sent to the Dutch East Indies to investigate "beri-beri," a disease endemic in those regions. Supposing that it was a germ disease, he took along some chickens as experimental animals in which to establish the germ. A highly fortunate piece of skul-duggery upset his plans. Without warning, most of his chickens came down with a paralytic disease from which some died, but after about four months those still surviving regained their health. Eijk-man, mystified by failing to find any germ responsible for the attack, finally investigated the chickens' diet. He discovered that the person originally in charge of feeding the chickens had economized (and no doubt profited) by using scraps of left-over food, mostly polished rice, from the wards of the military hospital. It happened that after a few months a new cook had arrived and taken over the feeding of the chickens; he had put a stop to the petty graft and supplied the animals with the usual chicken feed, containing unhulled rice. It was then that the chickens had recovered.

Eijkman experimented. He put chickens on a polished-rice diet and they fell sick. Back on the unhulled rice, they recovered. It was the first case of a deliberately produced dietary deficiency disease. Eijkman decided that this "polyneuritis" that afflicted fowls was similar in symptoms to human beri-beri. Did human beings get beri-beri because they ate only polished rice?

For human consumption, rice was stripped of its hulls mainly so that it would keep better, for the rice-germ removed with the hulls contains oils that go rancid easily. Eijkman and a co-worker, G. Grijns, set out to see what it was in rice hulls that prevented beri-beri. They succeeded in dissolving the crucial factor out of the hulls with water, and they found that it would pass through membranes which would not pass proteins. Evidently the substance in question must be a fairly small molecule. They could not, however, iden-tify it.

Meanwhile other investigators were coming across other mysteri-ous factors that seemed to be essential for life. In 1905 a Dutch nutritionist, C. A. Pekelharing, found that all his mice died within a month on an artificial diet which seemed ample as far as fats, carbo-hydrates, and proteins were concerned. But mice did fine when he added a few drops of milk to this diet. And in England the bio-

609

chemist Frederick Hopkins, who was demonstrating the importance of amino acids in the diet, carried out a series of experiments in which he, too, showed that something in the casein of milk would support growth if added to an artificial diet. This something was soluble in water. Even better than casein as the dietary supplement was a small amount of a yeast extract.

For their pioneer work in establishing that trace substances in the diet were essential to life, Eijkman and Hopkins shared the Nobel Prize in medicine and physiology in 1929.

THE NEXT TASK was to isolate these vital trace factors in food. By 1912 three Japanese biochemists, U. Suzuki, T. Shimamura, and S. Ohdake, had extracted from rice hulls a compound which was very potent in combatting beri-beri. Doses of 5 to 10 milligrams sufficed to effect a cure in fowl. In the same year the Polish-born biochemist Casimir Funk (then working in England and later to come to the United States) prepared the same compound from yeast.

Because the compound proved to be an amine (that is, one containing the amine group, NH_2), Funk called it a "vitamine," Latin for "life amine." He made the guess that beri-beri, scurvy, pellagra, and rickets all arose from deficiencies of "vitamines." Funk's guess was correct as far as his identification of these diseases as dietary-deficiency diseases was concerned. But it turned out that not all "vitamines" were amines.

In 1913 two American biochemists, Elmer Vernon McCollum and M. Davis, discovered another trace factor vital to health in butter and egg-yolk. This one was soluble in fatty substances instead of water. McCollum called it "fat-soluble A," to contrast it with "water-soluble B," which was the name he applied to the anti-beri-beri factor. In the absence of chemical information as to the nature of the factors, this seemed fair enough, and it started the custom of naming them by letters. In 1920 the British biochemist J. C. Drummond changed the names to "vitamin A" and "vitamin B," dropping the final *e* of "vitamine" as a gesture toward taking "amine" out of the name. He also suggested that the anti-scurvy factor was still a third such substance, which he named "vitamin C."

Vitamin A was quickly identified as a food factor required to prevent the development of abnormal dryness of the membranes around the eye, called "xerophthalmia," from Greek words meaning "dry eyes." In 1920 McCollum and his associates found that a substance in cod-liver oil, which was effective in curing both xerophthalmia and a bone disease called "rickets," could be so treated as to cure rickets only. They decided the anti-rickets factor must represent a fourth vitamin, which they named vitamin D. Vitamins D and A are fat-soluble; C and B are water-soluble.

By 1930 it had become clear that vitamin B was not a simple substance but a mixture of compounds with different properties. The food factor that cured beri-beri was named vitamin B_1, a second factor was called vitamin B_2, and so on. Some of the reports of new factors turned out to be false alarms, so that one doesn't hear of B_3, B_4 or B_5 any longer. However, the numbers worked their way up to B_{14}. The whole group of vitamins (all water-soluble) is frequently referred to as the "B-vitamin complex."

New letters also were added. Of these, vitamins E and K (both fat-soluble) remain as veritable vitamins, but "vitamin F" turned out to be not a vitamin and "vitamin H" turned out to be one of the B-complex vitamins.

Nowadays, with their chemistry identified, the letters of even the true vitamins are going by the board, and most of them are known by their chemical names, though the fat-soluble vitamins, for some reason, have held on to their letter designations more tenaciously than the water-soluble ones.

It was not easy to work out the chemical composition and structure of the vitamins, for these substances occur only in minute amounts. For instance, a ton of rice hulls contains only about five grams (a little less than a fifth of an ounce) of vitamin B_1. Not until 1926 did anyone extract enough of the reasonably pure vitamin to analyze it chemically. Two Dutch biochemists, B. C. P. Jansen and W. P. Donath, worked up a composition for vitamin B, from a tiny sample, but it turned out to be wrong. In 1932 the Japanese bio-chemist S. Ohdake tried again on a slightly larger sample and got it almost right. He was the first to detect a sulfur atom in a vitamin molecule.

Finally in 1934 Robert R. Williams, then director of chemistry at the Bell Telephone Laboratories, climaxed 20 years of research by painstakingly separating vitamin B_1 from tons of rice hulls until he had enough to work out a complete structural formula. The formula follows:

$$CH_3 - C = N - C - NH_2 \quad CH_3 \quad CH_2 - CH_2 - OH$$

Since the most unexpected feature of the molecule was the atom of sulfur ("theion" in Greek), the vitamin was named "thiamine."

Vitamin C was a different sort of problem. Citrus fruits furnish a comparatively rich source of this material, but one difficulty was finding an experimental animal that did not make its own vitamin C. Most mammals, aside from man and the other primates, have retained the capacity to form this vitamin. Without a cheap and simple experimental animal that would develop scurvy, it was difficult to follow the location of vitamin C among the various fractions into which the fruit juice was broken down chemically.

In 1918 the American biochemists B. Cohen and L. B. Mendel solved this problem by discovering that guinea pigs could not form the vitamin. In fact, guinea pigs developed scurvy much more easily than men did. But another difficulty remained. Vitamin C was found to be very unstable (it is the most unstable of the vitamins), so it was easily lost in chemical procedures to isolate it. A number of research workers ardently pursued the vitamin without success.

As it happened, vitamin C was finally isolated by someone who wasn't particularly looking for it. In 1928 the Hungarian-born biochemist Albert Szent-Györgyi, then working in London in Hopkins' laboratory and interested mainly in finding out how tissues made use of oxygen, isolated from cabbages a substance which helped transfer hydrogen atoms from one compound to another. Shortly afterward Charles Glen King and his coworkers at the University of Pittsburgh, who *were* looking for vitamin C, prepared some of the substance from cabbages and found that it was strongly protective against scurvy. What's more, they found it identical with crystals they had obtained from lemon juice. King determined its structure in 1933, and it turned out to be a sugar molecule of six carbons, belonging to the *L*-series instead of the *D*-series:

$$O = C \overset{\displaystyle O}{\diagup \diagdown} CH - CH - CH_2OH$$

$$\begin{array}{ccc} & O = C & CH - CH - CH_2OH \\ & \diagdown & \diagup \quad | \\ & C = C & OH \\ & \diagup \quad \diagdown & \\ & OH \quad\quad OH & \end{array}$$

It was named "ascorbic acid" (from Greek words meaning "no scurvy").

As for vitamin A, the first hint as to its structure came from the observation that the foods rich in vitamin A were often yellow or orange (butter, egg-yolk, carrots, fish-liver oil and so on). The substance largely responsible for this color was found to be a hydrocarbon named "carotene," and in 1929 the British biochemist T. Moore demonstrated that rats fed on diets containing carotene stored vitamin A in the liver. The vitamin itself was not colored yellow, so the deduction was that though carotene was not itself vitamin A, the liver converted it into something which was vitamin A. (Carotene is now considered an example of a "provitamin.")

In 1937 the American chemists H. N. Holmes and R. E. Corbet isolated vitamin A as crystals from fish-liver oil. It turned out to be a 20-carbon compound — half of the carotene molecule with a hydroxyl group added:

```
CH₃     CH₃
   \   /
     C
   /   \
 CH₂     C — CH = CH — C = CH — CH = CH — C = CH — CH₂ — OH
  |      ‖             |                  |
 CH₂     C — CH₃      CH₃                CH₃
   \    /
    CH₂
```

The chemists hunting for vitamin D found their best chemical clue by means of sunlight. As early as 1921 the McCollum group (who first demonstrated the existence of the vitamin) showed that rats did not develop rickets on a diet lacking vitamin D if they were exposed to sunlight. Biochemists guessed that the energy of sunlight converted some provitamin in the body into vitamin D. Since vitamin D was fat-soluble, they went searching for the provitamin in the fatty substances of food.

By breaking down fats into fractions and exposing each fragment separately to sunlight, they determined that the provitamin that sunlight converted into vitamin A was a steroid. What steroid? They tested cholesterol, the most common steroid of the body, and that was not it. Then in 1926 the British biochemists O. Rosenheim and T. A. Webster found that sunlight would convert a closely related sterol, "ergosterol," into vitamin D. The only trouble was that ergosterol did not occur in animals. Eventually the human provitamin was identified as "7-dehydrocholesterol," which differs from cholesterol only in having two hydrogen atoms fewer in its molecule. The vitamin D formed from it has this formula:

```
                                        CH₃                    CH₃
                         CH₃             |                      |
               CH₂        |             CH — CH₂ — CH₂ — CH₂ — CH — CH₃
        CH₂     |         C ／ CH
         |    CH₂  CH₂   |      ＼
   CH₂      ／  ‖    |    C — CH   CH₂
  ／    ＼ C    C    ‖       ＼  ／
 CH₂          |    CH        CH₂
  |    CH    C =
  CH   ／    ‖
 HO   CH₂   CH
```

614

Vitamin D in one of its forms is called "calciferol," from Latin words meaning "calcium-carrying," because it is essential to the proper laying down of bone structure.

Not all the vitamins show their absence by producing an acute disease. In 1922 Herbert McLean Evans and K. J. Scott at the University of California implicated a vitamin as a cause of sterility in animals. Evans and his group did not succeed in isolating this one, vitamin E, until 1936. It was then given the name "tocopherol" (from Greek words meaning "to bear children").

Unfortunately, whether human beings need vitamin E, or how much, is not yet known. Obviously dietary experiments designed to bring about sterility cannot be tried on human subjects. And even in animals, the fact that they can be made sterile by withholding vitamin E does not necessarily mean that natural sterility arises in this way.

In the 1930's the Danish biochemist Carl Peter Henrik Dam discovered by experiments on chickens that a vitamin was involved in the clotting of blood. He named it *Koagulationsvitamine,* and this was eventually shortened to vitamin K. Edward Doisy and his associates at St. Louis University then isolated vitamin K and determined its structure. Dam and Doisy shared the Nobel Prize in medicine and physiology in 1943.

Vitamin K is not a major vitamin nor a nutritional problem. Normally a more than adequate supply of this vitamin is manufactured by the bacteria in the intestines. In fact, they make so much of it that the feces may be richer in vitamin K than the food is. New-born infants are the most likely to run a danger of poor blood-clotting and consequent hemorrhage because of vitamin-K deficiency. In the hygienic modern hospital it takes infants three days to accumulate a reasonable supply of intestinal bacteria, and they are protected by injections of the vitamin into themselves directly or into the mother shortly before the birth. In the old days, the infants picked up the bacteria almost at once, and though they might die of various infections and disease, they were at least safe from the dangers of hemorrhage.

615

During the late 1930's and early 1940's biochemists identified several additional B-vitamins, which now go under the names of biotin, pantothenic acid, pyridoxine, folic acid, and cyanocobalamine. These vitamins are all made by intestinal bacteria; moreover, they are present so universally in foodstuffs that no cases of deficiency diseases have appeared. In fact, investigators have had to feed animals an artificial diet deliberately excluding them, and even to add "anti-vitamins" to neutralize those made by the intestinal bacteria, in order to see what the deficiency symptoms are. (Anti-vitamins are substances similar to the vitamin in structure. They immobilize the enzyme making use of the vitamin by means of competitive inhibition.)

The determination of the structure of each of the various vitamins was usually followed speedily (or even preceded) by synthesis of the vitamin. For instance, Williams and his group synthesized thiamine in 1937, three years after they had deduced its structure. The Polish-born Swiss biochemist Tadeus Reichstein and his group synthesized ascorbic acid in 1933, somewhat before the structure was completely determined by King. Vitamin A, for another example, was synthesized in 1936 (again somewhat before the structure was completely determined) by two different groups of chemists.

The use of synthetic vitamins has made it possible to prepare vitamin mixtures at reasonable prices and sell them over the drugstore counter. The need for vitamin pills varies with individual cases. Of all the vitamins, the one most apt to be deficient in supply is vitamin D. Young children in northern climates, where sunlight is weak in winter time, run the danger of rickets, so they may require irradiated foods or vitamin supplements. But the dosage of vitamin D (and of vitamin A) should be carefully controlled, because an overdose of these vitamins can be harmful. As for the B-vitamins, anyone eating an ordinary, rounded diet does not need to take pills for them. The same is true of vitamin C, which in any case should not present a problem, for there are few people who do not enjoy orange juice or who do not drink it regularly in these vitamin-conscious times.

On the whole, the wholesale use of vitamin pills, while redounding chiefly to the profit of drug houses, usually does people no harm and may be partly responsible for the fact that the current generation of Americans is taller and heavier than previous generations.

BIOCHEMISTS naturally were curious to find out how the vitamins, present in the body in such tiny quantities, exerted such important effects on the body chemistry. The obvious guess was that they had something to do with enzymes, also present in small quantities.

The answer finally came from detailed studies of the chemistry of enzymes. Protein chemists had known for a long time that some of the enzymes (as well as certain other proteins) were not made up solely of amino acids; their molecules also had non-amino acid portions loosely attached to them. The first discovery of this fact, at least in connection with enzymes, came when it was noticed that certain enzymes lost their activity if they were "dialyzed"—that is, allowed to diffuse in solution through a collodion membrane. Apparently some portion of the enzyme essential to its activity passed through the collodion membrane into the pure water on the other side. What remained within the collodion bag was the protein itself; the portion that escaped must be a molecule small enough to get through the collodion pores. The French biochemist Gabriel Emile Bertrand suggested in 1897 that this portion be called a "coenzyme." The activity of the enzyme depended on the cooperation of the protein portion proper ("apoenzyme") and its coenzyme.

In 1936 Otto Warburg and W. Christian succeeded in working out the structure of a coenzyme called "cozymase," a part of the yeast enzyme zymase. Cozymase consisted of an adenine molecule, two ribose molecules, two phosphate groups, and a molecule of "nicotinamide." Now this last was an unusual kind of thing to find in living tissue, and interest naturally centered on the nicotinamide. (It is called "nicotinamide" because it contains an amide group, $CONH_2$, and can be formed easily from "nicotinic acid." Nicotinic acid is structurally related to the tobacco alkaloid "nicotine," but they are utterly different in properties; for one thing, nicotinic acid is necessary to life, whereas nicotine is a deadly poison.) The formulas of nicotinamide and nicotinic acid are:

nicotinic acid   nicotinamide

Once the formula of cozymase was worked out, it was promptly renamed "diphosphopyridine nucleotide" (DPN) — "nucleotide" from the characteristic arrangement of the adenine, ribose, and phosphate, similar to that of the nucleotides making up nucleic acid, and "pyridine" from the name given to the combination of atoms making up the ring in the nicotinamide formula.

Soon a very similar coenzyme was found, differing from DPN only in the fact that it contained three phosphate groups rather than two. This, naturally, was named "triphosphopyridine nucleotide" (TPN). Both DPN and TPN proved to be coenzymes for a number of enzymes in the body, all serving to transfer hydrogen atoms from one molecule to another. (Such enzymes are called "dehydrogenases.") It was the coenzyme that did the actual job of hydrogen transfer; the enzyme proper in each case selected the particular substrate on which the operation was to be performed. The enzyme and the coenzyme each had a vital function, and if either was deficient in supply, the release of energy from foodstuffs via hydrogen transfer would slow to a limp.

What was immediately striking about all this was that the nicotinamide group represented the only part of the enzyme the body cannot manufacture itself. It can make all the protein it needs and all the ingredients of DPN and TPN except the nicotinamide. That it must find ready-made (or at least in the form of nicotinic acid) in the diet. If it doesn't, then the manufacture of DPN and TPN stops and all the hydrogen-transfer reactions they control slow down.

Was nicotinamide or nicotinic acid a vitamin? As it happened, Funk (who coined the word "vitamine") had isolated nicotinic acid from rice hulls. Nicotinic acid was not the substance that cured beri-beri, so he had ignored it. But on the strength of nicotinic acid's appearance now in connection with coenzymes, the University of Wisconsin biochemist C. A. Elvehjem and his coworkers tried it on another deficiency disease.

In the 1920's the American physician Joseph Goldberger had studied pellagra (sometimes called Italian leprosy), a disease endemic in the Mediterranean area and almost epidemic in the southern United States in the early part of this century. Pellagra's most noticeable symptoms are a dry, scaly skin, diarrhea, and an inflamed tongue; it sometimes leads to mental disorders. Goldberger noticed that the disease struck people who lived on a limited diet (*e.g.*, mainly cornmeal) and spared families that owned a milch cow. He began to experiment with artificial diets, feeding them to animals and inmates of jails (where pellagra seemed to blossom). He succeeded in producing "blacktongue" (a disease analogous to pellagra) in dogs, and in curing this disease with a yeast extract. He found he could cure jail inmates of pellagra by adding milk to their diet. Goldberger decided that a vitamin must be involved, and he named it the P-P ("pellagra-preventive") factor.

It was pellagra, then, that Elvehjem chose for the test of nicotinic acid. He fed a tiny dose to a dog with blacktongue, and the dog responded with a remarkable improvement. A few more doses cured him. Nicotinic acid was a vitamin, all right, and what's more, it was the P-P factor.

The American Medical Association, worried that the public might get the impression there were vitamins in tobacco, urged that the vitamin not be called nicotinic acid and suggested instead the name "niacin" (an abbreviation of *ni*cotinic *ac*id) or "niacinamide." Niacin has caught on fairly well.

Gradually it became clear that the various vitamins were merely portions of coenzymes, each consisting of a molecular group an animal or a human being cannot make for itself. In 1932 Warburg had found a yellow coenzyme that catalyzed the transfer of hydrogen atoms. The Austrian chemist Richard Kuhn and his associates shortly afterward isolated vitamin B_2, which proved to be yellow, and worked out its structure:

$$
\begin{array}{c}
CH_2 - OH \\
| \\
HO - CH \\
| \\
HO - CH \\
| \\
HO - CH \\
| \\
CH_2
\end{array}
$$

The carbon chain attached to the middle ring is like a molecule called "ribitol," so vitamin B_2 was named "riboflavin," "flavin" coming from a Latin word meaning "yellow." Since examination of its spectrum showed that riboflavin was very similar in color to Warburg's yellow coenzyme, Kuhn tested the coenzyme for riboflavin activity in 1935 and found such activity to be there. In the same year the Swedish biochemist Hugo Theorell worked out the structure of Warburg's yellow coenzyme and showed that it was riboflavin with a phosphate group added. (In 1954 a second and more complicated coenzyme also was shown to have riboflavin as part of its molecule.)

Kuhn was awarded the 1938 Nobel Prize in chemistry, and Theorell received the 1955 Nobel Prize in medicine and physiology. Kuhn, however, was unfortunate enough to be selected for his prize shortly after Austria had been absorbed by Nazi Germany, and (like Gerhard Domagk) he was compelled to refuse it.

In 1937 the German biochemists K. Lohmann and P. Schuster discovered an important coenzyme that contained thiamine as part of its structure. Through the 1940's other connections were found between B vitamins and coenzymes. Pyridoxine, pantothenic acid, folic acid, biotin — each in turn was found to be tied to one or more groups of enzymes.

The vitamins beautifully illustrate the economy of the human body's chemical machinery. The human cell can dispense with making them because they serve only one special function, and the cell can take the reasonable risk of finding the necessary supply in the diet. There are many other vital substances that the body needs only in trace amounts but must make for itself. ATP, for instance, is formed from much the same building blocks that make up the indispensable nucleic acids. It is inconceivable that any organism could lose any enzyme necessary for nucleic-acid synthesis and remain alive, for nucleic acid is needed in such quantities that the organism dare not trust to the diet for its supply. And to be able to make nucleic acid automatically implies the ability to make ATP. Consequently no organism is known that is incapable of manufacturing its own ATP, and in all probability no such organism will ever be found.

To make special products such as vitamins would be like setting up a special machine next to an assembly line to turn out nuts and bolts for the automobiles. The nuts and bolts can be obtained more efficiently from a parts supplier, without any loss to the apparatus for assembling the automobiles, and by the same token the organism can obtain vitamins in its diet, with a saving in space and material.

The vitamins illustrate another important fact of life. As far as is

621

known, all living cells require the B vitamins. The coenzymes are an essential part of the cell machinery of every cell alive — plant, animal or bacterial. Whether the cell gets the B vitamins from its diet or makes them itself, it must have them if it is to live and grow. This universal need for a particular group of substances is an impressive piece of evidence for the essential unity of all life and its descent (possibly) from a single original scrap of life formed in the primeval ocean.

WHILE THE ROLES of the B vitamins are now well known, the chemical functions of the other vitamins have proved rather hard nuts to crack. The only one on which any real advance has been made is vitamin A.

In 1925 the American physiologists L. S. Fridericia and E. Holm found that rats fed on a diet deficient in vitamin A had difficulty performing tasks in dim light. An analysis of their retinas showed that they were deficient in a substance called "visual purple."

There are two kinds of cells in the retina of the eye — "rods" and "cones." The rods specialize in vision in dim light, and they contain the visual purple. A shortage of visual purple therefore hampers only vision in dim light, and it results in what is known as "night blindness."

In 1938 the Harvard biologist George Wald began to work out the chemistry of vision in dim light. He showed that light causes visual purple, or "rhodopsin," to separate into two components: the protein "opsin" and a non-protein called "retinene." Retinene turned out to be very similar in structure to vitamin A.

The retinene always recombines with the opsin to form rhodopsin in the dark. But during its separation from opsin in the light, a small percentage of it breaks down, because it is unstable. However, the supply of retinene is replenished from vitamin A, which is converted to retinene by the removal of two hydrogen atoms with the aid of enzymes. Thus vitamin A acts as a stable reserve for retinene. If vitamin A is lacking in the diet, eventually the retinene supply and the amount of visual purple decline, and night blindness is the result.

Vitamin A must have other functions as well, for a deficiency causes dryness of the mucous membranes and other symptoms which can't very well be traced to troubles in the retina of the eye. But the other functions are still unknown.

The same has to be said about the chemical functions of vitamins C, D, E, and K.

MINERALS

IT IS NATURAL TO SUPPOSE that the materials making up anything as wonderful as living tissue must themselves be something pretty exotic. Wonderful the proteins and nucleic acids certainly are, but it is a little humbling to realize that the elements making up the human body are as common as dirt, and the whole lot could be bought for a few dollars. (It used to be cents, but inflation has raised the price of everything.)

In the early nineteenth century, when chemists were beginning to analyze organic compounds, it became quite clear that living tissue was made up, in the main, of carbon, hydrogen, oxygen and nitrogen. These four elements alone constituted about 96 per cent of the weight of the human body. Then there was also a little sulfur in the body. If you burned off these five elements, you were left with a bit of white ash, mostly the residue from the bones. The ash was a collection of minerals.

It was not surprising to find common salt, sodium chloride, in the ash. After all, salt is not a mere condiment to improve the taste of food — as dispensable as, say, basil, rosemary or thyme. It is a matter of life and death. You need only taste blood to realize that salt is a basic component of the body. Herbivorous animals, which presumably lack sophistication as far as the delicacies of food-preparation are concerned, will undergo much danger and privation to reach a "salt-lick," where they can make up the lack of salt in their diet of grass and leaves.

As early as the mid-eighteenth century, the Swedish chemist Johann Gottlieb Gahn had shown that bones were made up largely of calcium phosphate, and an Italian scientist, V. Menghini, had established that the blood contained iron. In 1847 Justus von Liebig found potassium and magnesium in the tissues. By the mid-nineteenth century, then, the mineral constituents of the body were known to include calcium, phosphorus, sodium, potassium, chlorine, magnesium, and iron. What's more, these were as active in life processes as any of the elements usually associated with organic compounds.

The case of iron is the clearest. If it is lacking in the diet, the blood becomes deficient in hemoglobin and transports less oxygen from the lungs to the cells. The condition is known as "iron-deficiency anemia." The patient is pale for lack of the red pigment and tired for lack of oxygen.

In 1882 the English physician Sidney Ringer found that a frog heart could be kept alive and beating outside its body on a solution (called "Ringer's solution" to this day) containing, among other things, sodium, potassium, and calcium in about the proportions found in the frog's blood. Each was somehow essential for functioning of the muscle. Calcium, moreover, was vital to blood clotting. In its absence blood would not clot, and no other element could substitute for calcium in this respect.

Of all the minerals, phosphorus was eventually discovered to perform the most varied and crucial functions in the chemical machinery of life. I have discussed these in Chapter 12.

Calcium, a major component of bone, makes up 2 per cent of the body; phosphorus, 1 per cent. The other minerals I have mentioned come in smaller proportions, down to iron, which makes up only 0.004 per cent of the body. (That still leaves the average adult male a tenth of an ounce of iron in his tissues.) But we are not at the end of the list; there are other minerals which, though present in tissue only in barely detectable quantities, are yet essential to life.

The mere presence of an element is not necessarily significant; it may be just an impurity. In our food we take in at least traces of every element in our environment, and some small amount of each finds its way into our tissues. But elements such as silicon and aluminum, for instance, contribute nothing. On the other hand, zinc is vital. How does one distinguish an essential mineral from an accidental impurity?

The best way is to show that some necessary enzyme contains the trace element as an essential component. (Why an enzyme? Because in no other way can any trace component possibly play an important role.) In 1939 David Keilin and T. Mann of England showed that zinc was an integral part of the enzyme carbonic anhydrase. Now carbonic anhydrase is essential to the body's handling of carbon dioxide, and the proper handling of that important waste material in turn is essential to life. It follows in theory that zinc is indispensable to life, and experiment shows that it actually is. Rats fed on a diet low in zinc stop growing, lose hair, suffer scaliness of the skin, and die prematurely for lack of zinc as surely as for lack of a vitamin.

In the same way it has been shown that copper, manganese, cobalt, and molybdenum are essential to animal life. Their absence from the diet gives rise to deficiency diseases. Molybdenum, the latest of the essential trace elements to be identified (in 1954), is a constituent of an enzyme called "xanthine oxidase." The importance of molybdenum was first noticed in the 1940's in connection with plants, when soil scientists found that plants would not grow well in soils deficient in the element. It seems that molybdenum is a component of certain enzymes in soil microorganisms that catalyze the conversion of the nitrogen of the air into nitrogen-containing compounds. Plants depend on this help from microorganisms because they cannot themselves take nitrogen from the air. (This is only one of an enormous number of examples of the close interdependence of all life on our planet. The living world is a long and intricate chain which may suffer hardship or even disaster if any link is broken.)

It is now realized that there are trace-element deserts, just as there are waterless deserts; the two usually go together but not always. In Australia soil scientists have found that an ounce of molybdenum in the form of some appropriate compound spread over 16 acres of molybdenum-deficient land results in a considerable increase in fertility. The dosage of trace elements is crucial. Too much is as bad as too little, for some substances that are essential for life in small quantities (*e.g.*, copper) become poisonous in large quantities.

ONE OF THE MOST DRAMATIC EPISODES in the discovery of mineral deficiencies has to do with cobalt. It involves the once incurably fatal disease called "pernicious anemia."

In the early 1920's the University of Rochester pathologist George Hoyt Whipple was experimenting on the replenishment of hemoglobin by means of various food substances. He would bleed dogs to induce anemia and then feed them various diets to see which would permit them to replace the lost hemoglobin most rapidly. He did this not because he was interested in pernicious anemia, or in any kind of anemia, but because he was investigating bile pigments, compounds produced by the body from hemoglobin. Whipple discovered that the food that enabled the dogs to make hemoglobin most quickly was liver.

In 1926 two Boston physicians, George Richards Minot and William Parry Murphy, considering Whipple's results, decided to try liver as a treatment for pernicious-anemia patients. The treatment worked. The incurable disease was cured, so long as the patients ate liver as an important portion of their diet. Whipple, Minot, and Murphy shared the Nobel Prize in physiology and medicine in 1934.

Unfortunately liver, although it is a great delicacy when properly cooked, then chopped and lovingly mixed with such things as eggs, onions, and chicken fat, becomes wearing as a steady diet. (After a while, a patient might be tempted to think pernicious anemia was preferable.) Biochemists began to search for the curative substance in liver, and by 1930 Edwin J. Cohn and his coworkers at the Harvard Medical School had prepared a concentrate a hundred times as potent as liver itself. To isolate the active factor, however, further purification was needed. Fortunately, chemists at the Merck

Laboratories discovered in the 1940's that the concentrate from liver could accelerate the growth of certain bacteria. This provided an easy test of the potency of any preparation from it, so the biochemists could proceed to break down the concentrate into fractions and test them in quick succession. Because the bacteria reacted to the liver substance in much the way that they reacted to, say, thiamine or riboflavin, the investigators now suspected strongly that the factor they were hunting for was a B vitamin. They called it "vitamin B_{12}."

By 1948, using bacterial response and chromatography, E. L. Smith in England and Karl A. Folkers at Merck succeeded in isolating pure samples of vitamin B_{12}. The vitamin proved to be a red substance, and both scientists thought it resembled the color of certain cobalt compounds. It was known by this time that a deficiency of cobalt caused severe anemia in cattle and sheep. Both Smith and Folkers burned samples of vitamin B_{12}, analyzed the ash, and found that it did indeed contain cobalt. The compound has now been named "cyanocobalamine." So far it is the only cobalt-containing compound that has been found in living tissue.

By breaking it up and examining the fragments, chemists quickly decided that vitamin B_{12} was an extremely complicated compound, and they worked out an empirical formula of $C_{63}H_{88}O_{14}N_{14}PCo$. Then a British chemist, Dorothy Hodgkin, determined its over-all structure by means of X-rays. The diffraction pattern given by crystals of the compound allowed her to build up a picture of the "electron densities" along the molecule, that is, those regions where the probability of finding an electron is high and those where it is low. If lines are drawn through regions of equal probability, a kind of skeletal picture is built up of the shape of the molecule as a whole. Into this skeletal picture she was able to fit the known fragments of the molecule in their proper places. To calculate the electron densities from the X-ray diffraction picture of this enormously complicated molecule she had to use a modern computer—the National Bureau of Standards Western Automatic Computer (SWAC).

The molecule of vitamin B_{12}, or cyanocobalamine, turned out to

6 2 7

be a lopsided porphyrin ring, with one of the carbon bridges connecting two of the smaller pyrrole rings missing, and with complicated side-chains on the pyrrole rings. It resembled the somewhat simpler heme molecule, with this key difference: where heme had an iron atom at the center of the porphyrin ring, cyanocobalamine had a cobalt atom.

Cyanocobalamine is active in very small quantities when injected into the blood of pernicious-anemia patients. The body can get along on only a thousandth as much of this substance as it needs of the other B vitamins. Any diet, therefore, ought to have enough cyanocobalamine for our needs. Even if it didn't, the bacteria in the intestines manufacture quite a bit of it. Why, then, should anyone ever have pernicious anemia?

Apparently the sufferers from this disease are simply unable to absorb enough of the vitamin into the body through the intestinal walls. Their feces are actually rich in the vitamin (for want of which they are dying). From feedings of liver, providing a particularly abundant supply, such a patient manages to absorb enough cyanocobalamine to stay alive. But he needs a hundred times as much of the vitamin if he takes it by mouth as he does when it is injected directly into the blood.

Something must be wrong with the patient's intestinal apparatus, preventing the passage of the vitamin through the walls of the intestines. It has been known since 1929, thanks to the researches of the British biochemist W. B. Castle, that the answer lies somehow in the gastric juice. Castle called the necessary component of gastric juice "intrinsic factor." And in 1954 investigators found a product from the intestinal linings of animals which assists the absorption of the vitamin and proved to be Castle's intrinsic factor. It is a small protein molecule with a molecular weight of 5,000. Apparently this substance is missing in pernicious-anemia patients. When a small amount of it is mixed with cyanocobalamine, the patient has no difficulty in absorbing the vitamin through the intestines. Just how this intrinsic factor helps absorption is still not known.

GETTING BACK TO THE TRACE ELEMENTS. . . . The first one discovered was not a metal; it was iodine, an element with properties like those of chlorine. This story begins with the thyroid gland.

In 1896 a German biochemist, E. Baumann, discovered that the thyroid was distinguished by containing iodine, practically absent from all other tissues. In 1905 a physician named David Marine, who had just set up practice in Cleveland, was amazed to find how widely prevalent goiter was in that area. Goiter is a conspicuous disease, sometimes producing grotesque enlargement of the thyroid and causing its victims to become either dull and listless or nervous, overactive, and pop-eyed. It is not contagious. Dr. Marine wondered whether the disease was due to a deficiency of iodine, the one element in which the thyroid specialized. Cleveland, being inland, might lack the iodine that was so plentiful in the soil near the ocean and in the seafood that is an important article of diet there.

The doctor experimented on animals and after ten years felt sure enough of his ground to try feeding iodine-containing compounds to goiter patients. He was probably not too surprised to find that it worked. Marine then suggested that iodine-containing compounds be added to table salt and to the water-supply of inland cities where the soil was poor in iodine. There was strong opposition to his proposal, however, and it took another ten years to get water-iodination and iodized salt generally accepted. Once the iodine supplements became routine, simple goiter declined in importance as one of mankind's woes.

Today American researchers (and the public) are engaged in studies and discussion of a similar health question — the fluoridation of water to prevent tooth decay. This issue is still a matter of bitter controversy in the non-scientific and political arena, and so far the opposition has been far more stubborn and successful than in the case of iodine. Perhaps one reason is that cavities in the teeth do not seem nearly as serious as the disfigurement of goiter.

629

In the early decades of this century dentists noticed that people in certain areas in the United States (*e.g.*, some localities in Arkansas) tended to have darkened teeth — a mottling of the enamel. Eventually this was traced to a higher-than-average content of fluorine compounds in the natural drinking water of those areas. With the attention of researchers directed to fluorine in the water, another interesting discovery turned up. Where the fluorine content of the water was above average, the population had an unusually low rate of tooth decay. For instance, the town of Galesburg in Illinois, with fluorine in its water, had only one-third as many cavities per youngster as the nearby town of Quincy, whose water contained practically no fluorine.

Tooth decay is no laughing matter, as anyone with a toothache will readily agree. It costs the people of the United States more than a billion and a half dollars a year in dental bills, and by the age of 35 two-thirds of all Americans have lost at least some of their teeth. Dental researchers succeeded in getting support for large-scale studies to find out whether fluoridation of water would be safe and would really help to prevent tooth decay. They found that one part per million of fluorine in the drinking water did not mottle teeth and yet showed an effect in decay-prevention. They therefore adopted one part per million as a standard for testing the results of fluoridation of community water supplies.

Fluorine is chemically akin to chlorine. In doses more concentrated than those recommended it is highly toxic, but in this respect it is like many other elements: everything depends on the dose. Chlorine, iodine, and the trace metals (*e.g.*, copper) also can be toxic in certain doses. A dosage of one part per million in water is very tiny indeed. Yet in some way not yet understood, fluorine in drinking water even in this minute dosage finds its way into the enamel of the teeth and fortifies the enamel against attack. It can be incorporated in the enamel only during childhood, when the teeth are being built, but once there, it protects the teeth throughout the person's lifetime.

In the past two decades, researchers have carried out several major tests of the effects of fluoridation. Perhaps the best known is the ten-year study in Newburgh, N. Y. Very careful records were kept of the children's cavities and general health, both in Newburgh, where the water was fluoridated, and in Kingston, a town just across the Hudson River where the water was not fluoridated. At the end of the ten years the population samples of the two towns (more than 400 children in each case) were compared. The Newburgh children who had drunk fluoridated water from birth had 58 per cent fewer cavities than their contemporaries in Kingston. Many had no tooth decay at all. And the medical examinations showed no ill-effects whatever; by every test the Newburgh children were just as healthy as the Kingston children.

Similar studies elsewhere have produced the same results. In Evanston, Ill., for example, 13 years of fluoridation of the water have greatly reduced the incidence of tooth decay among the city's children and saved a quarter of a million dollars in dental bills, according to the director of the study, J. Roy Blayney, emeritus professor of the University of Chicago.

The dental profession is now convinced, on the basis of a quarter of a century of research, that for a few pennies per person per year, tooth decay can be reduced by about two-thirds, with a saving of at least a billion dollars a year in dental costs and a relief of pain and of dental handicaps that cannot be measured in money. The nation's dental and medical organizations, the United States Public Health Service, and state health agencies recommend fluoridation of public water supplies. And yet, in the realm of politics fluoridation has lost a majority of its battles. More than 1,000 communities, totaling some 22 million people, have fluoridated water. But a group called the National Committee Against Fluoridation has aroused community after community to vote down fluoridation and even to repeal it in some localities where it had been adopted.

Two chief arguments have been employed by the opponents with the greatest effect. One is that fluorine compounds are poisonous. So they are, but not in the doses used for fluoridation! The other is that fluoridation is compulsory medication, infringing the individual's

6 3 1

freedom. That may be so, but it is questionable whether the individual in any society should have the freedom to expose others to preventable sickness. If compulsory medication is evil, then we have a quarrel not only with fluoridation but also with chlorination, iodination, and, for that matter, with all the forms of inoculation, including vaccination against smallpox, that are compulsory in most civilized countries today.

HORMONES

ENZYMES, VITAMINS, TRACE ELEMENTS — how potently these sparse substances decide life-or-death issues for the organism! But there is a fourth group of substances which in a way are even more potent. They conduct the whole performance: they are like a master switch that awakens a city to activity, or the throttle that controls an engine, or the red cape that excites the bull.

At the turn of the century two English physiologists, William Maddock Bayliss and Ernest Henry Starling, became intrigued by a striking little performance in the digestive tract. The gland behind the stomach known as the pancreas releases its digestive fluid into the upper intestines at just the moment when food leaves the stomach and enters the intestine. How does it get the message? What tells the pancreas that the right moment has arrived? The obvious guess was that the information must be transmitted via the nervous system, which was then the only known means of communication in the body. Presumably the entry of food into the intestines from the stomach stimulated nerve endings which relayed the message to the pancreas by way of the brain or the spinal cord.

To test this theory, Bayliss and Starling cut every nerve to the pancreas. Their maneuver failed! The pancreas still secreted juice at precisely the right moment.

The puzzled experimenters went hunting for an alternate signaling system. In 1902 they tracked down a "chemical messenger." It was a substance secreted by the walls of the intestine. When they injected this into an animal's blood, it stimulated the secretion of pancreatic juice even though the animal was not eating. Bayliss and Starling concluded that, in the normal course of events, food entering the intestines stimulates their linings to secrete the substance, which then travels via the bloodstream to the pancreas and triggers the gland to start giving forth pancreatic juice. The two investigators named the substance secreted by the intestines "secretin," and they called it a "hormone," from a Greek word meaning "rouse to activity." Secretin is now known to be a small protein molecule.

Several years earlier, physiologists had discovered that an extract of the adrenals (two small organs just above the kidneys) could raise blood pressure if injected into the body. The Japanese chemist Jokichi Takamine isolated the responsible substance in 1901 and named it "adrenalin." (This later became a trade name; the chemists' name for it now is "epinephrine.") Its structure resembles that of the amino acid tyrosine, from which it is derived in the body.

Plainly adrenalin, too, was a hormone. As the years went on, the physiologists found that a number of other "glands" in the body secreted hormones. (The word "gland" comes from the Greek word for acorn, and it was originally applied to any small lump of tissue in the body. But it became customary to give the name gland to any tissue that secreted a fluid, even large organs such as the liver and the mammaries. Small organs that did not secrete fluids gradually lost this name, so that the "lymph glands," for instance, were renamed the "lymph nodes." Even so, when lymph nodes in the throat or the armpit become enlarged during infections, physicians and mothers alike still refer to them as "enlarged glands.")

Many of the glands, such as those along the alimentary canal, the sweat glands, and the salivary glands, discharge their fluids through ducts. Some, however, are "ductless"; they release substances directly into the bloodstream, which then circulates the secretions through the body. It is the secretions of these ductless or "endocrine glands" that contain hormones. The study of hormones is for this reason termed "endocrinology."

When biochemists found that iodine was concentrated in the thyroid gland, they made the reasonable guess that the element was part of a hormone. In 1915 Edward Calvin Kendall of the Mayo Foundation in Minnesota isolated from the thyroid an iodine-containing amino acid which behaved like a hormone, and he named it "thyroxine." Each molecule of thyroxine contained four atoms of iodine. Like adrenalin, thyroxine has a strong family resemblance to tyrosine and is manufactured from it in the body. (Many years later, in 1952, the biochemist Rosalind Pitt-Rivers and her associates isolated another thyroid hormone — "tri-iodothyronine," so named because its molecule contains three atoms of iodine rather than four. It is less stable than thyroxine but three to five times as active.)

The thyroid hormones control the over-all rate of metabolism in the body: they arouse all the cells to activity. People with an underactive thyroid are sluggish, torpid, and after a time may become mentally retarded, because the various cells are running in low gear. Conversely, people with an overactive thyroid are nervous and jittery, because their cells are racing. Either an underactive or an overactive thyroid can produce goiter.

The thyroid controls the body's "basal metabolism," that is, its rate of consumption of oxygen at complete rest in comfortable environmental conditions — the "idling rate," so to speak. If a person's basal metabolism is above or below the norm, suspicion falls upon the thyroid gland. Measurement of the basal metabolism is a tedious affair, for the subject must fast for a period in advance and lie still for half an hour while the rate is measured, to say nothing of an even longer period beforehand. Instead of going through this troublesome procedure, why not go straight to the horse's mouth — that is, measure the amount of rate-controlling hormone that the thyroid is producing? In recent years researchers have developed a method of measuring the amount of "protein-bound iodine" (PBI) in the bloodstream; this indicates the rate of thyroid-hormone production and so has provided a simple, quick blood test to replace the basal-metabolism determination.

THE BEST-KNOWN HORMONE is insulin, the first protein whose structure was fully worked out (see Chapter 11). Its discovery was the culmination of a long chain of events.

Diabetes is the name of a whole group of diseases, all characterized by unusual thirst and, in consequence, an unusual output of urine. The name comes from a Greek word meaning "syphon" (apparently the coiner pictured water syphoning endlessly through the body). The most serious form of the disease is "diabetes mellitus." Mellitus comes from the Greek word for honey, and it refers to the fact that in advanced stages of certain cases of the disease the urine contains sugar (in the glucose form). The waste of sugar plainly indicates that the body is not utilizing its food efficiently. And in fact the diabetic patient, despite an increase in appetite, may steadily lose weight as the disease advances. Up to a generation ago there was no helpful treatment for the disease.

In the nineteenth century the German physiologists J. von Mering and O. Minkowski had found that removal of the pancreas gland from a dog produced a condition just like human diabetes. After Bayliss and Starling discovered the hormone secretin, it began to appear that a hormone of the pancreas might be involved in diabetes. But the only known secretion from the pancreas was the digestive juice; where did the hormone come from? A significant clue turned up. When the duct of the pancreas was tied off, so that it could not pour out its digestive secretions, the major part of the gland shriveled, but the groups of cells known as the "islets of Langerhans" (after the German physician Paul Langerhans, who had discovered them in 1869) remained intact.

In 1916 a Scottish physician, Albert Sharpey-Schafer, suggested, therefore, that the islets must be producing the anti-diabetes hormone. He named the assumed hormone "insulin," from the Latin word for "island."

Attempts to extract the hormone from the pancreas at first failed miserably. As we now know, insulin is a protein, and the protein-

6 3 5

splitting enzymes of the pancreas destroyed it even while the chemists were trying to isolate it. In 1921 the Canadian physician Frederick Grant Banting and the physiologist Charles Herbert Best (working in the laboratories of J. J. R. MacLeod at the University of Toronto) tried a new approach. First they tied off the duct of the pancreas. The enzyme-producing portion of the gland shriveled, the production of protein-splitting enzymes stopped, and the scientists were then able to extract the intact hormone from the islets. It proved indeed effective in countering diabetes. Banting called the hormone "isletin," but the older and more Latinized form proposed by Sharpey-Schafer won out. Insulin it became and still is.

In 1923 Banting and, for some reason, MacLeod (whose only service to the discovery of insulin was to allow the use of his laboratory over the summer while he was on vacation) received the Nobel Prize in physiology and medicine.

The effect of insulin within the body shows most clearly in connection with the level of glucose concentration in the blood. Ordinarily the body stores most of its glucose in the liver, in the form of a variety of starch called "glycogen," keeping only a small quantity of glucose in the bloodstream to serve the immediate energy needs of the cells. If the glucose concentration in the blood rises too high, this stimulates the pancreas to increase its production of insulin, which pours into the bloodstream and brings about a lowering of the glucose level. On the other hand, when the glucose level falls too low, the lowered concentration inhibits the production of insulin by the pancreas, so that the sugar level rises. Thus a balance is achieved. The production of insulin lowers the level of glucose which lowers the production of insulin which raises the level of glucose which raises the production of insulin which lowers the level of glucose — and so on. This is an example of what is called "feedback." The thermostat that controls the heating of a house works in the same fashion.

In the case of the blood-sugar concentration, a second hormone secreted by the islets of Langerhans refines the control. The islets are made up of two distinct kinds of cells, "alpha" and "beta." The beta cells produce insulin, while the alpha cells turn out a hormone called "glucagon." Glucagon opposes the effect of insulin, so the two hormonal forces push in opposite directions, and the balance shifts slightly this way and that under the stimulus of the glucose concentration in blood.

Now the trouble in diabetes is that the islets have lost the ability to turn out enough insulin. The glucose concentration in the blood therefore drifts upward. When the level rises to about 50 per cent higher than normal, it crosses the "renal threshold" — that is, glucose spills over into the urine. In a way this loss of glucose into the urine is the lesser of two evils, for if the glucose concentration were allowed to build up any higher, the resulting rise in viscosity of the blood would cause undue heartstrain. (The heart is designed to pump blood, not molasses.)

The classic way of checking for the presence of diabetes is to test the urine for sugar. For instance, a few drops of urine can be heated with "Benedict's solution" (named for the American chemist Francis Gano Benedict). The solution contains copper sulfate, which gives it a deep blue color. If glucose is not present in the urine, the solution remains blue. If glucose is present, the copper sulfate is converted to cuprous oxide. Cuprous oxide is a brick-red, insoluble substance. A reddish precipitate at the bottom of the test-tube therefore is an unmistakable sign of sugar in the urine, which usually means diabetes.

Nowadays an even simpler method is available. Small paper strips about two inches long are impregnated with two enzymes, glucose dehydrogenase and peroxidase, plus an organic substance called "orthotolidine." The yellowish strip is dipped into a sample of the patient's urine and then exposed to the air. If glucose is present, it combines with oxygen from the air with the catalytic help of the glucose dehydrogenase. In the process, hydrogen peroxide is formed. The peroxidase in the paper then causes the hydrogen peroxide to combine with the orthotolidine to form a deep blue compound. In short, if the yellowish paper is dipped into urine and turns blue, diabetes can be strongly suspected.

Once glucose begins to appear in the urine, diabetes mellitus is fairly far along in its course. It is better to catch the disease earlier by checking the glucose level in the blood before it crosses the renal threshold. The "glucose tolerance test" now in general use measures the rate of fall of the glucose level in the blood after it has been raised by feeding the person glucose. Normally the pancreas responds with a flood of insulin. In a healthy person the sugar level will drop to normal within two hours. If the level stays high for three hours or more, it shows a sluggish insulin response, and the person is likely to be in the early stages of diabetes.

Within a year of Banting's and Best's isolation of insulin, physicians were treating diabetics with injections of the hormone. But the necessity for regular insulin injections, while it allows diabetics to live reasonably normal lives, brings its difficulties. The sizable doses of insulin introduce comparatively violent oscillations in the blood level, instead of the normal continuous feedback and delicate balance. And, of course, hypodermic needles are a nuisance. Unfortunately, insulin cannot be taken by mouth, because it would promptly be broken down in the stomach. However, in 1954 investigators discovered an enzyme, "insulinase," which destroys insulin; its function in the body is to get rid of any excess of insulin in the blood quickly. Suppose this enzyme could be put out of action, so that a diabetic's meager natural supply of insulin would last longer. He might then be able to get along without injections of the hormone. Drugs that inactivate the enzyme have been developed.

In fact, two types of pills are now available for treating some cases of diabetes. One assists in the use of sugar by the cells.

IT IS POSSIBLE that insulin has something to do with controlling appetite.

In our well-fed nation, despite the fact that no people in history has ever been so diet-conscious, the incidence of overweight has reached epidemic proportions. Although insurance companies and physicians have worked hard to convince the public that overweight is an invitation to serious diseases such as diabetes mellitus and atherosclerosis, and can cut life expectancy sharply, there is no visible decline in the incidence of overweight.

An easy explanation is that the obese are simply willful gluttons. This is a view held only by thin people. Almost every fat person can testify that he has tried many times to diet himself thin, knowing full well the deleterious effect of fat on his or her comfort, health, and appearance. The dieter may succeed temporarily, only to gain the weight back. (If I may indulge in a personal comment, I am 30 pounds overweight and am willing to add my testimony.)

The psychiatrists offer a more complicated theory, to the effect that overeating is not a matter of willful folly but a compulsion beyond the individual's conscious control. Stout people, they say, are the victims of personality disturbances, generally originating during childhood as a result of the family environment. An unconscious drive forces them to overeat, against the advice of friends, doctors, and their own common sense.

Perhaps so, but psychiatry has yet to control the incidence of overweight by any treatment psychiatrists have managed to devise. In 1959 two nutritionists at Iowa State College, L. G. Buchinal and E. S. Eppright, reported an attempt to check the theory of the psychogenic origin of overweight. They studied 111 girls attending rural schools, dividing them into those who had been distinctly fat for at least three years and those of normal weight. No personality or behavioral distinctions could be found between the two groups. The one definite difference reported was that the parents of the fat girls were, on the average, fatter than the parents of the thin girls.

Does this suggest a hereditary tendency to fatness? It may be argued that children of fat parents simply learn bad eating habits at the family table. How, then, explain the fact that it is possible to breed strains of laboratory mice which, if allowed to eat at will, will eat themselves twice as fat as other strains allowed the same liberty?

It would seem that, regardless of whether a conscious love of food or an unconscious compulsion contributes to overeating, there is also in any case some physical inclination which can be inherited, just as surely as eye color can be. In other words, we are all born with what some physiologists call an "appestat," which regulates appetite as a thermostat regulates a furnace. If the appestat is set too high, the individual finds himself continually taking in more calories than he expends, unless he exerts a strenuous self-control which sooner or later wears him out.

In the early 1940's a physiologist, S. W. Ranson, showed that animals grew obese after destruction of a portion of the hypothalamus (located in the lower part of the brain). This seems to fix the location of the appestat. What controls its operation? "Hunger pangs" spring to mind. An empty stomach contracts in waves, and the entry of food ends the contractions. Perhaps it is these contractions that signal to the appestat. Not so; surgical removal of the stomach has never interfered with appetite control.

The Harvard physiologist Jean Mayer has advanced a more reasonable suggestion. He believes that the appestat responds to the level of glucose in the blood. After food has been digested, the glucose level in the blood slowly drops. When it falls below a certain level, the appestat is turned on. If, in response to the consequent urgings of the appetite, the person eats, the glucose level in his blood momentarily rises and the appestat is turned off.

This small rise and fall in the glucose level takes place despite the workings of the insulin-glucagon system. Any interference with that system ought, therefore, to exaggerate the effects. Sure enough, an injection of glucagon, which raises the glucose blood level above normal, has been reported to kill the appetite. (Perhaps stout people suffer from an underproduction of glucagon, which keeps the glucose level abnormally low and the appetite unnecessarily active. But this, as yet, is only speculation.)

If the glucose level controls appetite, what of diabetes? In diabetics the insulin deficiency keeps the glucose level abnormally high. This should kill the appetite, but it does not. Diabetics are always hungry.

Mayer suggests that insulin controls the rate at which glucose enters the cells of the hypothalamus. In diabetics the absence or diminution of insulin makes it more difficult for glucose to get into the cells of the appestat, which therefore acts as if there were a low glucose level in the blood. The appestat is permanently turned on, and diabetics remain hungry.

THE HORMONES I HAVE DISCUSSED so far are all either proteins (as insulin, glucagon, secretin) or modified amino acids (as thyroxine, tri-iodothyronine, adrenalin). We come now to an altogether different group — the steroid hormones.

The story of these begins in 1927, when two German physiologists, Bernhard Zondek and S. Aschheim, discovered that extracts of the urine of pregnant women, when injected into female mice or rats, aroused them to sexual heat. (Their discovery led to the first early test for pregnancy.) It was clear at once that they had found a hormone, specifically a "sex hormone."

Within two years pure samples of the hormone were isolated by Adolf Butenandt in Germany and by Edward Doisy at St. Louis University. It was named "estrone," from "estrus," the term for sexual heat in females. Its structure was quickly found to be that of a steroid, with the four-ring structure of cholesterol.

Estrone is now one of a group of known female sex hormones, called "estrogens" ("giving rise to estrus"). In 1931 Butenandt isolated the first male sex hormone, or "androgen" ("giving rise to maleness"). He called it "androsterone."

It is the production of sex hormones that governs the changes that take place during adolescence: the development of facial hair in the male and of enlarged breasts in the female, for instance. The complex menstrual cycle in females depends on the interplay of several estrogens.

The female sex hormones are produced in large part in the ovaries, the male sex hormones in the testes. Both of these organs therefore fall under the heading of "glands." With what can only be considered excessive coyness, the media of public communication tend to

641

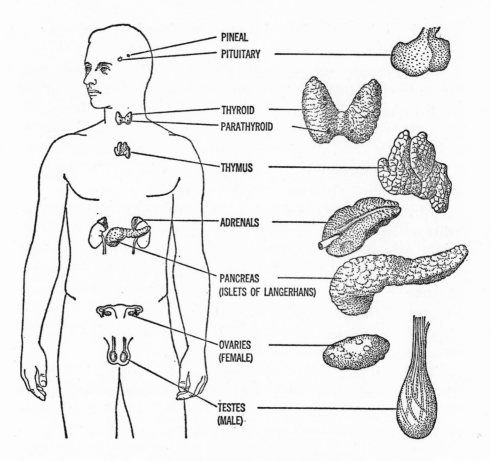

PINEAL
PITUITARY

THYROID
PARATHYROID

THYMUS

ADRENALS

PANCREAS
(ISLETS OF LANGERHANS)

OVARIES
(FEMALE)

TESTES
(MALE)

THE ENDOCRINE GLANDS.

use the euphemism "glands" for sexual organs which have the perfectly good and respectable names I have just used.

The sex hormones are not the only steroid hormones. The first non-sexual chemical messenger of the steroid type was discovered in the adrenals. These, as a matter of fact, are double glands, consisting of an inner gland called the adrenal "medulla" (the Latin word for "marrow") and an outer gland called the adrenal "cortex" (the Latin word for "bark"). It is the medulla that produces adrenalin. In 1929 investigators found that extracts from the cortex could keep animals alive after their adrenal glands had been removed—a 100 per cent fatal operation. Naturally a search immediately began for "cortical hormones."

The search had a practical medical reason behind it. The well-known affliction called "Addison's disease" (first described by the English physician Thomas Addison in 1855) had symptoms like those resulting from the removal of the adrenals. Clearly the disease must be caused by a failure in hormone production by the adrenal cortex. Perhaps injections of cortical hormones might deal with Addison's disease as insulin dealt with diabetes.

Two men were outstanding in this search. One was Tadeus Reichstein (who was later to synthesize vitamin C); the other was Edward Kendall (who had first discovered the thyroid hormone nearly 20 years before). By the late 1930's the researchers had isolated more than two dozen different compounds from the adrenal cortex. At least four showed hormonal activity. Kendall named the substances Compounds A, B, E, F, and so on. All the cortical hormones turned out to be steroids.

Now the adrenals are very tiny glands, and it would take the glands of countless numbers of animals to provide enough cortical extracts for general use. Apparently the only reasonable solution was to try to synthesize the hormones.

A false rumor drove cortical-hormone research forward under full steam during World War II. It was reported that the Germans were buying up adrenal glands in Argentine slaughter-houses to manufacture cortical hormones that improved the efficiency of their airplane pilots in high-altitude flight. There was nothing to it, but the rumor had the effect of stimulating the United States Government to place a high priority on research into methods for the synthesis of the cortical hormones; the priority was even higher than that given to the synthesis of penicillin or the anti-malarials.

Compound A was synthesized by Kendall in 1944, and by the following year Merck & Co. had begun to produce it in substantial amounts. It proved of little value for Addison's disease, to the disappointment of all. After a prodigious labor the Merck biochemist Lewis H. Sarrett then synthesized, by a process involving 37 steps,

643

Compound E, which was later to become known as "cortisone."

The synthesis of Compound E created little immediate stir in medical circles. The war was over; the rumor of cortical magic worked on German pilots had proved untrue; and Compound A had fizzled. Then, in an entirely unexpected quarter, Compound E suddenly came to life.

For 20 years the Mayo Clinic physician Philip Showalter Hench had been studying rheumatoid arthritis, a painful, sometimes paralytic disease. Hench suspected that the body possessed natural mechanisms for countering this disease, because the arthritis was often relieved during pregnancy or during attacks of jaundice. He could not think of any biochemical factor that jaundice and pregnancy held in common. He tried injections of bile pigments (involved in jaundice) and sex hormones (involved in pregnancy) but neither helped his arthritic patients.

However, various bits of evidence pointed toward cortical hormones as a possible answer, and in 1949, with cortisone available in reasonable quantity, Hench tried that. It worked! It did not cure the disease, any more than insulin cures diabetes, but it seemed to relieve the symptoms, and to an arthritic that alone is manna from heaven. What was more, cortisone later proved to be helpful as a treatment for Addison's disease, where Compound A had failed.

For their work on the cortical hormones, Kendall, Hench, and Reichstein shared the Nobel Prize in medicine and physiology in 1950.

Unfortunately, the influences of the cortical hormones on the body's workings are so multiplex that there are always side-effects, sometimes serious. Physicians are reluctant to use cortical-hormone therapy unless the need is clear and urgent. Synthetic substances related to cortical hormones (some with a fluorine atom inserted in the molecule) are being used in an attempt to avoid the worst of the side-effects, but nothing approaching a reasonable ideal has yet been found. One of the most active of the cortical hormones discovered so far is "aldosterone," isolated in 1953 by Reichstein and his co-workers.

WHAT CONTROLS all the varied and powerful hormones? All of them (including a number I have not mentioned), can exert more or less drastic effects in the body. Yet they are tuned together so harmoniously that they keep the body functioning smoothly without a break in the rhythm. Seemingly there must be a conductor somewhere that directs their cooperation.

The nearest thing to an answer is the pituitary, a small gland suspended from the bottom of the brain (but not part of it). The name of the gland arose from an ancient notion that its function was to secrete phlegm, the Latin word for which is *pituita* (also the source of the word "spit"). Because this notion is false, scientists have renamed the gland the "hypophysis" (from Greek words meaning "growing under" — *i.e.*, under the brain), but pituitary is still the more common term.

The gland has three parts: the anterior lobe, the posterior lobe, and, in some organisms, a small bridge connecting the two. The anterior lobe is the most important, for it produces at least six hormones (all small-molecule proteins) which seem to act specifically upon other ductless glands. In other words, the anterior pituitary can be viewed as the orchestra leader that keeps the other glands playing in time and in tune. (It is interesting that the pituitary is located just about in the center of the skull, as if deliberately placed in a spot of maximum security.)

One of the pituitary's messengers is the "thyroid-stimulating hormone" (TSH). It stimulates the thyroid on a feedback basis. That is, it causes the thyroid to produce thyroid hormone; the rise in concentration of thyroid hormone in the blood in turn inhibits the formation of TSH by the pituitary; the fall of TSH in the blood in its turn reduces the thyroid's production; that stimulates the production of TSH by the pituitary, and so the cycle maintains a balance.

In the same way, the "adrenal-cortical-stimulating hormone," or "adrenocorticotropic hormone" (ACTH), maintains the level of cortical hormones. If extra ACTH is injected into the body, it will raise the level of these hormones, and thus it can serve the same purpose as the injection of cortisone itself. ACTH has therefore been used to treat rheumatoid arthritis.

The most spectacular of the anterior pituitary hormones is the "somatotropic hormone" (STH), more popularly known as the "growth hormone." Its effect is a general one stimulating growth of the whole body. A child who cannot produce a sufficient supply of the hormone will become a dwarf; one who produces too much will turn into a circus giant. If the disorder that results in an oversupply of the growth hormone does not occur until after the person has matured (*i.e.*, when his bones have been fully formed and hardened), only the extremities, such as the hands, feet, and chin, grow grotesquely large — a condition known as "acromegaly" (Greek for "large extremities").

As to how the hormones work, in chemical terms, investigators have so far been up against a brick wall. They have not yet been able to determine precisely how any hormone performs its assignment.

It seems certain that the hormones do not act as enzymes. At least, no hormone has been found to catalyze a specific reaction directly. The next alternative is to suppose that a hormone, if not itself an enzyme, acts upon an enzyme — that it either promotes or inhibits an enzyme's activity. Insulin, the most thoroughly investigated of all the hormones, does seem to be definitely connected with an enzyme called "glucokinase," which is essential for the conversion of glucose to glycogen. This enzyme is inhibited by extracts from the anterior pituitary and the adrenal cortex, and insulin can nullify that inhibition. Thus insulin in the blood may serve to activate the enzyme and so speed up the conversion of glucose to glycogen. That would help to explain how insulin lowers the glucose concentration in the blood.

Yet the presence or absence of insulin affects metabolism at so many points that it is hard to see how this one action could bring about all the abnormalities that exist in the body chemistry of a diabetic. (The same is true for other hormones.) Some biochemists have therefore tended to look for grosser and more wholesale effects.

There is a growing belief that insulin somehow acts as an agent to get glucose into the cell. On this theory, a diabetic has a high glucose level in his blood for the simple reason that the sugar cannot get into his cells and therefore he cannot use it. (In explaining the insatiable appetite of a diabetic, Mayer, as I have already mentioned, suggested that glucose in the blood has difficulty in entering the cells of the appestat.)

If insulin assists glucose in entering the cell, then it must act on the cell membrane in some way. How? No one knows. In fact, not much is known about cell membranes in general, except that they are composed of protein and fatty substances. We can speculate that insulin, as a protein molecule, may somehow change the arrangement of amino-acid side-chains in the protein of the membrane and thus open doors for glucose (and possibly many other substances).

If we are willing to be satisfied with generalities of this kind (and at the moment there is no alternative), we can go on to suppose that the other hormones also act on the cell membranes, each in its own fashion because each has its own specific amino-acid arrangement. Similarly, steroid hormones, as fatty substances, may act on the fatty molecules of the membrane, either opening or closing the door to certain substances. Clearly, by helping a given material to enter the cell or preventing it from doing so, a hormone could exert a drastic effect on what goes on in the cell. It could supply one enzyme with plenty of substrate to work on and deprive another of material, thus controlling what the cell produces. Assuming that a single hormone may decide the entrance or non-entrance of several different substances, we can see how the presence or absence of a hormone could profoundly influence metabolism, as in fact it does in the case of insulin.

The picture is attractive, but even if it is correct, biochemists badly need a great deal more specific information. For that, alas, they must wait.

647

DEATH

THE ADVANCES MADE BY MODERN MEDICINE in the battle against infection, against cancer, against nutritional disorders, have increased the probability that any given individual will live long enough to experience old age. Half the people being born in this generation can be expected to reach the age of 70 (barring a nuclear war or some other prime catastrophe).

The rarity of survival to old age in earlier eras no doubt accounts in part for the extravagant respect paid to longevity in those times. The *Iliad*, for instance, makes much of "old" Priam and "old" Nestor. Nestor is described as having survived three generations of men, but at a time when the average length of life could not have been more than 20 to 25, Nestor need not have been older than 70 to have survived three generations. That is old, yes, but not extraordinary by present standards. Because Nestor's antiquity made such an impression on people in Homer's time, later mythologists supposed that he must have been something like 200 years old.

To take another example at random, Shakespeare's *Richard II* opens with the rolling words: "Old John of Gaunt, time-honoured Lancaster." John's own contemporaries, according to the chroniclers of the time, also considered him an old man. It comes as a slight shock to realize that John of Gaunt lived only to the age of 59. An interesting example from our own history is that of Abraham Lincoln. Whether because of his beard, or his sad, lined face, or songs of the time that referred to him as "Father Abraham," most people think of him as an old man at the time of his death. One could only wish that he had lived to be one. He was assassinated at the age of 56.

All this is not to say that really old age was unknown in the days before modern medicine. In ancient Greece Sophocles, the playwright, lived to be 90, and Isocrates, the orator, to 98. Flavius Cassiodorus of fifth-century Rome died at 95. Enrico Dandolo, the twelfth-century Doge of Venice, lived to be 97. Titian, the Renaissance painter, survived to 99. In the era of Louis XV, the Duc de Richelieu, grandnephew of the famous cardinal, lived 92 years.

This emphasizes the point that although the average life expectancy in medically advanced societies has risen greatly, the maximum life span has not. We expect very few men even today to attain or exceed the lifetime of an Isocrates or a Dandolo. Nor do we expect modern nonagenarians to be able to participate in the business of life with any greater vigor. Sophocles was writing great plays in his nineties, and Isocrates was composing great orations. Titian painted to the last year of his life; Dandolo was the indomitable war leader of a Venetian war against the Byzantine Empire at the age of 96. (Among comparably vigorous oldsters of our day, the best example I can think of is George Bernard Shaw, who lived to 94.)

Although a far larger proportion of our population reaches the age of 60 than ever before, beyond that age life expectancy has improved very little over the past. The Metropolitan Life Insurance Company estimates that the life expectancy of a 60-year-old American male in 1931 was just about the same as it was a century and a half earlier — that is, 14.3 years against the estimated earlier figure of 14.8. For the average American woman the corresponding figures were 15.8 and 16.1. Since 1931 the advent of antibiotics has raised the expectancy at 60 for both sexes by two and a half years. But on the whole, despite all that medicine and science have done, old age overtakes a person at about the same rate and in the same way as it always has. Man has not yet found a way to stave off the gradual weakening and eventual breakdown of the human machine.

As in other forms of machinery, it is the moving parts that go first. The circulatory system — the pulsing heart and arteries — is man's Achilles' heel in the long run. His progress in conquering premature death has raised disorders of this system to the rank of the number one killer. Circulatory diseases are responsible for just over half the deaths in the United States, and of these diseases, a single one, atherosclerosis, accounts for one death out of four.

Atherosclerosis (from Greek words meaning "mealy hardness") is characterized by grainlike fatty deposits along the inner surface of the arteries, which force the heart to work harder to drive blood through the vessels at a normal pace. The blood pressure rises, and the consequent increase in strain on the small blood vessels may burst them. If this happens in the brain (a particularly vulnerable area) there is a cerebral hemorrhage, or "stroke." Sometimes the bursting of a vessel is so minor that it occasions only a trifling and temporary discomfort or even goes unnoticed, but a massive collapse of vessels will bring on paralysis or a quick death.

The roughening and narrowing of the arteries introduces another hazard. Because of the increased friction of the blood scraping along the roughened inner surface of the vessels, blood clots are more likely to form, and the narrowing of the vessels heightens the chances that a clot will completely block the blood flow. In the coronary artery, feeding the heart muscle itself, a block ("coronary thrombosis") can produce almost instant death.

Just what causes the formation of deposits on the artery walls is a matter of much debate among medical scientists. Cholesterol certainly seems to be involved, but how it is involved is still far from clear. The plasma of human blood contains "lipoproteins," which consist of cholesterol and other fatty substances bound to certain proteins. Some of the fractions making up lipoprotein maintain a constant concentration in the blood — in health and in disease, before and after eating, and so on. Others fluctuate, rising after meals. Still others are particularly high in obese individuals. One fraction, rich in cholesterol, is particularly high in overweight people and in those with atherosclerosis.

Atherosclerosis tends to go along with a high blood-fat content, and so does obesity. Overweight people are more prone to atherosclerosis than are thin people. Diabetics also have high blood-fat levels, and they are more prone to atherosclerosis than are normal individuals. And, to round out the picture, the incidence of diabetes among the stout is considerably higher than among the thin.

It is thus no accident that those who live to a great age are so often scrawny, little fellows. Large, fat men may be jolly, but they don't keep the sexton waiting unduly, as a rule. (Of course, there are always exceptions, and one can point to men such as Winston Churchill and Herbert Hoover, who have reached a green old age although they have never been noted for leanness.)

The key question, at the moment, is whether atherosclerosis can be fostered or prevented by the diet. Animal fats, such as those in milk, eggs, and butter, are particularly high in cholesterol; plant fats are particularly low in it. Moreover, the fatty acids of plant fats are mainly of the unsaturated type, which has been reported to counter the deposition of cholesterol. Despite the fact that investigations of these matters have yielded no conclusive results one way or the other, people have been flocking to "low-cholesterol diets," in the hope of staving off thickening of the artery walls. No doubt this will do no harm.

Of course, the cholesterol in the blood is not derived from the cholesterol of the diet. The body can and does make its own cholesterol with great ease, and even though you live on a diet that is completely free of cholesterol, you will still have a generous supply of cholesterol in your blood lipoproteins. It therefore seems reasonable to suppose that what matters is not the mere presence of cholesterol but the individual's tendency to deposit it where it will do the most harm. It may be that there is a hereditary tendency to manufacture excessive amounts of cholesterol. Biochemists are seeking drugs that will inhibit cholesterol formation, in the hope that such drugs may forestall the development of atherosclerosis in those who are prone to the disease.

BUT EVEN THOSE who escape atherosclerosis grow old. Old age is a disease of universal incidence. Nothing can stop the creeping enfeeblement, the increasing brittleness of the bones, the weakening of the muscles, the stiffening of the joints, the slowing of reflexes, the dimming of sight, the declining agility of the mind. The rate at which this happens is somewhat slower in some than in others, but, fast or slow, the process is inexorable.

Why? What is old age, anyway? So far there are only speculations. Some have suggested that the body's resistance to infection slowly decreases with age (at a rate depending on heredity). Others speculate that "clinkers" of one kind or another accumulate in the cells (again at a rate that varies from individual to individual). These supposed side-products of normal cellular reactions, which the cell can neither destroy nor get rid of, slowly build up in the cell as the years pass, until they eventually interfere with the cell's metabolism so seriously that it ceases to function. When enough cells are put out of action, so the theory goes, the body dies. A variation of this notion holds that the protein molecules themselves become clinkers, because cross-links develop between them so that they become stiff and brittle and finally bring the cell machinery grinding to a halt.

The most concretely investigated theory is that of Albert I. Lansing of Washington University, who has found evidence of a connection between aging and accumulation of insoluble calcium in the cells. Working with rotifers — tiny, wheel-like animals — he finds also that the offspring of aging rotifers are shorter-lived than those born of young parents.

There is no reason to believe that a century is man's immutable, maximum life span. Continued advances in biochemistry may well produce, some day, methods of slowing down the degenerative changes that bring about the diseases of the circulatory system and of old age. If we can't achieve immortality, we may at least achieve a longer life.

Whether, in view of the population explosion, such a consummation is devoutly to be wished (inviting though it may sound to us as individuals), is more than a little uncertain.

CHAPTER

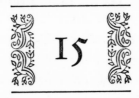

15

THE
SPECIES

VARIETIES OF LIFE

MAN'S KNOWLEDGE OF HIS OWN BODY is incomplete without a knowledge of his relationship to the rest of life on the earth. In primitive cultures, the relationship was often considered to be close indeed. Many tribes regarded certain animals as their ancestors or blood-brothers, and made it a crime to kill or eat them, except under certain ritualistic circumstances. This veneration of animals as gods or near-gods is called "totemism" (from an American Indian word), and there are signs of it in cultures that are not so primitive. The animal-headed gods of Egypt were a hangover of totemism, and so, perhaps, is the modern Hindu veneration of cows and monkeys.

On the other hand, Western culture, as exemplified in Greek and Hebrew ideas, very early made a sharp distinction between man and the "lower animals." Thus the Bible emphasizes that man was produced by a special act of creation in the image of God, "after our likeness" (Genesis 1:26). Yet the Bible attests, nevertheless, to man's remarkably keen interest in the lower animals. Genesis mentions that Adam, in his idyllic early days in the Garden of Eden, was given the task of naming "every beast of the field, and every fowl of the air."

Offhand, that seems not too difficult a task — something that one could do in perhaps an hour or two. The scriptural chroniclers put "two of every sort" of animal in Noah's Ark, whose dimensions were 450 by 75 by 45 feet (if we take the cubit to be 18 inches). The Greek natural philosophers thought of the living world in similarly limited terms: Aristotle could list only about 500 kinds of animals, and his pupil Theophrastus, the most eminent botanist of ancient Greece, listed only about 500 different plants.

Such a list might make some sense if one thought of an elephant as always an elephant, a camel as just a camel, or a flea as simply a flea. Things began to get a little more complicated when naturalists realized that animals had to be differentiated on the basis of whether they could breed with each other. The Indian elephant could not interbreed with the African elephant; therefore they had to be considered different "species" of elephant. The Arabian camel (one hump) and the Bactrian camel (two humps) also are separate species. As for the flea, the small biting insects (all resembling the common flea) are divided into 500 different species!

Through the centuries, as naturalists counted new varieties of creatures in the field, in the air, and in the sea, and as new areas of the world came into view through exploration, the number of identified species of animals and plants grew astronomically. By 1800 it had reached 70,000. Today more than 1,250,000 different species are known, and no biologist supposes that the count is complete.

THE LIVING WORLD would be mighty confusing if we couldn't classify this enormous variety of creatures according to some scheme of relationships. One can begin by grouping together the cat, the tiger, the lion, the panther, the leopard, the jaguar, and other catlike animals in the "cat family"; likewise, the dog, the wolf, the fox, the jackal, and the coyote form a "dog family"; and so on. On the basis of obvious general criteria one can go on to classify some animals as meat-eaters and others as plant-eaters. The ancients also set up general classifications based on habitat, and so they considered all animals that lived in the sea to be fishes and all that flew in the air to be birds. But this made the whale a fish and the bat a bird. Actually, in a fundamental sense the whale and the bat are more like each other than the one is like a fish or the other like a bird. Both bear live young. Moreover, the whale has air-breathing lungs, rather than the gills of a fish, and the bat has hair instead of the feathers of a bird. Both are classed with the mammals, which give birth to living babies (instead of laying eggs) and feed them on mother's milk.

One of the earliest attempts to make a systematic classification was that of an Englishman named John Ray (or Wray), who in the seventeenth century classified all the known species of plants (about 18,600), and later the species of animals, according to systems which seemed to him logical. For instance, he divided flowering plants into two main groups, on the basis of whether the seed contained one embryonic leaf or two. The tiny embryonic leaf or pair of leaves had the name "cotyledon," from the Greek word for a kind of cup ("kotyle"), because it lay in a cuplike hollow in the seed. Ray therefore named the two types respectively "monocotyledonous" and "dicotyledonous." The classification proved so useful that it is still in effect today. The difference between one embryonic leaf and two in itself is unimportant, but there are a number of important ways in which all monocotyledonous plants differ from all dicotyledonous ones. The difference in the embryonic leaves is just a handy tag which is symptomatic of many general differences. (In the same way, the distinction between feathers and hair is minor in itself but is a handy marker for the vast array of differences that separates birds from mammals.)

Although Ray and others contributed some useful ideas, the real founder of the science of classification, or "taxonomy" (from a Greek word meaning "arrangement"), was a Swedish botanist best known by his Latinized name of Carolus Linnaeus, who did the job so well that the main features of his scheme still stand today. Linnaeus set forth his system in 1737 in a book entitled *Systema Naturae*. He grouped species resembling one another into a "genus" (from a Greek word meaning "race" or "sort"), put related genera in turn into an "order," and grouped similar orders in a "class." Each species was given a double name, made up of the name of the genus and of the species itself. (This is much like the system in the telephone book, which lists Smith, John; Smith, William, and so on.) Thus the members of the genus of cats are *Felis domesticus* (the pussy-cat), *Felis leo* (the lion), *Felis tigris* (the tiger), *Felis pardus* (the leopard), and so on. The genus to which the dog belongs includes *Canis familiaris* (the dog), *Canis lupus* (the European gray wolf), *Canis occidentalis* (the American timber wolf), etc. The two species of camels are *Camelus bactrianus* (the Bactrian camel) and *Camelus dromedarius* (the Arabian camel).

Around 1800 the French naturalist Georges Leopold Cuvier went beyond "classes" and added a more general category called the "phylum" (from a Greek word for "tribe"). A phylum includes all animals with the same general body plan. For instance, the mammals, birds, reptiles, amphibia, and fishes are placed in one phylum because all have backbones, a maximum of four limbs, and red blood containing hemoglobin. Insects, spiders, lobsters, and centipedes are placed in another phylum; clams, oysters, and mussels in still another; and so on.

The tree of life now is arranged as I shall describe in the following paragraphs, going from the most general divisions to the more specific.

We start with the "kingdoms"—plant, animal, and in-between (that is, those microorganisms, such as the bacteria, that cannot be classed definitely as plant or animal in nature).

The plant kingdom, according to one system of classification, is divided into two subkingdoms. In the first subkingdom, called Thallophyta, are placed all the plants that do not have roots, stems or leaves—that is, the algae (one-celled green plants and various sea-weeds) and the fungi (the one-celled molds plus such organisms as mushrooms). The members of the second subkingdom, the Embryophyta, are divided into two main phyla — the Bryophyta (the various mosses) and the Tracheophyta (plants with systems of tubes for the circulation of sap), which includes all the species that we ordinarily think of as plants.

This last great phylum is made up of three main classes: the Filicineae, the Gymnospermae, and the Angiospermae. In the first class are the ferns, which reproduce by means of spores. The gymnosperms, forming seeds on the surface of the seed-bearing organs, include the various evergreen cone-bearing trees. The angiosperms, with the seeds enclosed in ovules, make up the vast majority of the familiar plants.

As for the animal kingdom, I shall list the more important phyla only.

The Protozoa ("first animals") are, of course, the one-celled animals. Next there are the Porifera, animals consisting of colonies of cells within a pore-bearing skeleton; these are the sponges. The individual cells show signs of specialization but retain a certain independence, for after all are separated by straining through a silk cloth, they may aggregate to form a new sponge.

The first phylum whose members can be considered truly multicelled animals is the Coelenterata (meaning "hollow gut"). These animals have the shape of a cup and consist of two layers of cells — the ectoderm ("outer skin") and the endoderm ("inner skin"). The most common examples of this phylum are the jellyfish and the sea-anemones.

All the rest of the animal phyla have a third layer of cells — the mesoderm ("middle skin"). From these three layers are formed the many organs of even the most complex animals, including man.

The mesoderm arises during the development of the embryo, and the manner in which it arises divides the animals involved into two "superphyla." Those in which the mesoderm forms at the junction

657

of the ectoderm and the endoderm are called the Annelid super-phylum; those in which the mesoderm arises in the endoderm alone are the Echinoderm superphylum.

Let us consider the Annelid superphylum first. Its simplest phylum is Platyhelminthes (Greek for "flat worms"). This includes not only the parasitic tapeworm but also free-living forms. The flat-worms have contractile fibers that can be considered primitive muscles, and they also possess a head, a tail, special reproductive organs, and the beginnings of excretory organs. In addition, the flatworms display bilateral symmetry: that is, they have left and right sides which are mirror images of each other. They move head first, and their sense organs and rudimentary nerves are concentrated in the head area, so that the flatworm can be said to possess the first step toward a brain.

Next comes the phylum Nematoda (Greek for "thread worm"), whose most familiar member is the hookworm. These creatures possess a primitive bloodstream — a fluid within the mesoderm that bathes all the cells and conveys food and oxygen to them. This allows the nematodes, in contrast to animals such as the flat tapeworm, to have bulk, for the fluid can bring nourishment to interior cells. The nematodes also possess a gut with two openings, one for the entry of food, the other (the anus) for ejection of wastes.

The next two phyla in this superphylum have hard external "skeletons" — that is, shells (which are found in some of the simpler phyla, too). These two groups are the Brachiopoda, which have calcium carbonate shells on top and bottom and are popularly called "lampshells," and the Mollusca (Latin for "soft"), whose soft bodies are enclosed in shells originating from the right and left sides instead of the top and bottom. The most familiar molluscs are the clams, oysters, and snails.

A particularly important phylum in the Annelid superphylum is Annelida. These are worms, but with a difference: they are composed of segments, each of which can be looked upon as a kind of organism in itself. Each segment has its own nerves branching off the main nerve stem, its own blood-vessels, its own tubules for carrying off wastes, its own muscles, and so on. In the most familiar annelid, the earthworm, the segments are marked off by little constrictions of flesh which look like little rings around the animal; in fact, Annelida is from a Latin word meaning "little ring."

Segmentation apparently endows an animal with superior efficiency, for all the most successful species of the animal kingdom, including man, are segmented. (Of the non-segmented animals, the most complex and successful is the squid.) If you wonder how the human body is segmented, think of the vertebrae and the ribs; each vertebra of the backbone and each rib represents a separate segment of the body, with its own nerves, muscles, and blood vessels.

The annelids, lacking a skeleton, are soft and relatively defenseless. The phylum Arthropoda ("jointed feet"), however, combines segmentation with a skeleton, the skeleton being as segmented as the rest of the body. The skeleton is not only more maneuverable for being jointed; it is also light and tough, being made of a polysaccharide called "chitin" rather than of heavy, inflexible limestone or calcium carbonate. On the whole, the arthropods, which include the lobsters, spiders, centipedes, and insects, are the most successful phylum in existence. At least the phylum contains more species than all the other phyla put together.

This accounts for the main phyla in the Annelid superphylum. The other superphylum, the Echinoderm, contains only two important phyla. One is Echinodermata ("spiny-skin"), which includes such creatures as the starfish and the sea urchin. The echinoderms differ from other mesoderm-containing phyla in possessing radial symmetry and having no clearly-defined head and tail (though in early life echinoderms do show bilateral symmetry, which they lose as they mature).

The second important phylum of the Echinoderm superphylum is important indeed, for it is the one to which man himself belongs.

THE GENERAL CHARACTERISTIC that distinguishes the members of this phylum (which embraces man, ostrich, snake, frog, mackerel, and a varied host of other animals) is an internal skeleton. No animal outside this phylum possesses one. The particular mark of such a skeleton is the backbone. In fact, the backbone is so important a feature that in common parlance all animals are loosely divided into vertebrates and invertebrates. Actually there is an in-between group which has a rod of cartilage called a "notochord" ("backcord") in the place of the backbone. The notochord seems to represent a rudimentary backbone; in fact, it makes its appearance even in mammals during the development of the embryo. So the animals with notochords (various wormlike, sluglike, and mollusclike creatures) are classed with the vertebrates. The whole phylum is named Chordata, and it is divided into four subphyla, three of which have only a notochord. The fourth, with a true backbone and general internal skeleton, is Vertebrata.

The vertebrates in existence today form two superclasses: the Pisces ("fishes") and the Tetrapoda ("four-footed" animals).

The Pisces group is made up of three classes: (1) the Agnatha ("jawless") fishes, which have true skeletons but no limbs or jaws — the best known representative, the lamprey, possessing a rasping set of files in a round sucker-like mouth; (2) the Chondrichthyes ("cartilage-fish"), with a skeleton of cartilage instead of bone, sharks being the most familiar example; and (3) the Osteichthyes, or "bony fishes."

The tetrapods, or four-footed animals, all of which breathe by

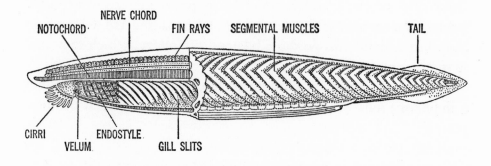

AMPHIOXUS, *a primitive, fishlike chordate with a notochord.*

means of lungs, make up four classes. The simplest are the Amphibia ("double life") — for example, the frogs and toads. The double life means that in their immature youth (*e.g.*, as tadpoles) they have no limbs and breathe by means of gills; then as adults they develop four feet and lungs. The amphibians, like fishes, lay their eggs in the water.

The second class are the Reptilia (from a Latin word meaning "creeping"). They include the snakes, lizards, alligators, and turtles. They breathe with lungs from birth, and hatch their eggs (enclosed in a hard shell) on land. The reptiles have an essentially four-chambered heart, whereas the amphibians' heart has three chambers and the fishes' heart only two.

The final two groups of tetrapods are the Aves (birds) and the Mammalia (mammals). All are warm-blooded: that is, their bodies possess devices which maintain an even internal temperature regardless of the temperature outside (within reasonable limits). Since the internal temperature is usually higher than the external, these animals require insulation. As aids to this end, the birds are equipped with feathers and the mammals with hair, serving to trap a layer of insulating air next to the skin. The birds lay eggs like those of reptiles. The mammals, of course, bring forth their young already "hatched" and supply them with milk produced by mammary glands (*mammae* in Latin).

In the nineteenth century zoologists heard reports of a great curiosity so amazing that they refused to believe it. The Australians had found a creature that had hair and produced milk yet laid eggs! Even when the zoologists were shown specimens of the animal (not living, unfortunately, because it is not easy to keep alive away from its natural habitat), they were inclined to brand it a clumsy fraud. The beast was a land-and-water animal that looked a good deal like a duck: it had a bill and webbed feet. Eventually the "duckbilled platypus" had to be recognized as a genuine phenomenon and a new kind of mammal. Another egg-laying mammal, the echidna, has since been found in Australia and New Guinea.

So the mammals are now divided into three subclasses. These egg-

661

laying mammals form the first class, Prototheria (Greek for "first beasts"). The embryo in the egg is actually pretty well developed by the time the egg is laid, and it hatches out not long afterward. The second subclass of mammals, Metatheria ("mid-beasts"), includes the opossums and kangaroos. Their young, though born alive, are in a very undeveloped form and will die in short order unless they managed to reach the mother's protective pouch and stay at the mammary nipples until they are strong enough to move about. These animals are called "marsupials" (from *marsupium*, Latin for pouch).

Finally, at the top of the mammalian hierarchy, we come to the subclass Eutheria ("true beasts"). Their distinguishing feature is the placenta, a blood-suffused tissue which enables the mother to supply the embryo with food and oxygen and carry off its wastes, so that she can develop the offspring for a long period inside her body (nine months in the case of the human being, two years in the case of elephants and whales). The eutherians are usually referred to as "placental mammals."

The placental mammals are divided into well over a dozen orders, of which the following are examples:

Insectivora ("insect-eating") — shrews, moles, and others.

Chiroptera ("hand-wings") — the bats.

Carnivora ("meat-eating") — the cat family, the dog family, weasels, bears, seals, and so on, but not including man.

Rodentia ("gnawing") — mice, rats, rabbits, squirrels, guinea pigs, beavers, porcupines, and so on.

Edentata ("toothless") — the sloths and armadillos, which have teeth, and anteaters, which do not.

Artiodactyla ("even toes") — hoofed animals with an even number of toes on each foot, such as cattle, sheep, goats, swine, deer, antelopes, camels, giraffes, and so on.

Perissodactyla ("odd-toes") — horses, donkeys, zebras, rhinoceroses, and tapirs.

Proboscidea ("long nose") — the elephants, of course, among others.

Odontoceti ("toothed whales") — the sperm whale and others with teeth.

Mysticeti ("mustached whales") — the right whale, the blue whale, and others that filter their small sea-food through fringes of whalebone that look like a colossal mustache inside the mouth.

Primates ("first") — man, apes, monkeys, and a number of creatures with which man may be surprised to find himself associated.

The primates are characterized by hands and sometimes feet that are equipped for grasping, with opposable thumbs and big toes. The digits are tipped with flattened nails rather than with sharp claws or enclosing hooves. The brain is enlarged, and the sense of vision is more important than the sense of smell. There are many other, less obvious, anatomical criteria.

The primates are divided into some nine families. Some have so few primate characteristics that it is hard to think of them as primates, but so they must be classed. One is the family Tupaiidae, which includes the insect-eating tree-shrews! Then there are the lemurs — nocturnal, tree-living creatures with fox-like muzzles and a rather squirrely appearance, found particularly in Madagascar.

The families closest to man are, of course, the monkeys and apes. There are three families of monkeys (a word possibly derived from the Latin *homunculus*, meaning "little man").

The two monkey families in the Americas, known as the "new-world monkeys," are the Cebidae (*e.g.*, the organ-grinder's monkey) and the Callithricidae (*e.g.*, the marmoset). The third, the "old-world" family, are the Cercopithecidae; they include the various baboons.

The apes all belong to one family, called Pongidae. They are native to the Eastern Hemisphere. Their most noticeable outward differences from the monkeys are, of course, their larger size and their lack of tails. The apes fall into four types: the gibbon, smallest, hairiest, longest-armed, and most primitive of the family; the orang-utan, larger, but also a tree-liver like the gibbon; the gorilla, rather larger than a man, mainly ground-dwelling, and a native of Africa;

and the chimpanzee, also a dweller in Africa, rather smaller than a man and the most intelligent primate next to man himself.

As for our own family, Hominidae, it consists today of only one genus, and as a matter of fact, only one species. Linnaeus named the species *Homo sapiens* ("man the wise"), and no one has dared change the name, despite provocation.

EVOLUTION

IT IS ALMOST IMPOSSIBLE to run down the roster of living things, as we have just done, without ending with a strong impression that there has been a slow development of life from the very simple to the complex. The phyla can be arranged so that each seems to add something to the one before. Within each phylum, the various classes can be arranged likewise, and within each class the orders.

Furthermore, the species often seem to melt together, as if they are still evolving along their slightly separate roads from common ancestors not very far in the past. Some species are so close together that under special circumstances they will interbreed, as in the case of the horse and donkey, which, by appropriate cooperation, can produce the mule. Cattle can interbreed with buffaloes, and lions with tigers. There are also intermediate species, so to speak — creatures that link together two larger groups of animals. The cheetah is a cat with a smattering of doggish characteristics, and the hyena is a dog with some cattish characteristics. The platypus is a mammal only half-way removed from a reptile. There is a creature called "peripatus" which seems half worm, half centipede. The dividing lines become particularly thin when we look at certain animals in their youthful stages. The infant frog seems to be a fish, and there is a primitive chordate called "balanoglossus" which as a youngster is so like a young echinoderm that at first it was so classified.

We can trace practically a re-enactment of the passage through the phyla even in the development of a human being from the fertilized egg. It starts as a single cell (a kind of protozoon), then becomes a small colony of cells (as in a sponge), each of which at first is capable of separating and starting life on its own, as happens when identical twins develop. The developing embryo passes through a two-layered stage (like a coelenterate), then adds a third layer (like an echinoderm), and so it continues to add complexities in roughly the order that the higher and higher species do. The human embryo has at some stage in its development the notochord of a primitive chordate, later gill pouches reminiscent of a fish, and still later the tail and body hair of a lower mammal.

From Aristotle on, many men speculated on the possibility that organisms had evolved from one another. But as Christianity grew in power, such speculations were discouraged. The first chapter of Genesis in the Bible stated flatly that each living thing was created "after his kind," and, taken literally, this had to mean that the species were "immutable" and had had the same form from the very beginning. Even Linnaeus, who must have been struck by the apparent kinships among living things, insisted firmly on the immutability of species.

The literal story of Creation, strong as its hold was on the minds of men, eventually had to yield to the evidence of the "fossils" (from the Latin word meaning "to dig"). These petrified remnants of once living things were often found buried so deeply under layers of rock that they had to be older than the few thousand years that had elapsed since the Creation. Moreover, on close inspection many of the fossil organisms turned out to be different from any living species. John Ray, the early classifier, wondered if they might represent extinct species. A Swiss naturalist named Charles Bonnet went farther. In 1770 he suggested that fossils were indeed remnants of extinct species which had been destroyed in ancient geological catastrophes going back to long before the Flood.

It was an English land-surveyor named William Smith who laid a scientific foundation for the study of fossils ("paleontology"). While working on excavations for a canal in 1791, he was impressed by the fact that the rock through which the canal was being cut was marked by clearly defined layers (strata), and that each stratum contained its own characteristic fossils. It now became possible to put fossils in a chronological order, depending on their place in the series of successive layers, and to associate each fossil with a particular type of rock stratum which would represent a certain period in geological history.

About 1800, Cuvier (the man who invented the notion of the "phylum") classified fossils according to the Linnaean system. Although many were of species and genera not found among living creatures, all fitted neatly into one or another of the known phyla and so made up an integral part of the scheme of life. Furthermore, the older the fossil, the simpler and less highly developed it seemed. Not only that, but fossils sometimes represented intermediate forms connecting two groups of creatures which, as far as living forms were concerned, seemed entirely separate. A particularly startling example, discovered after Cuvier's time, is a very primitive bird called Archaeopteryx (Greek for "ancient wing"). This now-extinct creature had wings and feathers, but it also had a lizard-like tail and a beak that contained reptilian teeth! In these and other respects it was clearly midway between a reptile and a bird.

Cuvier still supposed that terrestrial catastrophes, rather than evolution, had been responsible for the disappearance of the extinct forms of life, but in the 1830's Charles Lyell's new view of fossils and geological history in his history-making work *The Principles of Geology* killed "catastrophism" deader than a doornail (see Chapter 3). Some reasonable theory of evolution became a necessity, if any sense at all was to be made of the paleontological evidence.

If animals had evolved from one form to another, what had caused them to do so? This was the main stumbling block in the efforts to explain the varieties of life. The first to attempt an explanation was the French naturalist Jean Baptiste de Lamarck. In 1809 he published a book, entitled *Zoological Philosophy*, in which he suggested that the environment caused organisms to acquire small changes which were then passed on to their descendants. Lamarck

FOSSIL OF A CRINOID, *or sea lily, a primitive animal of the echinoderm superphylum. This specimen was found in Indiana.*

A palm-leaf fossil, *found in Colorado.*

FOSSIL OF A BRYOZOAN, *a tiny, mosslike water animal, here magnified about 20 times. It was brought up from an oil drill-hole on Cape Hatteras.*

FOSSIL OF A FORAMINIFER, *also found in a Cape Hatteras drill-hole. Chalk and some limestones are composed mainly of the shells of these microscopic, one-celled animals.*

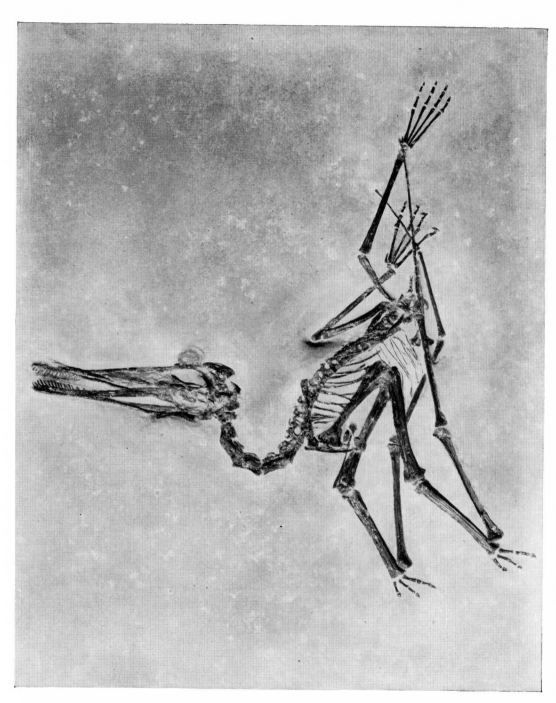

SKELETON OF A PTERODACTYL, *an extinct flying reptile.*

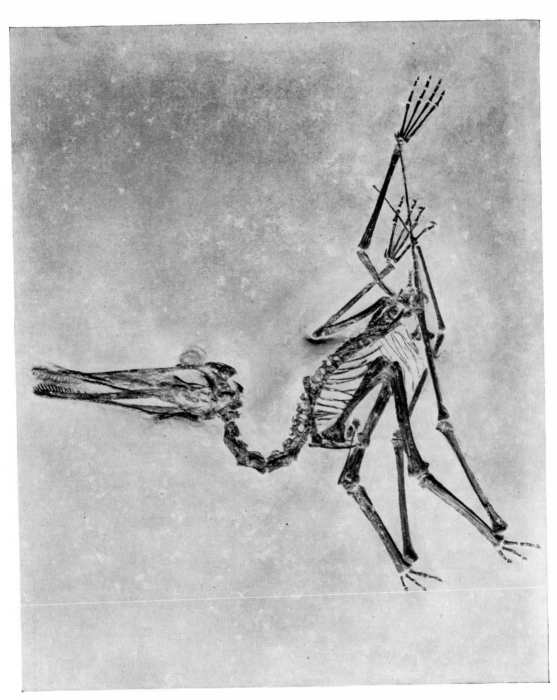

SKELETON OF A PTERODACTYL, *an extinct flying reptile.*

MODEL OF AN EXTINCT LUNG-FISH *found in Germany. The lung-fishes, living in tidal waters, were forerunners of the land animals.*

CAST OF A COELACANTH. *This ancient fish was found still living in deep water near Madagascar.*

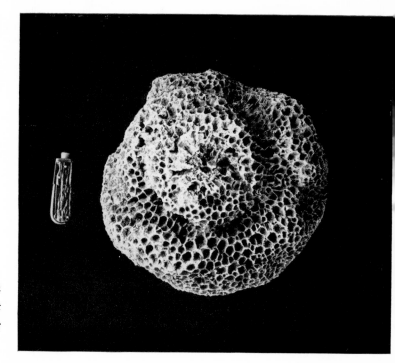

FOSSIL OF A CORAL, *an ancient coelenterate that lived in the sea. This was found in Indiana.*

A FOSSILIZED FISH.

Fossil of a trilobite, *a long-extinct sea arthropod of the Paleozoic era, whose name comes from the fact that it was divided into three lobes. The specimen was found in Vermont.*

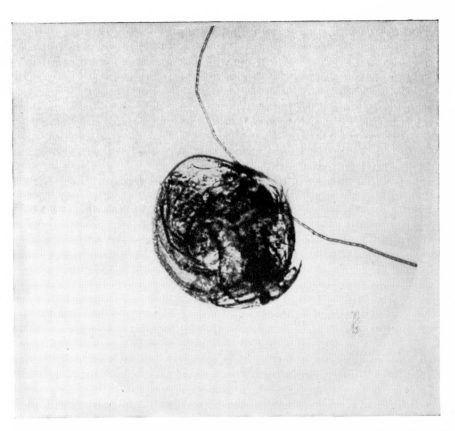

A 3,000-YEAR-OLD CRUSTACEAN. *It was found in a frozen deposit and revived on being thawed, according to Soviet paleontologists.*

AN ANCIENT ANT *delicately preserved in amber.*

FOSSIL OF A BRYOZOAN, *a tiny, mosslike water animal, here magnified about 20 times. It was brought up from an oil drill-hole on Cape Hatteras.*

FOSSIL OF A FORAMINIFER, *also found in a Cape Hatteras drill-hole. Chalk and some limestones are composed mainly of the shells of these microscopic, one-celled animals.*

ARCHAEOPTERYX.

illustrated his idea with the giraffe (a newly discovered sensation of the time). Suppose that a primitive, antelope-like creature that fed on tree leaves ran out of food within easy reach and had to stretch its neck as far as it could to get more food. By habitual stretching of its neck, tongue, and legs, it would gradually lengthen those append-ages. It would then pass on these developed characteristics to its offspring, which in turn would stretch further and pass on a still longer neck to its descendants, and so on. Little by little, by genera-tion after generation of stretching, the primitive antelope would evolve into a giraffe.

Lamarck's notion of the "inheritance of acquired characteristics" quickly ran afoul of difficulties. How had the giraffe developed its blotched coat, for instance? Surely no action on its part, deliberate or otherwise, could have effected this change. Furthermore, a skep-tical experimenter cut off the tails of mice for generation after gen-eration and reported that the last generation grew tails not one whit shorter than the first. (He might have saved himself the trouble by considering the case of the circumcision of Jewish males, which after more than a hundred generations had produced no shriveling of the foreskin.)

Despite its rejection by most biologists, Lamarckism lingered on into the twentieth century and even had a strong but apparently temporary revival in the form of Lysenkoism (hereditary modification of plants by certain treatments) in the Soviet Union. Modern geneticists do not exclude the possibility that the action of the environment may bring about certain transmittable changes in simple organisms, but the Lamarckian idea as such was demolished by the discovery of genes and the laws of heredity.

In 1831 a young Englishman named Charles Darwin, a dilettante and sportsman who had spent a more or less idle youth and was restlessly looking for something to do to overcome his boredom, was persuaded by a ship captain and a Cambridge professor to sign on as naturalist on a ship setting off on a five-year voyage around the world. The expedition was to study continental coastlines and make observations of flora and fauna along the way. Darwin, aged 22, made the voyage of the *Beagle* the most important sea-voyage in the history of science.

As the ship sailed slowly down the east coast of South America and then up its west coast, Darwin painstakingly collected information on the various forms of plant and animal life. His most striking discovery came in a group of islands in the Pacific, about 650 miles west of Ecuador, called the Galapagos Islands because of giant tortoises living on them (Galapagos coming from the Spanish word for tortoise). What attracted Darwin's attention was the variety of finches on the islands; they are known as "Darwin's finches" to this day. He found the birds divided into at least 14 different species, distinguished from one another mainly by differences in the size and shape of their bills. These particular species did not exist anywhere else in the world, but they resembled an apparently close relative on the South American mainland.

What accounted for the special character of the finches on these islands? Why did they differ from ordinary finches, and why were they themselves divided into no fewer than 14 species? Darwin decided that the most reasonable theory was that all of them were descended from the mainland type of finch and had differentiated during long isolation on the islands. The differentiation had resulted from varying methods of obtaining food. Three of the Galapagos species still fed on seeds, as the mainland finch did, but each ate a different kind of seed and varied correspondingly in size, one species being rather large, one medium, and one small. Two other species fed on cacti; most of the others fed on insects.

The problem of the changes in the finches' eating habits and physical characteristics preyed on Darwin's mind for many years. In 1838 he began to get a glimmering of the answer on reading a book that had been published 40 years before by an English clergyman named Thomas Robert Malthus. It was entitled *An Essay on the Principle of Population*, and in it Malthus maintained that a population always outgrew its food supply, so that eventually starvation, disease or war cut it back. Thinking of his finches, Darwin at once realized that competition for food would act as a mechanism favoring the more efficient ones. When the finches that had colonized the Galapagos multiplied to the point of outrunning the seed supply, only the stronger birds or those particularly adept at obtaining seeds or those able to get new kinds of food would survive. A bird that happened to be equipped with slight variations of the finch characteristics which enabled it to eat bigger seeds or tougher seeds or, better still, insects, would find an untapped food supply. A bird with a slightly thinner and longer bill could reach food that others could not, or one with an unusually massive bill could use otherwise unusable food. Such birds, and their descendants, would gain in numbers at the expense of the original variety of finch. Each of the adaptive types would find and fill a new, unoccupied niche in the environment. On the Galapagos Islands, virtually empty of bird life to begin with, all sorts of niches were there for the taking, with no established competitors to bar the way. On the South American

669

mainland, with all the niches occupied, the ancestral finch did well merely to hold its own. It proliferated into no further species.

Darwin suggested that every generation of animals was composed of an array of individuals varying randomly from the average. Some would be slightly larger; some would possess organs of slightly altered shape; some abilities would be a trifle above or below normal. The differences might be minute, but those whose makeup was even slightly better suited to the environment would tend to live slightly longer and have more offspring. Eventually an accumulation of favorable characteristics might be coupled with an inability to breed with the original type or other variations of it, and thus a new species would be born.

Darwin called this process "natural selection." According to his view, the giraffe got its long neck not by stretching but because some giraffes were born with longer necks than their fellows, and the longer the neck, the more chance a giraffe had of reaching food. By natural selection, the long-necked species won out. Natural selection explained the giraffe's blotched coat just as easily: an animal with blotches on its skin would blend against the sun-spotted vegetation and thus have more chance of escaping the attention of a prowling lion.

Darwin's view of the way in which species were formed also made clear why it was often so difficult to make clear-cut distinctions between species or between genera. The evolution of species is a continuous process, and, of course, takes a very long time. There must be any number of species with members which are even now slowly drifting apart into separate species.

Darwin spent many years collecting evidence and working out his theory. He realized that it would shake the foundations of biology and man's thinking about his own place in the scheme of things, and he wanted to be sure of his ground in every possible respect. Darwin started his book on the theory of evolution by natural selection in 1844, and in 1858 he was still working on it. His friends (including Lyell, the geologist) knew what he was working on and several had read his preliminary drafts. They urged him to hurry, lest he be anticipated. Darwin wouldn't (or couldn't) hurry, and he *was* anticipated.

The man who anticipated him was Alfred Russel Wallace, 14 years younger than Darwin. Wallace's life paralleled that of Darwin. He, too, went on an around-the-world scientific expedition as a young man. In the East Indies, he noticed that the plants and animals in the eastern islands were completely different from those in the western islands. A sharp line could be drawn between the two types of life-forms; it ran between Borneo and Celebes, for instance, and between the small islands of Bali and Lombok farther to the south. The line is still called "Wallace's Line."

Now the mammals in the eastern islands and in Australia were distinctly more primitive than those in the western islands and Asia, or indeed in the rest of the world. It looked as if Australia and the eastern islands had split off from Asia at some early time when only primitive mammals existed, and the placental mammals had developed later only in Asia. New Zealand must have been isolated even longer, for it lacked mammals altogether and was inhabited by primitive flightless birds, of which the best-known survivor today is the kiwi.

How had the higher mammals in Asia arisen? Wallace first began puzzling over this in 1855, and in 1858 he, too, came across Malthus's book and from it, he, too, drew the conclusions Darwin had drawn. But Wallace did not spend 14 years writing his conclusions. Once the idea was clear in his mind, he sat down and wrote a paper on it in two days. Wallace decided to send his manuscript to some well-known competent biologist for criticism and review, and he chose Charles Darwin.

When Darwin received the manuscript, he was thunderstruck. It expressed his own thoughts in almost his own terms. At once he passed Wallace's paper to other important scientists and offered to collaborate with Wallace on reports summarizing their joint conclusions. Their reports appeared in the *Journal of the Linnaean Society* in 1858.

The next year Darwin's book was finally published. Its full title is "On the Origin of Species by Means of Natural Selection, or the Preservation of Favoured Races in the Struggle for Life." We know it simply as *The Origin of Species.*

The theory of evolution has been modified and sharpened since Darwin's time, through knowledge of the mechanism of inheritance, of genes, and of mutations (see Chapter 12). But his basic conception of evolution by natural selection has stood firm, and indeed the evolutionary idea has been extended to every field of science — physical, biological, and social.

THE ANNOUNCEMENT of the Darwinian theory naturally blew up a storm. The Fundamentalists (literal interpreters of the Bible) were outraged by the implication that man might be a mere descendent from an apelike ancestor. Benjamin Disraeli (later to be Prime Minister of Great Britain) created an immortal phrase by remarking acidly: "The question now placed before society is this, 'Is man an ape or an angel?' I am on the side of the angels." Churchmen, rallying to the angels' defense, carried the attack to Darwin.

Darwin himself was not equipped by temperament to enter violently into the controversy, but he had an able champion in the eminent biologist Thomas Henry Huxley. As "Darwin's bulldog," Huxley fought the battle tirelessly in the lecture halls of England. He won his most telling victory almost at the very beginning of the struggle, in the famous debate with Samuel Wilberforce, a bishop of the Anglican Church, a mathematician, and so accomplished and glib a speaker that he was familiarly known as "Soapy Sam."

Bishop Wilberforce, after apparently having won the audience, turned at last to his solemn, humorless adversary. As the report of the debate quotes him, Wilberforce "begged to know whether it was through his grandfather or his grandmother that [Huxley] claimed his descent from a monkey."

While the audience roared with glee, Huxley rose slowly to his feet and answered: "If, then, the question is put to me, would I rather have a miserable ape for a grandfather, or a man highly endowed by nature and possessing great means and influence, and yet who employs those faculties and that influence for the mere purpose of introducing ridicule into a grave scientific discussion — I unhesitatingly affirm my preference for the ape."

Huxley's smashing return apparently not only crushed Wilberforce but also put the Fundamentalists on the defensive.

Another powerful proponent of evolutionary ideas was the English philosopher Herbert Spencer, who popularized the phrase "survival of the fittest" and the word "evolution" — a word Darwin himself rarely used. Spencer tried to apply the theory of evolution to the development of human societies (he is considered the founder of the science of sociology). His arguments, contrary to his intention, were later misused to support war and racism.

The last open battle against evolution took place in 1925; it ended with the anti-evolutionists winning the battle and losing the war.

The Tennessee legislature had passed a law forbidding teachers in publicly-supported schools of the state from teaching that man had evolved from lower forms of life. To challenge the law's constitutionality, scientists and educators persuaded a young high-school biology teacher named John T. Scopes to tell his class about Darwinism. Scopes was thereupon charged with violating the law and brought to trial in Dayton, Tenn., where he taught. The world gave fascinated attention to his trial.

The local population and the judge were solidly on the side of anti-evolution. William Jennings Bryan, the famous orator, three times unsuccessful candidate for the Presidency, and outstanding Fundamentalist, served as one of the prosecuting attorneys. Scopes had as his defenders the noted criminal lawyer Clarence Darrow and associated attorneys.

The trial was for the most part disappointing, for the judge refused to allow the defense to place scientists on the stand to testify to the evidence behind the Darwinian theory and restricted testimony to the question whether Scopes had or had not discussed evolution. But the issues nevertheless emerged in the courtroom when Bryan, over the protests of his fellow-prosecutors, volunteered to submit to cross-examination on the Fundamentalist position. Darrow promptly showed that Bryan was ignorant of modern developments in science and had only a stereotyped Sunday-school acquaintance with religion and the Bible.

Scopes was found guilty and fined $100. (The conviction was later reversed on technical grounds by the Tennessee Supreme Court). But the Fundamentalist position (and the state of Tennessee) had stood in so ridiculous a light in the eyes of the educated world that the anti-evolutionists have not made any serious stand since then — at least not in broad daylight.

A STUDY OF THE FOSSIL RECORD has enabled paleontologists to divide the history of the earth into a series of "eras." They start some five or six hundred million years ago with the first fossils (when all the phyla except Chordata were already established). The first fossils do not, of course, represent the first life. For the most part, it is only the hard portions of a creature that fossilize, so the clear fossil record contains only animals that possessed shells or bones. Even the simplest and oldest of these creatures are already far advanced and must have a long evolutionary background.

The broad divisions of geological time are the Paleozoic (Greek for "ancient life"), the Mesozoic ("middle life"), and the Cenozoic ("new life"). According to modern methods of geological dating, the Paleozoic era covered a span of perhaps 350 million years, the Mesozoic 150 million years, and the Cenozoic the last 50 million years of the earth's history.

Each era in turn is subdivided into ages. The Paleozoic begins with the Cambrian age (named for a location in Wales — actually an ancient tribe that occupied it — where these strata were first uncovered). During the Cambrian period shellfish were the highest form of life. The next age is the Ordovician (another Welsh tribe); this was the time when the chordates made their first appearance. Then came the Silurian (still another Welsh tribe) and the Devonian (from Devonshire). The Devonian was the age of fishes. It was also the period when life first invaded the land.

The move toward the land probably began as competition for

food in the crowded sea drove some organisms into shallow tidal waters, up to then unoccupied because the bottom was exposed for hours at a time at low tide. As more and more species crowded into the tide-waters, relief from competition could be attained only by moving farther and farther up the shore, until eventually some mutant organisms were able to establish themselves on dry land.

The first life forms to manage the transition were plants. This took place about 350 million years ago. The pioneers belonged to a now extinct plant group called "psilopsids" — the first multicellular plants. Once plant life had begun to grow on dry land, animal life could follow suit. Within a few million years the land was occupied by arthropods, molluscs, and worms. All these first land animals were small, because heavier animals, without an internal skeleton, would have collapsed under the force of gravity. (In the ocean, of course, buoyancy largely negated gravity, which was not therefore a factor. Even today the largest animals live in the sea.) The first land creatures to gain much mobility were the insects; thanks to their development of wings, they were able to counteract the force of gravity, which held other animals to a slow crawl.

Finally, a hundred million years after the first invasion of the land, there came a new invasion by creatures that could afford to be bulky despite gravity because they had a bracing of bone within. The new colonizers from the sea were bony fishes belonging to the subclass Crossopterygii ("fringed-fins"). Some of their fellow members had migrated to the uncrowded sea deeps; among them was the coelacanth, which biologists recently found to their amazement is still in existence. The crossopterygians that moved on to the land managed the trick by developing a primitive lung in place of the swim-bladder, an air-filled organ used by fishes for buoyancy. Some evolved into "lung-fishes," a few species of which still exist in Africa and Australia. These live in stagnant water where ordinary fishes would suffocate, and they can even survive summer droughts when their habitat dries up. By the end of the Devonian era some of the primitive-lunged crossopterygians found themselves standing on the dry land, propped up shakily on four stubby legs.

675

After the Devonian came the Carboniferous ("coal-bearing") age, so named by Lyell because it was the period of the vast, swampy forests that eventually were buried and became coal beds. This was the age of the amphibians; the crossopterygians by then were spending their entire adult lives on land. Next came the Permian age (named for a district in the Urals). The first reptiles now made their appearance. They ushered in the Mesozoic era, in which reptiles were to dominate the earth so thoroughly that it has become known as the age of the reptiles.

The Mesozoic is divided into three ages — the Triassic (it was found in three strata), the Jurassic (from the Jura mountains in France), and the Cretaceous ("chalk-forming"). In the Triassic arose the dinosaurs (Greek for "terrible lizards"). The dinosaurs reached their peak form in the Cretaceous, when *Tyranossaurus rex* thundered over the land — the largest carnivorous land animal in the history of our planet.

It was during the Jurassic that the earliest mammals and birds developed, each from a separate group of reptiles. For millions of years these creatures remained inconspicuous and unsuccessful. With the end of the Cretaceous, however, the gigantic reptiles began to disappear, perhaps killed off by some vast climatic change, and the mammals and birds came into their own. The Cenozoic era that followed became the age of mammals; it brought in placental mammals and the world we know.

THE UNITY OF PRESENT LIFE is demonstrated in part by the fact that all organisms are composed of proteins built from the same amino acids. The same kind of evidence has recently established our unity with the past as well. Biochemists at the Carnegie Institution in Washington showed that certain 300-million-year-old fossils contained remnants of proteins consisting of precisely the same amino acids that make up proteins today. Not one of the ancient amino acids differed from present ones.

From our knowledge of biochemistry we can deduce some of the biochemical changes that may have played a part in the evolution of animals.

Let's take the excretion of nitrogenous wastes. Apparently the simplest way to get rid of nitrogen is to excrete it in the form of the small ammonia molecule (NH_3), which can easily pass through cell membranes into the blood. Ammonia happens to be extremely poisonous; if its concentration in the blood exceeds one part in a million, the organism will die. But for a sea animal this is no great problem; it can discharge the ammonia into the ocean continuously through its gills. For a land animal, however, the ammonia method is out of the question. To discharge ammonia as quickly as it is formed would require such an excretion of urine that the animal would quickly be dehydrated and die. Therefore a land organism must produce its nitrogenous wastes in a less toxic form than ammonia. The answer is urea. This substance can be carried in the blood in concentrations up to one part in a thousand without serious danger.

Now fish eliminate nitrogenous wastes as ammonia, and so do tadpoles. But when a tadpole matures to a frog, it begins to eliminate nitrogenous wastes as urea. This change in the chemistry of the organism is every bit as crucial for the changeover from life in the water to life on land as is the visible change from gills to lungs.

Such a biochemical change must have taken place when the cross opterygians invaded the land and became amphibians. Thus there is every reason to believe that biochemical evolution played as great a part in the development of organisms as "morphological" evolution (that is, changes in form and structure).

Another biochemical change was necessary before the great step from amphibian to reptile could be taken. If the embryo in a reptile's egg excreted urea, it would build up to toxic concentrations in the limited quantity of water within the egg. The change that took care of this problem was the formation of uric acid instead of urea. Uric acid (a purine molecule resembling the adenine and guanine that occur in nucleic acids) is insoluble in water; it is therefore precipitated in the form of small granules and thus cannot enter the cells.

677

This changeover from urea excretion to uric-acid excretion was as essential in the development of reptiles as was the changeover, for instance, from a three-chambered heart to an essentially four-chambered one.

In adult life, reptiles continue eliminating nitrogenous wastes as uric acid. They have no urine in the liquid sense. Instead, the uric acid is eliminated as a semi-solid mass through the same body opening that serves for the elimination of feces. This single body opening is called the "cloaca" (Latin for "sewer").

Birds and egg-laying mammals, which lay eggs of the reptilian type, preserve the uric-acid mechanism and the cloaca. In fact, the egg-laying mammals are often called "monotremes" (from Greek words meaning "one hole").

Placental mammals, on the other hand, can easily wash away the embryo's nitrogenous wastes, for the embryo is connected to the mother's circulatory system. Mammalian embryos, therefore, make do nicely with urea. It is dumped into the mother's bloodstream and passes out through the mother's kidneys.

An adult mammal has to excrete substantial amounts of urine to get rid of its urea. This calls for two separate openings: an anus to eliminate the indigestible solid residues of food and a urethral opening for the liquid urine.

Other facets of biochemical evolution have been worked out in recent years, and so far all the deductions based upon biochemistry have agreed with those arrived at independently by the students of morphological evolution.

THE DESCENT OF MAN

JAMES USSHER, a seventeenth-century Irish archbishop, dated the creation of man precisely in the year 4004 B.C.

Before Darwin, few men dared to question the Biblical interpretation of man's early history. The earliest reasonably definite date to which the events recorded in the Bible can be referred is the reign of Saul, the first king of Israel, who is believed to have become king about 1025 B.C. (I *Samuel* 10–31). Bishop Ussher and other Biblical scholars who worked back through the chronology of the Bible came to the conclusion that man and the Universe could not be more than a few thousand years old.

The documented history of man, as recorded by Greek historians, began only about 700 B.C. Beyond this hard core of history, dim oral traditions went back to the Trojan War, about 1200 B.C., and more dimly to a pre-Greek civilization on the island of Crete under a King Minos.

At the beginning of the nineteenth century, archaeologists began to get their first glimpses of human civilizations that came before the periods described by the Greek and Hebrew historians. In 1799, during General Bonaparte's invasion of Egypt, an officer in his army, named Boussard, discovered an inscribed stone in the town of Rosetta, on one of the mouths of the Nile. The slab of black basalt had three inscriptions, one in Greek, one in an ancient form of Egyptian picture writing called "hieroglyphic" ("sacred writing"), and one in a simplified form of Egyptian writing called "demotic" ("of the people").

The inscription in Greek was a routine decree of the time of Ptolemy V, dated the equivalent of March 27, 196 B.C. Plainly it must be a translation of the same decree given in the other two languages on the slab (compare the no-smoking signs and other official notices that often appear in three languages in public places, especially airports, today). Archaeologists were overjoyed: at last they had a "pony" with which to decipher the previously undecipherable Egyptian scripts. It fell to the lot of a French student of antiquities, Jean François Champollion, to solve the "Rosetta stone." He made the guess that Coptic, a still remembered language of certain Christian sects in Egypt, could be used as a guide to the ancient Egyptian language. By 1821 he had cracked the hieroglyphs and the demotic script and opened the way to reading all the inscriptions found in the ruins of ancient Egypt.

An almost identical find later broke the undeciphered writing of ancient Mesopotamia. On a high cliff near the ruined village of Behistun in western Iran, scholars found an inscription that had been carved about 520 B.C. at the order of the Persian emperor Darius I. It announced the manner in which he had come to the throne after defeating a usurper, and to make sure that everyone could read it, Darius had had it carved in three languages — Persian, Sumerian and Babylonian. The Sumerian and Babylonian writings were based on pictographs formed by indenting clay with a stylus; these had developed into a "cuneiform" ("wedge-shaped") script.

An English army officer, Henry Creswicke Rawlinson, climbed the cliff, transcribed the entire inscription and, by 1846, after ten years of work, managed to work out a complete translation, using local dialects as his guide where necessary. The decipherment of the cuneiform scripts made it possible to read the history of the ancient civilizations between the Tigris and the Euphrates.

Expedition after expedition was sent to Egypt and Mesopotamia to look for tablets and the remains of the ancient civilizations. In 1854 a Turkish scholar, Hurmuzd Rassam, discovered the remnants of a library of clay tablets in the ruins of Nineveh, the capital of ancient Assyria — a library that had been collected by the last great Assyrian king, Asshurbanipal, about 650 B.C. In 1873 the English Assyriologist George Smith discovered clay tablets giving legendary accounts of a Flood so like the story of Noah that it became clear that much of the first part of the book of Genesis was based on Babylonian legend. Presumably the Jews picked up the legends during their Babylonian captivity in the time of Nebuchadrezzar, a century after the time of Asshurbanipal.

Yet Egypt and Mesopotamia were not quite in the same league with Greece when it came to dramatic finds on the origins of modern Western culture. Perhaps the most exciting moment in the history of archaeology came in 1873 when a German ex-grocer's boy found the most famous of all legendary cities.

Heinrich Schliemann as a boy developed a mania for Homer. Although most historians regarded the *Iliad* as mythology, Schliemann lived and dreamed of the Trojan War. He decided that he must find

Troy, and by nearly superhuman exertions he raised himself from grocer's boy to millionaire so that he could finance the quest. In 1868, at the age of 46, he set forth. He persuaded the Turkish government to give him permission to dig in Asia Minor; following only the meager geographical clues afforded by Homer's accounts, he finally settled upon a mound near the village of Hissarlik. He browbeat the local population into helping him dig into the mound. Excavating in a completely amateurish and unscientific manner, he began to uncover a series of buried ancient cities, each built on the ruins of the other. And then, at last, success: he uncovered Troy — or at least a city he proclaimed as Troy. Actually the particular ruins he named Troy are now known to be far older than Homer's Troy, but Schliemann had proved that Homer's tales were not mere legends.

Inexpressibly excited by his triumph, Schliemann went on to mainland Greece and began to dig at the site of Mycenae, a ruined village which Homer had decribed as the once powerful city of Agamemnon, leader of the Greeks in the Trojan War. Again he uncovered an astounding find — the ruins of a city with gigantic walls which we now know to date back to 1500 B.C.

Schliemann's successes prompted the British archaeologist Arthur John Evans to start digging on the island of Crete, described in Greek legends as the site of a powerful early city under a King Minos. Evans, exploring the island in the 1890's, laid bare a brilliant, lavishly ornamented "Minoan" civilization which stretched back many centuries before the time of Homer's Greece. Here, too, written tablets were found. They were in two different scripts, one of which, called "Linear B," was finally deciphered in the 1950's through a remarkable feat of cryptography and linguistic analysis by a young English architect named Michael Vestris.

As other early civilizations were uncovered — the Hittites and the Mittanni in Asia Minor, the Indus civilization in India, and so on — it became obvious that the history recorded by Greece's Herodotus and the Hebrews' Old Testament represented comparatively advanced stages of human civilization. Man's earliest cities were at least several thousand years old, and his prehistoric existence in less civilized modes of life must stretch back far into the past.

ANTHROPOLOGISTS FIND IT CONVENIENT to divide cultural history into three major periods: the Stone Age, the Bronze Age, and the Iron Age (a division first suggested by the Roman poet and philosopher Lucretius). The Bronze and Iron ages are, of course, very recent; as soon as we delve into the time before written history, we are back in the Stone Age. What we call civilization (from the Latin word for "city") began perhaps around 6000 B.C., when man first turned from hunting to agriculture, learned to domesticate animals, invented pottery and new types of tools, and started to develop permanent communities and a settled way of life. Because the archaeological remains from this period of transition are marked by advanced stone tools formed in new ways, it is called the New Stone Age, or the "Neolithic" period.

This Neolithic Revolution seems to have started in the Near East, at the crossroads of Europe, Asia, and Africa (where later the Bronze and Iron ages also were to originate). From there, it appears, the revolution slowly spread in widening waves to the rest of the world. It did not reach western Europe and India until 3000 B.C., northern Europe and eastern Asia until 2000 B.C., and central Africa and Japan until perhaps 1000 B.C. or later. And southern Africa and Australia remained in the Old Stone Age stage until the eighteenth and nineteeth centuries. Most of America also was still in the hunting phase when the Europeans arrived in the sixteenth century, although a well-developed civilization, possibly originated by the Mayas, had developed in Central America and Peru as early as the first centuries of the Christian era.

Evidences of man's pre-Neolithic cultures began to come to light in Europe at the end of the eighteenth century. In 1797 an Englishman named John Frere dug up in Suffolk some crudely-fashioned flint tools too primitive to have been made by Neolithic man. They were found 13 feet underground, which, allowing for the normal rate of sedimentation, testified to great age. In the same stratum with the tools were bones of extinct animals. More and more signs of the great antiquity of tool-making man were discovered, notably by two nineteenth-century French archeologists, Jacques Boucher de Perthes and Edouard Armand Lartet. Lartet, for instance, found a mammoth-tooth on which some early man had scratched an excellent drawing of the mammoth, obviously from living models. The mammoth was a hairy species of elephant that disappeared from the earth well before the beginning of the New Stone Age.

Archaeologists launched upon an active search for early stone tools. They found that these could be assigned to a relatively short Middle Stone Age ("Mesolithic") and a long Old Stone Age ("Paleolithic"). The Paleolithic was divided into Lower, Middle, and Upper periods. The earliest objects that could be considered tools ("eoliths," or "dawn-stones") seemed to date back nearly a million years!

What sort of creature had made the Old Stone Age tools? It turned out that Paleolithic man, at least in his late stages, was far more than a hunting animal. In 1879 a Spanish nobleman, the Marquis de Sautuola, explored some caves he had just discovered at Altamira in northern Spain near the city of Santander. While he dug into the floor of a cave, his five-year old daughter, who had come along to watch papa dig, suddenly cried: *Toros! Toros!* ("Bulls! Bulls!"). The father looked up, and there on the walls of the cave were drawings of various animals, in vivid color and vigorous detail.

Anthropologists found it hard to believe that these sophisticated drawings could have been made by primitive man. But some of the pictured animals were plainly extinct types, and all the evidence finally forced them to conclude that the artists must have lived in the late Paleolithic, say about 10,000 B.C.

Something was already known about the physical appearance of these Paleolithic men. In 1868 workmen excavating a roadbed for a railroad had uncovered the skeletons of five human beings in the so-called Cro-Magnon caves in southwest France. The skeletons were unquestionably *Homo sapiens,* yet some of them, and similar skeletons soon found elsewhere, seemed to be up to 35,000 or 40,000 years old, according to the geological evidence. They were given the name "Cro-Magnon man." Taller than the average modern man and equipped with a large braincase, Cro-Magnon man is pictured by artists as a handsome, stalwart fellow, modern enough, it would certainly appear, to be able to interbreed with present-day human beings.

Homo sapiens, it seems, originated in the Upper Paleolithic. Up to that time man and his ancestors had been confined to Africa, Asia, and Europe, but now hunting bands began to migrate across the Bering Straits into the Americas (some time between 25000 and 15000 B.C.), into Australia, to the far-flung islands of the Pacific, and to all the habitable parts of the globe.

Thanks to a new dating technique, we can now give fairly definite dates to the remains and settlements of Upper Paleolithic man. Known as the carbon-dating method, it was originated in 1946 by the chemist Willard F. Libby (who was later appointed a member of the United States Atomic Energy Commission). Libby reasoned that radioactive carbon 14 created in the atmosphere by cosmic rays would enter all living tissue via carbon dioxide, first absorbed by plants and then passed on to animals. As long as a plant or animal lived, it would continue to receive radiocarbon and maintain it at a certain level in its tissues. But when the organism died and ceased to take in carbon dioxide, the radiocarbon in its tissues would begin to diminish by radioactive breakdown, at a rate determined by its 5,600-year half-life. Therefore any piece of preserved bone, any bit of charcoal from an ancient campfire, or organic remains of any kind could be dated by measuring the amount of radiocarbon left. The method is reasonably accurate for objects up to 30,000 years old, and this covers archaeological history from the ancient civilizations back to the beginnings of *Homo sapiens* as we know him.

Cro-Magnon was not the first early man dug up by the archaeologists. In 1857, in the Neanderthal valley of the German Rhineland, a digger discovered part of a skull and some long bones that looked human in the main but only crudely human. The skull had a sharply sloping forehead and very heavy brow ridges. Some archaeologists maintained that they were the remains of a human being whose bones had been deformed by disease, but as the years passed other such skeletons were found, and a detailed and consistent picture of Neanderthal man was developed. Neanderthal was a short, squat, stooping biped, the men averaging a little taller than five feet, the women somewhat shorter. The skull was roomy enough for a brain nearly as large as modern man's. Anthropological artists picture the creature as barrel-chested, hairy, beetle-browed, chinless, and brutish in expression. Actually he was probably not so inhuman as pictured. Give Neanderthal a shave and a haircut, dress him in well-fitted clothes, and he could probably walk down New York's Fifth Avenue without getting much notice.

Traces of Neanderthal man were eventually found not only in Europe but also in northern Africa, in Russia and Siberia, in Palestine, and in Iraq. And skeletal remains somewhat resembling Neanderthal were discovered in still more widely separated places; these were Rhodesian man, dug up in Rhodesia in southern Africa, and Solo man, found on the banks of the Solo River in Java. They were considered separate species of the genus Homo, and so the three types were named *Homo neanderthalensis, Homo rhodesiensis,* and *Homo solensis.* But some anthropologists and evolutionists maintain that all three should be placed in the same species as *Homo sapiens,* as "varieties" or "subspecies" of man. There were men that we call *sapiens* living at the same time as Neanderthal, and intermediate forms have been found which suggest that there may have been interbreeding between them. If Neanderthal and his cousins can be classed as *sapiens,* then our species is perhaps 200,000 years old. Another apparent relative of Neanderthal, "Heidelberg man" (of which only a jawbone has been discovered), is much older, and if we include him in our species, the history of *Homo sapiens* can be pushed even farther back. And indeed, at Swanscombe in England archaeologists have found skull fragments which seem to be definitely *sapiens* and to be vastly older than Neanderthal.

Darwin's *Origin of Species* of course launched a great hunt for man's ancestors — what the popular press came to call the "missing link" between man and his presumably apelike forerunners.

In the 1880's a Dutch paleontologist named Eugene Dubois got it into his head that the ancestors of man might be found in Java, where the great apes still flourished (and where he could work conveniently because Java belonged to the Netherlands). Surprisingly enough, Dubois did turn up a creature somewhere between an ape and a man! After three years of hunting, he found the top of a skull which was larger than an ape's but smaller than any recognized as human. The next year he found a similarly intermediate thighbone. Dubois named his "Java man" *Pithecanthropus erectus* ("erect ape-man"). Half a century later, in the 1930's, another Dutchman, G. H. R. von Koenigswald, discovered more bones of Pithecanthropus, and they composed a clear picture of a small-brained, very beetling-browed creature with a distant resemblance to Neanderthal.

Meanwhile other diggers had found in a cave near Peking skulls, jaws, and teeth of a primitive man called *Sinanthropus pekinensis* ("Chinese man of Peking"). The Peking man is considered by some to belong to the same genus as Java man but is more advanced, with a somewhat larger brain and more human teeth.

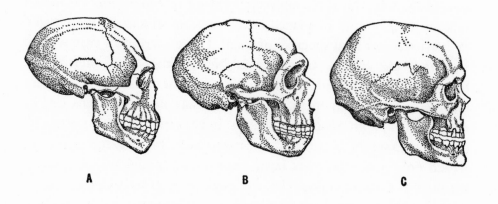

A   B   C

RECONSTRUCTED SKULLS *of* (A) *Pithecanthropus,* (B) *Neanderthal,* and (C) *Cro-Magnon man.*

But by far the most striking finds of the twentieth century are those made in Africa by two English scientists, Raymond Dart and Robert Broom. One spring day in 1924, workers blasting in a limestone quarry near Taungs in South Africa picked up a small skull that looked nearly human. They sent it to Dart, an anatomist working in Johannesburg. Dart immediately identified it as a being between an ape and a man, and he called it *Australopithecus africanus* ("southern ape of Africa"). When his paper announcing the find was published in London, anthropologists thought he had blundered, mistaking a chimpanzee for an ape-man. But Broom, an ardent fossil-hunter who had long been convinced that man originated in Africa, rushed to Johannesburg and proclaimed Australopithecus the closest thing to a missing link that had yet been discovered.

Through the following decades Dart, Broom, and several anthropologists searched for and found many more bones and teeth of the South African ape-man, as well as clubs that he used to kill game, the bones of animals that he killed, and caves in which he lived. Australopithecus was a short, small-brained creature with a snoutlike face, in many ways less human than Java man. But he had more human brows and more human teeth than Pithecanthropus. He walked erect, used tools, and probably had a primitive form of speech. In short, he was much closer to a man than to an ape. And he lived at least half a million years ago!

Where, then, is man's original ancestor — the primate from which the apes as well as man descended? So far back in time, undoubtedly, that it cannot be considered even vaguely human. There are fossil remnants of a small creature, about the size of a gibbon, which seems more human than does any existing ape. It is called Oreopithecus ("mountain ape"), and it may be about ten million years old. Possibly this is in the line from which all the pre-humans and humans descended. There are also fossils of a primitive ape called Proconsul, perhaps 25 million years old, which may represent the line of descent to the modern apes — chimpanzees, gorillas, and orang-utans. Farther back, then, there must be a common ancestor of Proconsul and

Oreopithecus. Such a true missing link would date back perhaps 40 million years.

FOR MANY YEARS anthropologists were greatly puzzled by a fossil that did look like a missing link, but of a curious and incredible kind. In 1911, near a place called Piltdown Common in Sussex, England, workmen building a road found an ancient, broken skull in a gravel bed. The skull came to the attention of a lawyer named Charles Dawson, and he took it to a paleontologist, Arthur Smith Woodward, at the British Museum. The skull was high-browed, with only slight brow ridges; it looked more modern than Neanderthal. Dawson and Woodward went searching in the gravel pit for other parts of the skeleton. One day Dawson, in Woodward's presence, came across a jawbone in about the place where the skull fragments had been found. It had the same reddish-brown hue as the other fragments, and therefore appeared to have come from the same head. But the jawbone, in contrast to the human upper skull, was like that of an ape! Equally strange, the teeth in the jaw, though apelike, were ground down as human teeth are by chewing.

Woodward decided that this half-ape, half-man might be an early creature with a well-developed brain and a backward jaw. He presented the find to the world as the "Piltdown Man," or *Eoanthropus dawsoni* ("Dawson's dawn-man").

Piltdown man became more and more of an anomaly as anthropologists found that in all other fossil finds that included the jaw, jawbone development did keep pace with skull development. Finally in the early 1950's three British scientists, Kenneth Oakley, W. E. Le Gros Clark, and J. S. Wiener, decided to investigate the possibility of fraud.

A close inspection of the teeth indicated that they had been ground down not by chewing but by a file. Their rust color turned out to be artificial; the bone surfaces had been dyed with potassium dichromate. The clinching evidence came when the investigators analyzed the fluorine and nitrogen content of the skull and the jawbone. Bones lying in the ground gradually accumulate fluorine from the ground water and lose nitrogen. The skull showed a fluorine and nitrogen content indicating it had been lying in the soil for perhaps 25,000 years. It was a true fossil, of *Homo sapiens*. But the jawbone had virtually no fluorine and a good deal of nitrogen. It had not been buried in the soil at all; it had been put there for Woodward and Dawson to find. The jawbone looked like a chimpanzee's because it was indeed a chimpanzee's.

The whole business had been a fake to take in Woodward. He died in 1944 and was fortunately spared the humiliation of the exposure. Perhaps Dawson had planted the jawbone (and other misleading evidences) to have some fun at Woodward's expense and then found himself too involved to back out. Dawson died in 1916, three years after the prank was perpetrated, leaving Piltdown Man to baffle and confuse anthropologists for more than a generation.

It is impossible to reconstruct any confident history of man's evolution on the basis of the few human fossils that have turned up. Anthropologists can only guess at some plausible hypotheses.

Perhaps something like a million years ago a manlike creature (as opposed to an advanced ape) arose somewhere in Africa or Asia and slowly spread over the Eastern Hemisphere. This early hominid may have given rise to a number of small-brained varieties, such as Australopithecus in Africa, Sinanthropus in east Asia, Pithecanthropus in Indonesia. One of the small-brained hominids in turn may have evolved, in different places, into different varieties of men — Rhodesian man, Solo man, Neanderthal man, and *Homo sapiens*. Neanderthal was long supposed to be the direct ancestor of *sapiens*, but this is now in considerable doubt; some remarkably modern-looking fossils seem to be at least as old as Neanderthal if not older. In any case, *sapiens* in the end was the sole successful survivor, and all the other varieties of hominids and men disappeared. Since his emergence as the dominant species of the earth, *sapiens* has undergone only minor differentiation into the varieties called "races."

MAN'S PRESENT AND FUTURE

EVER SINCE THE DAWN OF CIVILIZATION, men have been more or less acutely conscious of racial differences, and usually they have viewed other races with the emotions generally evoked by strangers, ranging from curiosity to contempt to hatred. But seldom has racism had such tragic and long-persisting results as the modern conflict between white men and Negroes.

It started in the fifteenth century, when Portuguese expeditions down the west coast of Africa began a profitable business of carrying off Negroes into slavery. As the trade grew and nations built their economies on slave labor, rationalizations to justify the Negroes' enslavement were invoked in the name of the Scriptures, of social morality, and even of science.

According to the slave-holders' interpretation of the Bible — an interpretation believed by many to this day — Negroes were descendants of Ham and as such an inferior tribe subject to Noah's curse . . . "a servant of servants shall he be unto his brethren" (Genesis 9:25). Actually the curse was laid upon Ham's son, Canaan, and on his descendents the "Canaanites," who were reduced to servitude by the Israelites when the latter conquered the land of Canaan. No doubt the words in Genesis 9:25 represent a comment after the fact, written by the Hebrew writers of the Bible to justify the enslavement of the Canaanites. In any case, the point of the matter is that the reference is to the Canaanites only, and the Canaanites were certainly white men. It was a twisted interpretation of the Bible that the slave-holders used, with telling effect in centuries past, to defend their subjugation of the Negro.

The "scientific" racists of more recent times took their stand on even shakier ground. They argued that the Negro was inferior to the white man because he obviously represented a lower stage of evolution. Were not his dark skin and wide nose, for instance, reminiscent of the ape? Unfortunately for their case, this line of reasoning actually leads to the opposite conclusion. The Negro is the least hairy of all the groups of mankind; in this respect and in the fact that his hair is crisp and woolly, rather than long and straight, the Negro is farther from the ape than the white man is! The same can be said of the Negro's thick lips; they resemble those of an ape less than do the white man's thin lips.

The fact of the matter is that to attempt to rank the various groups of *Homo sapiens* on the evolutionary ladder is to try to do fine work with blunt tools. Humanity consists of but one species, and so far the variations that have developed in response to natural selection are quite superficial.

The dark skin of dwellers in the earth's tropical and subtropical regions has obvious value in preventing sunburn. The fair skin of northern Europeans is useful to absorb as much ultraviolet radiation as possible from the comparatively feeble sunlight in order that enough vitamin D be formed from the sterols in the skin. The narrowed eyes of the Eskimo and the Mongol have survival value in lands where the glare from snow or desert sands is intense. The high-bridged nose and narrow nasal passages of the European serve to warm the cold air of the northern winter. And so on.

Since the tendency of *Homo sapiens* has been to make our planet one world, no basic differences in the human constitution have developed in the past, and they are even less likely to develop in the future. Interbreeding is steadily evening out man's inheritance. The American Negro is one of the best cases in point. Despite social barriers against intermarriage, nearly four-fifths of the Negroes in the United States, it is estimated, have some white ancestry. By the end of the twentieth century probably there will be no "pure-blooded" Negroes in North America.

ANTHROPOLOGISTS NEVERTHELESS are keenly interested in race, primarily as a guide to the migrations of early man. It is not easy to identify specific races. Skin color, for instance, is a poor guide; the Australian aborigine and the African Negro are both dark in color but are no more closely related to each other than either is to the European. Nor is the shape of the head — "dolichocephalic" (long) versus "brachycephalic" (wide) — much better despite the classifications of Europeans into subgroups on the basis of head shape, which were popular in the late nineteenth century. The differences from one group to another are small, and the spread within a group is wide. In addition, the shape of the skull is affected by environmental factors such as vitamin deficiencies, the type of cradle in which the infant slept, and so on.

But the anthropologists have found an excellent marker for race in blood groups. The Boston University biochemist William Clouser Boyd was prominent in this connection. He pointed out that blood groups are inherited in a simple and known fashion, are unaltered by the environment, and show up in distinctly different distributions in the various races.

The American Indian is a particularly good example. Some tribes are almost entirely O; others are O but with a heavy admixture of A; virtually no Indians have B or AB blood. An American Indian testing as a B or AB is almost certain to possess some European ancestry. The Australian aborigines are likewise high in O and A, with B virtually non-existent. But they are distinguished from the American Indian in being high in the more recently discovered blood group M and low in blood group N, while the American Indian is high in N and low in M.

In Europe and Asia, where the population is more mixed, the differences between peoples are smaller, yet still distinct. For instance, in London 70 per cent of the population has O blood, 26 per cent A, and 5 per cent B. In the city of Kharkov, Russia, on the other hand, the corresponding distribution is 60, 25 and 15. In general, the percentage of B increases as one travels eastward in Europe, reaching a peak of 40 per cent in central Asia.

Now the blood-type genes show the not-yet-entirely-erased marks of past migrations. The infiltration of the B gene into Europe may be a dim mark of the invasion by the Huns in the fifth century and by the Mongols in the thirteenth. Similar blood studies in the Far

East seem to indicate a comparatively recent infiltration of the A gene into Japan from the southwest and of the B gene into Australia from the north.

A particularly interesting, and unexpected, echo of early human migrations in Europe showed up in Spain. It came out in a study of Rh blood distribution. (The Rh blood groups are so named from the reaction of the blood to anti-sera developed against the red cells of a Rhesus monkey. There are at least eight alleles of the responsible gene; seven are called Rh positive, and the eighth, recessive to all the others, is called "Rh negative" because it shows its effect only when a person has received the allele from both parents.) In the United States about 85 per cent of the population is Rh positive, 15 per cent Rh negative. The same proportion holds in most of the European peoples. But curiously, the Basques of northern Spain stand apart, with something like 60 per cent Rh negative to 40 per cent Rh positive. And the Basques are also notable in having a language unrelated to any other European language.

The conclusion that can be drawn from this is that the Basques are a remnant of a prehistoric invasion of Europe by an Rh-negative people. Presumably a later wave of invasions by Rh-positive tribes penned them up in their mountainous refuge in the western corner of the continent, where they remain the only sizable group of survivors of the "early Europeans." The small residue of Rh-negative genes in the rest of Europe and in the American descendants of the European colonizers may represent a legacy from those early Europeans.

The peoples of Asia, the African Negroes, the American Indians, and the Australian aborigines are almost entirely Rh positive.

IN HIS MILLION YEARS OF EVOLUTION, man has been subjected to the great climatic and geological changes brought on by the coming and going of the ice ages. These probably intensified the pressures of natural selection and helped evolve man at a relatively rapid rate, as evolutionary rates go. In the past 6,000 years he has had to adapt himself to the more subtle but equally drastic pressures of crowded city life, with its infectious diseases. In the past two centuries he has experienced a still more subtle change in his environment, which may have the most radical effects of all upon his mental and emotional evolution. This is the change to the machine-ridden, time-conscious world of technology.

Be that as it may, at the moment man is preparing with some excitement and a good deal of trepidation to make his first plunge into a completely alien and almost completely unknown world — the world of outer space. The one thing he does know is that it is an environment for which he is completely unadapted. He will have to take a livable environment along with him.

Man has already had some experience along these lines in descending into the ocean depths in submarines and vessels such as the bathyscaphe. As on those voyages, he will go into space in a bubble of air enclosed in a strong metal shell, carrying a full supply of the food, water, and other necessities he will require for the journey. But the takeoff into space is complicated enormously by the problem of overcoming gravity. In the space ship, a large proportion of the weight and volume must be devoted to the engine and fuel, and the possible "payload" of crew and supplies will at first be small indeed.

The food supply will have to be extremely compact: there will be no room for any indigestible constituents. The condensed, artificial food might consist of lactose, a bland vegetable oil, an appropriate mixture of amino acids, vitamins, minerals, and a dash of flavoring, the whole enclosed in a tiny carton made of edible carbohydrate. A carton containing 180 grams of solid food would suffice for one meal. Three such cartons would supply 3,000 calories. To this a gram of water per calorie (two and a half to three liters per day per person) would have to be added; some of it might be mixed in the food to make it more palatable, increasing the size of the carton. In addition, the ship would have to carry oxygen for breathing in the amount of about one liter (1,150 grams) of oxygen in liquid form per day per person.

Thus the daily requirement for each person would be 540 grams of dry food, 2,700 grams of water and 1,150 grams of oxygen. Total, 4,390 grams, or roughly nine and a half pounds. Imagine a trip to the moon, then, taking one week each way and allowing two days on the moon's surface for exploration. Each man on the ship would require about 150 pounds of food, water, and oxygen. This can probably be managed at present levels of technology.

For an expedition to Mars and back, the requirements are vastly greater. Such an expedition might well take two and a half years, allowing for a wait on Mars for a favorable phase of the planetary orbital positions to start the return trip. On the basis I have just described, such a trip would call for about five tons of food, water, and oxygen per man. To transport such a supply in a space ship is, under present technological conditions, unthinkable.

The only reasonable solution for a long trip is to make the space ship self-sufficient, in the same sense that the earth, itself a massive "ship" traveling through space, is self-sufficient. The food, water, and air taken along to start with would have to be endlessly re-used by recycling the wastes.

Such "closed systems" have already been constructed in theory. The recycling of wastes sounds unpleasant, but this is, after all, the process that maintains life on the earth. Chemical filters on the ship could collect the carbon dioxide and water vapor exhaled by the crew members; urea, salt, and water could be recovered by distillation and other processes from the urine and feces; the dry fecal residue could be sterilized of bacteria by ultraviolet light; and along with the carbon dioxide and water could then be fed to algae growing in tanks. By photosynthesis the algae would convert the carbon dioxide and nitrogenous compounds of the feces to organic food, plus oxygen, for the crew. The only thing that would be required from outside the system is energy for the various processes, including photosynthesis, and this could be supplied by the sun.

It has been estimated that as little as 250 pounds of algae per man could take care of the crew's food and oxygen needs for an indefinite period. Adding the weight of the necessary processing equipment, the total weight of supplies per man would be perhaps 350 pounds, certainly no more than 1,000 pounds. The system would be elaborate and expensive, uneconomic for a short trip such as to the moon, but in the present state of technology it represents the only possible way to solve the supply problem for any trip more ambitious than that.

Experiments dealing with these various possibilities are underway. One problem is making algae palatable. Several groups have worked on this, and in 1959 biochemists with the Boeing Airplane Company reported that by blanching algae with appropriate radiation, they had improved the taste. Dried and ground, the algae yielded a nutritious kind of flour which passed muster when prepared in the form of cookies and cupcakes.

Problems such as supply are at least familiar enough to be subject to calculation. Not so some of the other problems man will encounter in space. One of the major unknowns is the effect of prolonged weightlessness.

In a ship coasting freely through space, subject only to gravitational forces (a condition known as "free fall"), the crew and everything else will be virtually weightless. Unless anchored or holding on to something, the men will tend to float about in the ship with every slight movement of their muscles. The carbon dioxide exhaled by a person may stay close to his nose and mouth and suffocate him unless the air is continually stirred by fans. Water poured out of a glass will hang in the air; to drink, a man will have to suck from a bottle. A massive object standing on the floor will be as hard to lift as ever, for, though weightless, it still has inertia. By the same token, if a heavy object is set in motion it will be very hard to stop; for instance, a worker on the construction of a space station who happened to get in the way of a slowly moving steel beam and was pinned against the structure by it would be crushed to death by its inertial motion, despite its weightlessness.

By and large, the phenomenon of weightlessness looks rather comic to earthbound man. But it has its serious aspects. We have no significant information so far on how the human body will react to long periods of weightlessness. Laika, the dog in Sputnik II, lived through seven days in this state (she died of other causes, apparently), and mice and monkeys sent up in rockets have come through short experiences of weightlessness none the worse for wear. Man himself, however, has yet to make a real test of the condition. He has experienced up to 45 seconds of free fall in airplane experiments that have produced weightlessness by means of a coasting dive with the engines shut off. Some men have found the experience enjoyable, notably Herbert D. Stallings of the United States Air Force, who has logged a total of scores of hours on such flights. But even in exposures of these under-a-minute durations, some of the subjects have suffered nausea and anxiety. When the weightlessness follows a period of rapid acceleration, men become disoriented and lose coordination. This sort of reaction has also been experienced by men who have gone through simulated weightlessness for extended periods by lying in water (the buoyancy of the body making it virtually weightless in the water). In 1959 Captain Duane E. Graveline of the Air Force spent an entire week in the water (except for a one-hour break each night) in such an experiment. He became adapted to the weightless condition, but when he emerged, he found himself unable to react properly to normal gravity. He was weak; his neuro-muscular coordination out of the water was gone; and his mental activity was confused.

Even if weightlessness should prove a serious problem of space flight, however, there are ways to counteract it. A slow rotation of the space vehicle, for instance, could produce the sensation of weight by virtue of the centrifugal force, acting like the force of gravity.

More serious and less easily countered are the hazards of high acceleration and sudden deceleration, which space travelers will inevitably encounter in taking off and landing on rocket flights.

The normal force of gravity at the earth's surface is called one g. Weightlessness is zero g. An acceleration (or deceleration) that doubles the body's weight is two *g*, a force tripling the weight is three *g*, and so on.

The body's position during acceleration makes a big difference. If you are accelerated head first (or decelerated feet first), the blood rushes away from your head. At a high enough acceleration (say six *g* for five seconds), this means "blackout." On the other hand, if you are accelerated feet first (called "negative acceleration," as opposed to the "positive" head-first acceleration), the blood rushes to your head. This is more dangerous, because the heightened pressure may burst blood vessels in the eyes or brain. The investigators of acceleration call it "redout." An acceleration of two and a half *g* for ten seconds is enough to damage some of the vessels.

By far the easiest to tolerate is "transverse" acceleration — *i.e.*, with the force applied at right angles to the long axis of the body, as in a sitting position. Men have withstood transverse accelerations as high as ten *g* for more than two minutes in a centrifuge without losing consciousness.

For shorter periods the tolerances are much higher. Astounding records in sustaining high-*g* decelerations were made by Colonel John P. Stapp and other volunteers on the sled track of the Holloman Air Force Base in New Mexico. On his famous ride of December 10, 1954, Stapp took a deceleration of 25 *g* for about a second. His sled was brought to a full stop from a speed of more than 600 miles per hour in just 1.4 seconds. This, it was estimated, amounted to driving an automobile into a brick wall at 120 miles per hour! Of course, Stapp was strapped in the sled in a manner to minimize injury. He suffered only bruises, blisters, and painful eye shocks which produced two black eyes.

Astronautical investigators estimate that the accelerations required for the takeoff of a space ship can be kept under ten *g*. They are now fairly confident that devices such as contour couches, harnesses, and perhaps even immersion in water in a water-filled capsule or space suit will give a sufficient margin of safety against high *g*-forces.

Similar studies and experiments are being made on the radiation hazards, the boredom of long isolation, the strange experience of

TRACKS OF DINOSAUR. *The living example of youthful* Homo sapiens *was planted to indicate the size of the tracks.*

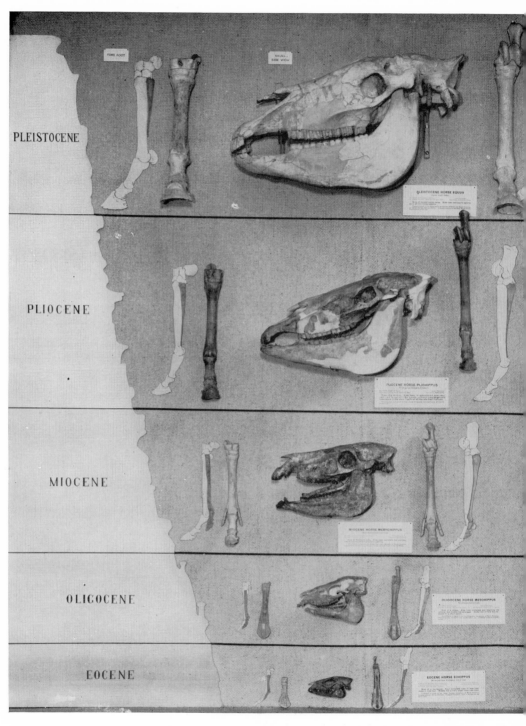

PLEISTOCENE

PLIOCENE

MIOCENE

OLIGOCENE

EOCENE

THE EVOLUTION OF THE HORSE, *illustrated by the skull and foot bones.*

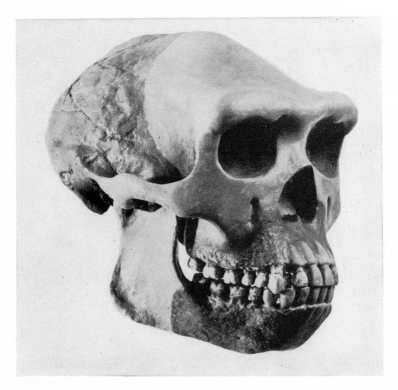

SKULL OF PITHECANTHROPUS, *as reconstructed by the anthropologist Franz Weidenreich.*

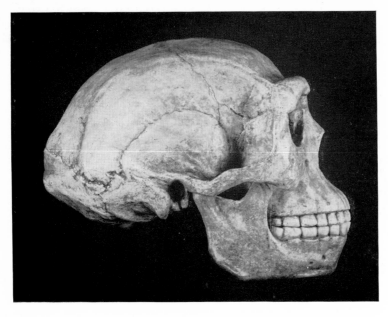

SKULL OF SINANTHROPUS.

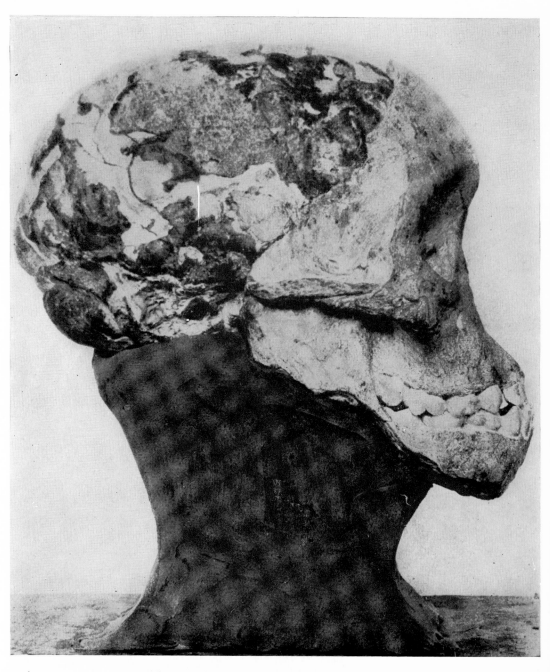

AUSTRALOPITHECUS, *the South African ape-man, reconstructed by Raymond Dart.*

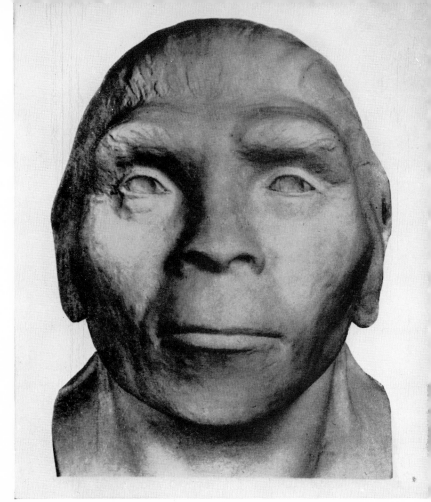

SINANTHROPUS WOMAN, *as reconstructed by Franz Weidenreich and Lucile Swan. Below is a restored skull.*

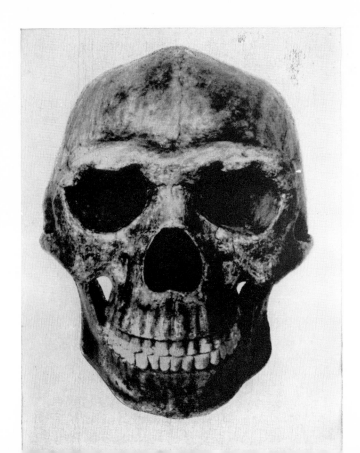

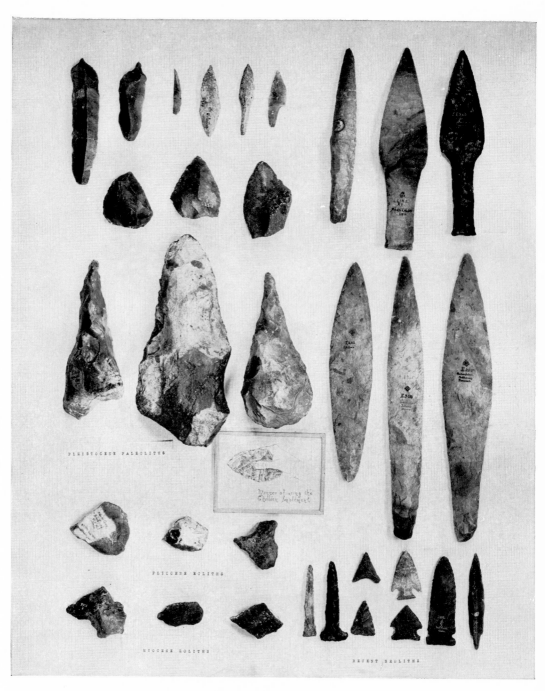

PLEISTOCENE PALEOLITHS

Dagger of using the
Chellean Implement

PLIOCENE EOLITHS

MIOCENE EOLITHS

RECENT EOLITHS

STONE TOOLS *of early men. The oldest, from the Miocene period, are
at the lower left; the most recent, at the lower right.*

being in soundless space where night never falls, and other eerie conditions that space fliers will have to endure. All in all, those preparing for man's first venture away from his home planet see no insurmountable obstacles ahead.

ATTEMPTING TO FORETELL THE FUTURE of the human race is a risky proposition that had better be left to mystics and science-fiction writers. But of one thing we can be fairly sure. Provided there are no worldwide catastrophes, such as a full-scale nuclear war or a massive attack from outer space or a pandemic of a deadly new disease, the human population will increase rapidly. It is now nearly three times as large as it was only a century and a half ago. Some estimates are that 5 per cent of all the human beings who have ever lived are living at this moment. And the world population is still growing at a tremendous rate.

Since we have no censuses of ancient populations, we must estimate them roughly on the basis of what we know about the conditions of human life. Ecologists have estimated that the pre-agricultural food supply—obtainable by hunting, fishing, collecting wild fruit and nuts, and so on — could not have supported a world population of more than 20 million, and in all likelihood the actual population during the Paleolithic was only a third or half of this at most. This means that as late as 6000 B.C. it could not have numbered more than six to ten million people — roughly the population of a single present city such as Tokyo or New York. (When America was discovered, the food-gathering Indians occupying what is now the United States probably numbered not much more than 250,000, which is like imagining the population of Dayton, Ohio, spread out across the continent.)

The first big jump in world population came with the Neolithic Revolution and agriculture. The British biologist Julian Sorrell Huxley (grandson of the Huxley who was "Darwin's bulldog") estimates that the population began to increase at a rate which doubled its numbers every 1,700 years or so. By the opening of the Bronze

699

Age, the world population may have been about 25 million; by the beginning of the Iron Age, 70 million; by the start of the Christian era, 150 million; but even by 1600, the earth's population totaled perhaps 500 million, less than the present population of China alone.

At that point the smooth rate of growth ended and the population began to explode. World explorers opened up some 18 million square miles of almost empty land on new continents to colonization by the Europeans. The eighteenth-century Industrial Revolution accelerated the production of food and of people. And even backward China and India shared in the population explosion. The doubling of the world's population now took place not in a period of nearly two millennia but in less than two centuries. The population expanded from 500 million in 1600 to 900 million in 1800. Since then it has grown at an ever faster rate. By 1900 it had reached 1.6 billion. In the first 60 years of the twentieth century it has climbed to 2.5 billion, despite two world wars.

With improved medical care and sanitation cutting down the death rate in high-birth-rate countries such as India and China, we must expect the population explosion to become still more vigorous. By the end of this century, the world population probably will exceed four billion.

At the moment students of the population explosion are leaning strongly toward the Malthusian view, which has been unpopular ever since it was advanced in 1798. As I said earlier in the chapter, Thomas Robert Malthus maintained in *An Essay on the Principle of Population* that population always tends to grow faster than the food supply, with the inevitable result of periodic famines and wars. Despite his predictions, the world population has grown apace without any serious setbacks in the past century and a half. But for this postponement of catastrophe we can thank, in large measure, the fact that large areas of the earth were still open for the expansion of food production. Now we are running out of tillable new lands. The optimism of the anti-Malthusians is beginning to look like a fool's paradise. A majority of the world's population is underfed, and the new mouths to feed are multiplying so fast that man is steadily falling farther behind.

Suppose that by miracles of technology we raise the productivity of the earth ten-fold; suppose that we mine the metals of the ocean, bring up gushers of oil in the Sahara, find coal in Antarctica, harness the energy of sunlight, develop fusion power. Then what? If the rate of increase of the human population continues unchecked at its present rate, all our science and technical invention will still leave us struggling uphill like Sisyphus.

If the earth's population went on doubling every 80 years (as it is doing now), by 3500 A.D. it would reach 630,000 billion! Our planet would have standing room only, for there would be only two and a half square feet per person on the entire land surface, including Greenland and Antarctica. In fact, if the human species could be imagined as continuing to multiply further at the same rate, by 5500 A.D. the total mass of human tissue would be equal to the mass of the earth. Such is the power of a geometric progression.

If there are those who see a way out in emigration to other planets, they may find food for thought in the fact that, assuming there were 1,000 billion other inhabitable planets in the Universe and people could be transported to any of them at will, at the present rate of increase of human numbers every one of those planets would be crowded literally to standing room only by 10,000 A.D. By 13,500 A.D. the mass of humanity would be equal to the mass of the known Universe!

Obviously the human race cannot increase at the present rate for very long, regardless of what is done with respect to the supply of food, water, minerals, and energy. I do not say "will not" or "dare not" or "should not"; I say quite flatly "cannot."

How, then, is the rate of population increase to be cut down? There are only two possible ways: (1) increase the death rate, or (2) reduce the birth rate.

The classic Malthusian limitation by famine, disease, and war would achieve the first end automatically. Man might forestall these methods by means of euthanasia or infanticide. None of this is at all palatable.

As for the birth rate, Malthus's ideal solution was moral restraint. But he was inclined to doubt that limiting sexual activity to rare occasions could be expected of humanity, and somehow I doubt it, too.

So we are pushed finally to the one rational and painless way out: the use of artificial methods to prevent conception. To reduce this to the simplest possible terms, what would be needed would be some cheap, readily available chemical that could be taken orally and would accomplish the desired end without important side effects. It might be designed either to inhibit sexual desire or to inhibit, temporarily, the production or the union of egg and sperm. Several oral contraceptives are being tested by researchers. Most of them are synthetic analogues of progesterone, a female sex hormone, and they act by preventing ovulation — that is, the formation of egg cells.

There are religious groups, of course, that have serious doubts as to the morality of such contraception. I cannot quarrel with their sincerity in this matter, but I am at a loss to see what reasonable alternative can be offered as a solution to the population explosion.

Nuclear war and a fresh start from the Paleolithic?

CHAPTER

16

THE MIND

THE NERVOUS SYSTEM

PHYSICALLY SPEAKING, man is a rather unimpressive specimen, as organisms go. He cannot compete in strength with most other animals his size. He walks awkwardly, compared with, say, the cat; he cannot run with the dog or the deer; in vision, hearing, and the sense of smell he is inferior to a number of other animals. His skeleton is ill-suited to his erect posture: man is probably the only animal that develops "low back pain" from his normal posture and activities. When we think of the evolutionary perfection of other organisms — the beautiful efficiency of the fish for swimming or of the bird for flying, the great fecundity and adaptability of the insects, the perfect simplicity and efficiency of the virus — man seems a clumsy and poorly designed creature indeed. As sheer organism, he could scarcely compete with the creatures occupying any specific environmental niche on earth. He has come to dominate the earth only by grace of one rather important specialization — his brain.

A CELL IS SENSITIVE to a change in its surroundings ("stimulus") and will react appropriately ("response"). Thus a protozoon will swim toward a drop of sugar solution deposited in the water near it, or away from a drop of acid. Now this direct, automatic sort of response is fine for a single cell, but it would mean chaos for a collection of cells. Any organism made up of a number of cells must have a system that coordinates their responses. Without such a system, it would be like a city of men completely out of communication with one another and acting at cross purposes. So even the coelenterates, the most primitive multicelled animals, have the beginnings of a nervous system. We can see in them the first nerve cells ("neurons") — special cells with fibers that extend from the main cell body and put out extremely delicate branches.

The functioning of nerve cells is so subtle and complex that even at this simple level we are already a little beyond our depth when it comes to explaining just what happens. In some way not yet understood, a change in the environment acts upon the nerve cell. It may be a change in the concentration of some substance, or in the temperature, or in the amount of light, or in the movement of the water,

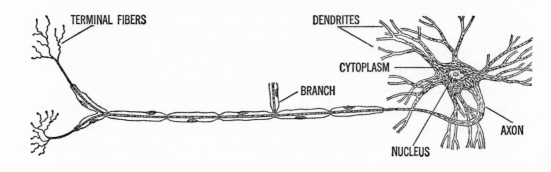

A NERVE CELL.

or it may be an actual touch by some object. Whatever the stimulus, it sets up an "impulse" that travels along the nerve fiber; at the end of the fiber the impulse jumps a tiny gap ("synapse") to the next nerve cell; and so it is transmitted from cell to cell. In the case of a coelenterate, such as a jellyfish, the impulse is communicated throughout the organism. The jellyfish responds by contracting some part or all of its body. If the stimulus is a contact with a food particle, the organism engulfs the particle by contraction of its tentacles.

All this is strictly automatic, of course, but since it helps the jellyfish, we like to read purpose into the organism's behavior. Indeed, man, as a creature who behaves in a purposeful, motivated way, naturally tends to attribute purpose even to inanimate Nature. Scientists call this attitude "teleological," and they try to avoid such a way of thinking and speaking as much as they can. But in describing the results of evolution it is so convenient to speak in terms of development toward more efficient ends that even among scientists all but the most fanatical purists occasionally lapse into teleology. (Readers of this book have noticed, of course, that I have sinned often.) Let us, however, try to avoid teleology in considering the development of the nervous system and the brain. Nature did not design the brain; it came about as the result of a long series of evolutionary accidents, so to speak, which happened to produce helpful features that at each stage gave an advantage to organisms possessing them. In the fight for survival, an animal that was more sensitive to changes in the environment than its competitors, and could respond to them faster, would be favored by natural selection. If, for instance, an animal happened to possess some spot on its body that was exceptionally sensitive to light, the advantage would be so great that evolution of eye-spots, and eventually of eyes, would follow almost inevitably.

Specialized groups of cells that amount to rudimentary "sense organs" begin to appear in the Platyhelminthes, or flatworms. Furthermore, the flatworms also show the beginnings of a nervous system that avoids sending nerve impulses indiscriminately throughout

705

the body and speeds them to the critical points of response. The development that accomplishes this is a central nerve cord. The flatworms are the first to develop a "central nervous system."

This is not all. The flatworm's sense organs are localized in its head end, the first part of its body that encounters the environment as it moves along, and so naturally the nerve cord is particularly well developed in the head region. That knob of development is the beginning of a brain.

Gradually the more complex phyla add new features. The sense organs increase in number and sensitivity. The nerve cord and its branches grow more elaborate, developing a widespread system of afferent ("carrying to") nerve cells that bring messages to the cord and efferent ("carrying away") fibers that transmit messages to the organs of response. The knot of nerve cells at the crossroads in the head becomes more and more complicated. Nerve fibers evolve into forms that can carry the impulses faster. In the squid, the most highly developed of the unsegmented animals, this faster transmission is accomplished by a thickening of the nerve fiber. In the segmented animals, the fiber develops a sheath of fatty material ("myelin") which is even more effective in speeding the nerve impulse. In man some nerve fibers can transmit the impulse at 100 meters per second (about 225 miles per hour), compared to only about one-tenth of a mile per hour in some of the invertebrates.

The chordates introduce a radical change in the location of the nerve cord. In them this main nerve trunk (better known as the spinal cord) runs along the back instead of along the belly, as in all lower animals. This may seem a step backward — putting the cord in a more exposed position. But the vertebrates have the cord well protected within the bony spinal column. The backbone, though its first function was protecting the nerve cord, produced amazing dividends, for it served as a girder upon which chordates could hang bulk and weight. From the backbone they can extend ribs that enclose the chest, jawbones that carry teeth for chewing, and long bones that form limbs.

THE CHORDATE BRAIN develops from three structures which are already present in simple form in the most primitive vertebrates. These structures, at first mere swellings of nerve tissue, are the "forebrain," "midbrain," and "hindbrain." At the head end of the spinal cord, the cord widens smoothly into the hindbrain section known as the "medulla oblongata." On the front side of this section in all but the most primitive chordates is a bulge called the "cerebellum" ("little brain"). Forward of this is the midbrain. In the lower vertebrates the midbrain is concerned chiefly with vision and has a pair of "optic lobes," while the forebrain is concerned with smell and taste and contains "olfactory bulbs." The forebrain, reading from front to rear, is divided into the olfactory-bulb section, the "cerebrum," and the "thalamus," the lower portion of which is the "hypothalamus." (Cerebrum is Latin for "brain"; in man, at least, the cerebrum is the largest and most important part of the organ.)

It is the roof of the cerebrum, the cap called the cerebral cortex, that is the star of the whole show. In fishes and amphibians this is merely a smooth covering (called the "pallium," or cloak). In reptiles a patch of new nerve tissue, called the "neopallium" ("new cloak") appears. This is the real forerunner of things to come. It will eventually take over the supervision of vision and other sensations. In the reptiles the clearing house for visual messages has already moved from the midbrain to the forebrain in part; in birds this move is completed. With the first mammals, the neopallium begins to take charge. It spreads virtually over the entire surface of the cerebrum. At first it remains a smooth coat, but as it goes on growing in the higher mammals, it becomes so much larger in area than the surface of the cerebrum that it is bent into folds, or "convolutions." This folding is responsible for the complexity and capacity of the brain of a higher mammal, notably that of man.

More and more the cerebrum comes to dominate the brain. The midbrain fades to almost nothing. In the case of the primates, which gain in the sense of sight at the expense of the sense of smell, the

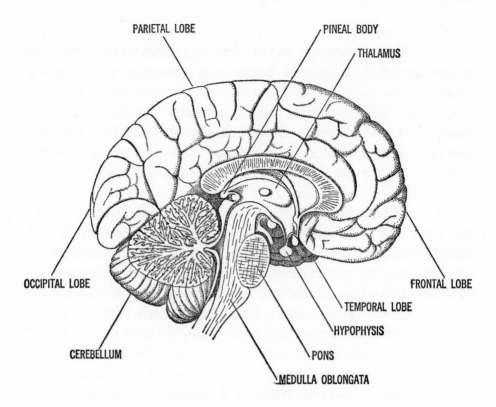

PARIETAL LOBE

PINEAL BODY

THALAMUS

OCCIPITAL LOBE

FRONTAL LOBE

TEMPORAL LOBE

HYPOPHYSIS

CEREBELLUM

PONS

MEDULLA OBLONGATA

THE HUMAN BRAIN.

olfactory lobes of the forebrain shrink to mere blobs. By this time the cerebrum has expanded over the thalamus and the cerebellum.

Even the most primitive known manlike fossils had considerably larger brains than the most advanced apes. Whereas the brain of the chimpanzee or of the orang-utan weighs less than 400 grams (under 14 ounces), and the gorilla, though far larger than a man, has a brain that averages about 540 grams, Pithecanthropus's brain apparently weighed about 850 grams and Sinanthropus's perhaps 1,000 grams. And these were the "small-brained" hominids. Rhodesian man's brain weighed about 1,300 grams; the brain of Neanderthal and of modern *Homo sapiens* comes to about 1,500 grams (53 ounces). Modern man's mental gain over Neanderthal apparently lies in the fact that a larger proportion of his brain is concentrated in the fore-regions, which apparently control the higher aspects of mental function. Neanderthal was a low-brow whose brain bulged in the rear; present-day man, in contrast, is a high-brow whose brain bulges in front.

Of course, the human brain is not the largest in the animal kingdom. The elephant's brain weighs 2,500 grams (some five and a half pounds), and the brains of the biggest whales are twice that size. Nor does man rank highest in the ratio of brain weight to body weight. While man's brain is about 1/45 of his total body weight, in some of the smaller primates the proportion runs as high as 1/18. But their brains are much smaller than man's on an absolute basis. Even allowing for the extreme cases of a big brain in a huge body (for example, the elephant, whose brain is only 1/2000 of its body weight) and of a relatively big brain in a tiny body (for example, the hummingbird), man is far and away outstanding in the animal kingdom for the effective size of his brain.

ODDLY ENOUGH, many of the ancient philosophers almost completely missed the significance of the organ under man's skull. Aristotle considered the brain merely an air-conditioning device, so to speak, designed to cool the overheated blood. The ancient and medieval thinkers often tended to place the seat of emotions and personality in organs such as the heart, the liver, and the spleen (*vide* the expressions "broken-hearted," "lily-livered," "vents his spleen").

The first modern investigator of the brain was a seventeenth-century English physician and anatomist named Thomas Willis; he traced the nerves that led to the brain. Later a French anatomist named Felix Vicq d'Azur and others roughed out the anatomy of the brain itself. But it was the eighteenth-century Swiss physiologist Albrecht von Haller who made the first crucial discovery about the functioning of the nervous system.

Von Haller found that he could make a muscle contract much more easily by stimulating a nerve than by stimulating the muscle itself. Furthermore this contraction was involuntary; he could even produce it by stimulating a nerve after the organism had died. Von Haller went on to show that the nerves carried sensations. When he cut the nerves attached to specific tissues, these tissues could no longer react. The physiologist concluded that the brain received sensations by way of nerves and then sent out, again by way of nerves, messages which led to such responses as muscle contraction. He supposed that the nerves all came to a junction at the center of the brain.

In 1811 the Austrian physician Franz Joseph Gall focused attention on the "gray matter" on the surface of the cerebrum (which is distinguished from the "white matter" in that the latter consists merely of the fibers emerging from the nerve-cell bodies, these fibers being white because of their fatty sheaths). Gall suggested that the nerves did not collect at the center of the brain, as von Haller had thought, but that each ran to some definite portion of the gray matter, which he considered the coordinating region of the brain. Gall reasoned that different parts of the cerebral cortex were in charge of collecting sensations from different parts of the body and sending out the messages for responses to specific parts as well.

If a specific part of the cortex was responsible for a specific property of the mind, what was more natural than to suppose that the degree of development of that part would reflect a person's character or mentality? By feeling for bumps on a person's skull one might find out whether this or that portion of the brain was enlarged and so judge whether he was particularly generous or particularly depraved or particularly something else. With this reasoning, some of Gall's followers founded the pseudo-science of "phrenology," which had quite a vogue in the nineteenth century and is not exactly dead even today.

But the fact that phrenology, as developed by charlatans, is nonsense, doesn't mean that Gall's original notion of the specialization of functions in particular parts of the cerebral cortex was wrong. Even before specific explorations of the brain were attempted, it had been noticed that accidental damage to a local portion of the brain might impair speech or some other single function. And as early as 1870 two German scientists, Gustav Fritsch and Eduard Hitzig, began to map the supervisory functions of the brain by stimulating various parts of it and observing what muscles responded.

By that time experimenters had learned that a great deal of an organism's behavior is controlled not by the brain but by the spinal cord, acting as a coordinating center in its own right. Its gray matter, located in the interior of the cord, is a crossroads for certain incoming and outgoing nerves, and these are largely concerned with the internal organs—the heart, digestive system, and so on.

These nerves form two systems: the "sympathetic" and the "parasympathetic." (The terms date back to semi-mystical notions of Galen.) Both systems act on almost every internal organ, exerting control by opposing effects. For instance, the sympathetic nerves act to accelerate the heartbeat, the parasympathetic nerves to slow it; the sympathetic nerves slow up secretion of digestive juices, the parasympathetic stimulate such secretions; and so on. Thus the spinal cord, together with primitive portions of the brain such as the medulla oblongata, regulates the workings of the organs in an automatic fashion. This set of involuntary controls was investigated in detail by the British physiologist John Newport Langley in the 1890's, and he named it the "autonomic nervous system."

In the 1830's the English physiologist Marshall Hall had studied another type of behavior which seemed to have voluntary aspects but proved to be really quite involuntary. When you accidentally touch a hot object with your hand, the hand draws away instantly. If the sensation of heat had to go to the brain, be considered and interpreted there, and evoke the appropriate message to the hand, your hand would be pretty badly scorched by the time it got the message. The unthinking spinal cord disposes of the whole business automatically and much faster. It was Hall who gave the process the name "reflex."

In man, reflexes are decidedly subordinate to the conscious will. You can force your hand to remain in a fire; you can deliberately speed up your rate of breathing when ordinary reflex action would

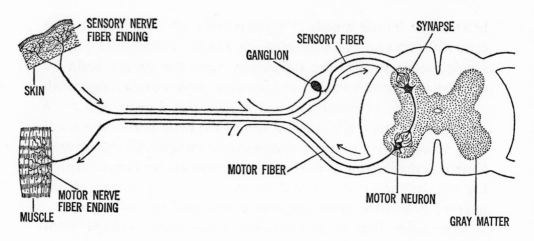

SENSORY NERVE
FIBER ENDING

SYNAPSE

SENSORY FIBER

GANGLION

SKIN

MOTOR NERVE
FIBER ENDING

MUSCLE

MOTOR FIBER

MOTOR NEURON

GRAY MATTER

THE REFLEX ARC.

keep it slow; and so on. The lower phyla of animals, on the other hand, not only are much more strictly controlled by their reflexes but also have them far more highly developed.

One of the best examples is a spider spinning its web. Here the reflexes produce such an elaborate pattern of behavior that it is difficult to think of it as mere reflex action; instead, it is usually called "instinctive" behavior. (Because the word "instinct" is often misused, biologists prefer the term "innate" behavior.) The spider is born with a nerve-wiring system in which the switches have been pre-set, so to speak. A particular stimulus sets it off on weaving a web, and each act in the process in turn acts as a stimulus determining the next response.

Looking at the spider's intricate web, built with beautiful precision and effectiveness for the function it will serve, it is almost impossible to believe that the thing has been done without purposeful intelligence. Yet the very fact that the complex task is carried through so perfectly and in exactly the same way every time is itself proof that intelligence has nothing to do with it. Conscious intelligence, with the hesitations and weighings of alternatives that are inherent in deliberate thought, will inevitably give rise to imperfections and variations from one construction to another.

With increasing intelligence, animals tend more and more to shed instincts and inborn skills. Thereby they doubtless lose something of value. A spider can build its amazingly complex web perfectly the first time, although it has never seen web-spinning, or even a web, before. Man, on the other hand, is born almost completely unskilled and helpless. A new-born baby can automatically suck on a nipple and wail if it is hungry and hold on for dear life if about to fall; but it can do very little else. Every parent knows how painfully and with what travail a child comes to learn the simplest forms of suitable behavior. And yet, a spider or an insect, though born with perfection, cannot deviate from it. The spider builds a beautiful web, but if its pre-ordained web should fail, it cannot learn to build another type of web. A boy, on the other hand, reaps great benefits from being unfettered by inborn perfection. He may learn slowly and attain only imperfection at best, but he can attain a variety of imperfection of his own choosing. What man has lost in convenience and security, he has gained in an almost limitless flexibility.

From our own standpoint it seems beyond question that the chordates have followed the better path and that man is a more advanced form of life than the ant. That, however, does not necessarily mean that man will survive the ant.

FEW PROBLEMS have fascinated biologists more than the question as to how the nerves carry impulses. Most of the early students of the nervous system held to a semi-mystical notion, inherited from Galen, that the brain generated a mysterious fluid, called "animal spirits," which traveled through the presumably hollow nerves. Even von Haller went along with this idea. But after Luigi Galvani and Alessandro Volta showed that "animal electricity" flowed along the nerves and that an electrical flow could be generated by chemical reactions, it became reasonable to suspect that nerve impulses were tiny charges of electricity originated and propagated by chemical changes in the nerve. This was elevated from mere speculation to experimental demonstration by the nineteenth-century German physiologist Emil Du Bois-Reymond, who by means of a delicate galvanometer was able to detect tiny electric currents in stimulated nerves.

With modern instruments, researches into the electrical properties of the nerve have been incredibly refined. By placing tiny electrodes at different spots on a nerve fiber and by detecting electrical changes through an oscilloscope, it is possible to measure a nerve impulse's strength, duration, speed of propagation, and so on.

If you apply small electric pulses of increasing strength to a single nerve cell, up to a certain point there is no response whatever. Then suddenly the cell fires: an impulse is initiated and travels along the fiber. The cell has a threshold; it will not react at all to a stimulus below the threshold, and to any stimulus above the threshold it will respond only with an impulse of a certain fixed intensity. The response, in other words, is all or nothing. And the nature of the impulse elicited by the stimulus seems to be the same in all nerves.

How can such a simple yes-no affair, identical everywhere, lead to the complex sensations of sight, for instance, or to the complex finger responses involved in playing a violin? It seems that a nerve, such as the optic nerve, contains a large number of individual fibers, some of which may be "firing" and others not, forming a pattern, possibly a complex one, shifting continuously with changes in the overall stimulus. Such a changing pattern may be continually "scanned" by the brain and interpreted appropriately. But nothing is known about how the interpretation is made or how the pattern is translated into action such as the contraction of a muscle or secretion by a gland.

The firing of the nerve cell itself apparently depends on the movement of ions across the membrane of the cell. Ordinarily the inside of the cell has a comparative excess of potassium ions, while outside the cell there is an excess of sodium ions. Somehow the cell holds potassium ions in and keeps sodium ions out so that the concentrations on the two sides of the cell membrane do not equalize.

THE ORIGINAL UNIVAC, *first of the large electronic computers.*

PROGRAM ON TAPE (at left) *is being fed into* Univac 1105, *a computer used by the U.S. Census Bureau.*

DISK MEMORY UNIT *of the IBM* Ramac 305. *The access arm shown can write information bits on a disk or read them off. Such a unit can hold up to 20 million bits.*

TAPE MEMORIES *for a transistorized* Univac.

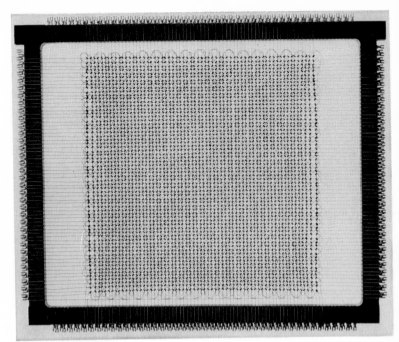

AN ARRAY OF FERRITE CORES *used for the memory of an IBM computer. The complete memory consists of many such matrices stacked above one another.*

READING BY MACHINE. *This IBM apparatus can read writing or printing on documents. The small "write" head at the lower left first magnetizes the ink of the printed characters, and the "read" head to the right of it then reads the magnetic patterns that identify the characters.*

It is now believed that a "sodium pump" of some kind inside the cell keeps pumping out sodium ions as fast as they come in. In any case, there is an electric potential difference of about one-tenth of a volt across the cell membrane, with the inside negatively charged with respect to the outside. Now when the nerve cell is stimulated, the potential difference across the membrane collapses, and this represents the firing of the cell. It takes a couple of thousandths of a second for the potential difference to be re-established, and during that interval the nerve will not react to another stimulus. This is the "refractory period."

Once the cell fires, the nerve impulse travels down the fiber by a series of firings, each successive section of the fiber exciting the next in turn. The impulse can travel only in the forward direction, because the section that has just fired cannot fire again until after a resting pause.

Thanks to the electric currents involved in nerve impulses, it is possible to "read" the brain's activity, in a way, though no one has yet been able to translate what the brain waves are saying. In 1929 a German psychiatrist, Hans Berger, applied electrodes to various parts of the head and was able to detect rhythmic waves of electrical activity, now known as alpha waves, beta waves, and so on. Electro-encephalograms ("electrical writings of the brain") have since been extensively studied, and they show that each individual has his own pattern, varying with excitement and in sleep. Although the electro-encephalogram is still far from being a method of "reading thoughts" or tracing the mechanism of the intellect, it does help in the diagnosis of major upsets of brain function, particularly epilepsy. It can also help locate areas of brain damage or brain tumors.

Something has been learned about the chemicals involved in the transmission of nerve impulses. One of the chemicals definitely known to stimulate the nerves is the hormone adrenalin. It acts upon nerves of the sympathetic system, which slows the activity of the digestive system and accelerates the rate of respiration and the heart-beat. When anger or fear excites the adrenal glands to secrete the hormone, its stimulation of the sympathetic nerves sends a faster surge of blood through the body, carrying more oxygen to the tissues, and by slowing down digestion for the duration it saves energy during the emergency.

In the normal course, the nerve endings of the sympathetic nervous system themselves secrete a compound very like adrenalin, called "noradrenalin." This chemical serves to carry the nerve impulses across the synapses, transmitting the message by stimulating the nerve endings on the other side of the gap.

In the early 1920's the English physiologist Henry Dale and the German physiologist Otto Loewi (who were to share the Nobel Prize in physiology and medicine in 1930) studied a chemical which performed this function for most of the nerves other than those of the sympathetic system. The chemical is called acetylcholine. It is now believed to be involved not only at the synapses but also in conducting the nerve impulse along the nerve fiber itself. Perhaps acetylcholine acts upon the "sodium pump." At any rate, the substance seems to be formed momentarily in the nerve fiber and to be broken down quickly by an enzyme called "cholinesterase." Anything that inhibits the action of cholinesterase will interfere with this chemical cycle and will stop the transmission of nerve impulses. The deadly substances now known as "nerve gases" are cholinesterase inhibitors. By blocking the conduction of nerve impulses they can stop the heartbeat and produce death within minutes. The application to warfare is obvious. They can be used, less immorally, as insecticides.

HUMAN BEHAVIOR

UNLIKE PHYSICAL PHENOMENA, such as the motions of planets or the behavior of light, the behavior of living things has never been reduced to rigorous natural laws and perhaps never will be. There are many who insist that the study of human behavior cannot become a true science, in the sense of being able to explain or predict behavior in any given situation on the basis of universal natural laws.

Yet life is no exception to the rule of natural law, and it can be argued that living behavior would be fully explainable if all the factors were known. The catch lies in that last phrase. It is unlikely that all the factors will ever be known; they are too many and too complex. Man need not, however, despair of ever being able to understand himself. There is yet room for better knowledge of his own mental complexities, and even if we never reach the end of the road, we may yet hope to travel along it quite a way. The question at the moment is: how far can we now go in predicting behavior? Can we isolate specific factors and trace their effects?

In the simple organisms we can see direct, automatic responses of the kind called "tropisms" (from a Greek word meaning to "turn"). Plants show "phototropism" (turning toward light), "hydrotropism" (turning toward water, in this case by the roots), and "chemotropism" (turning toward particular chemical substances). Chemotropism is also characteristic of many animals, from protozoa to ants. Certain moths are known to fly toward a scent as far as two miles away. That tropisms are completely automatic is shown by the fact that a phototropic moth will even fly into a candle flame.

Reflexes, even in the very highest organisms, have something as invariant and mechanical about them as the lowliest tropisms. They indicate that even in man there is something of the machine. The question is: how much? To put it another way: does man possess "free will" (as he likes to think) or is his behavior in some respects absolutely determined by the stimulus?

One can argue for the existence of free will on philosophical or theological grounds, but I know of no one who has ever found a way to demonstrate it experimentally. To demonstrate "determinism," the reverse of free will, is not exactly easy, either. Attempts in that direction, however, have been made. Most notable were those of the Russian physiologist Ivan Petrovich Pavlov.

Pavlov started with a specific interest in the mechanism of digestion. He showed in the 1880's that gastric juice was secreted in the stomach as soon as food was placed on a dog's tongue; the stomach would secrete this juice even if food never reached it. But if the vagus nerve (which runs from the medulla oblongata to various parts of the alimentary canal) was cut near the stomach, the secretions stopped. For his work on the physiology of digestion, Pavlov received the Nobel Prize in physiology and medicine in 1904. But like some other Nobel laureates (notably Ehrlich and Einstein) Pavlov went on to other discoveries that dwarfed the accomplishments for which he actually received the prize.

He decided to investigate the automatic, or reflex, nature of secretions, and he chose the secretion of saliva as a convenient, easy-to-observe example. The sight or odor of food causes a dog (and a man, for that matter) to salivate. What Pavlov did was to ring a bell every time he placed food before a dog. Eventually the dog salivated when it heard the bell even though no food was present. An association had been built up. The nerve impulse that carried the sound of the bell to the cerebrum had become equivalent to one representing the sight or odor of food.

Pavlov called this a "conditioned reflex;" the salivation was a "conditioned response." Willy-nilly, the dog salivated at the sound of the bell just as it would at the sight of food. Of course, the conditioned response could be wiped out — for instance, by repeatedly denying food to the dog when the bell was rung and subjecting it to a mild electric shock instead. Eventually the dog would not salivate but instead would wince at the sound of the bell, even though it received no electric shock.

In theory, all learning can be considered to consist of conditioned responses. In learning to type, for instance, you start by watching the typewriter keyboard and gradually substitute certain automatic movements of the fingers for visual selection of the proper key. Thus the thought "k" is accompanied by a specific movement of the middle finger of the right hand; the thought "the" causes the first finger of the left hand, the first finger of the right hand, and the second finger of the left hand to hit certain spots in that order. These responses involve no conscious thought. Eventually a practiced typist has to stop and think to recall where the letters are. I am myself a rapid and completely mechanical typist, and if I am asked where the letter "f," say, is located on the keyboard, the only way I can answer (short of looking at the keyboard) is to move my fingers in the air as if typing and try to catch one of them in the act of typing "f." Only my fingers know the keyboard; my conscious mind does not.

The same principle may apply to more complex learning, such as reading or playing a violin. Why, after all, does the design CRAYON in black print on this piece of paper automatically evoke a picture of a pigmented stick of wax and a certain sound that represents a word? You do not need to spell out the letters or search your memory or reason out the possible message contained in the design; from repeated conditioning you automatically associate the symbol with the thing itself.

In the early decades of this century the American psychologist John Broadus Watson built a whole theory of human behavior, called "behaviorism," on the basis of conditioning. Watson went so far as to suggest that people had no deliberate control over the way they behaved; it was all determined by conditioning. Although his theory was popular for a time, it never gained wide support among psychologists. In the first place, even if the theory is basically correct — if behavior is dictated solely by conditioning — behaviorism is not very enlightening on those aspects of human behavior that are of most interest to us, such as creative intelligence, artistic ability, and the sense of right and wrong. It would be impossible to identify all the conditioning influences and relate them to the pattern of thought and belief in any measurable way, and something that cannot be measured is not subject to any really scientific study.

In the second place, what does conditioning have to do with a process such as intuition? The mind suddenly puts two previously unrelated thoughts or events together, apparently by sheer chance, and creates an entirely new idea or response. Even apes, whose patterns of behavior are simpler and more mechanical than man's, show some spontaneous insight. The Gestalt psychologist Wolfgang Köhler discovered some striking illustrations of this in his famous experiments with chimpanzees. In one case a chimp, after trying in vain to reach bananas with a stick that was too short, suddenly picked up another bamboo stick that the experimenter had left lying handy, joined the two sticks together, and so brought the fruit within reach. In another instance a chimp piled one box on another to reach bananas hanging overhead. These acts had not been preceded by any training or experience that might have formed the association for the animal; apparently they were sheer flashes of inspiration.

So behavior very often cannot be explained merely in terms of conditioning. Nevertheless, conditioning experiments have become a powerful tool in psychology. Through them, animals sometimes almost "talk" to the experimenter. The technique has made it possible to investigate the learning abilities of various animals, their instincts, their visual abilities, their ability to distinguish colors, and so on. Of all the investigations, not the least remarkable are those of the Austrian naturalist Karl von Frisch. Von Frisch trained bees to go to dishes placed in certain locations for their food, and he learned that these foragers soon told the other bees in their hive where the food was located. From his experiments von Frisch learned that the bees communicated with one another by means of a dance on the honeycombs, that the nature and vigor of the dance told the direction and distance of the food dish from the hive and even how plentiful or scarce the food supply was, and that the bees were able to tell direction from the polarization of light in the sky. Von Frisch's fascinating discoveries about the language of the bees opened up a whole new field of study of animal behavior.

NEARLY TWO CENTURIES AGO an Austrian physician named Franz Anton Mesmer became the sensation of Europe for his experiments with a powerful tool for probing human behavior. By what he called "animal magnetism" (soon renamed "mesmerism") he would put a patient into a trance and pronounce the patient cured of his illness. He may well have produced some cures (since some disorders can be treated by suggestion), but Mesmer, an ardent astrologer and all-around mystic, was denounced as a fake and eventually retired in disgrace.

Nevertheless, he had started something. In the 1850's a British surgeon named James Braid revived hypnotism (he was the first to use this term) as a medical device, and other physicians also took it up. Among these was a Viennese doctor named Josef Breuer, who in the 1880's began to use hypnosis specifically for mental and emotional disorders.

Hypnotism (Greek for "putting to sleep") had been known, of course, since ancient times, and had often been used by mystics. But Breuer and others now began to interpret its effects as evidence of the existence of an "unconscious" level of the mind. Motivations of which the individual was unaware were buried there, and they could be brought to light by hypnosis. It was tempting to suppose that these motivations were suppressed from the conscious mind because they were associated with shame or guilt, and that they might account for useless, irrational or even vicious behavior.

Breuer set out to employ hypnosis to probe the hidden causes of hysteria and other behavior disorders. Working with him was a pupil named Sigmund Freud. For a number of years they treated patients together, putting the patients under light hypnosis and encouraging them to speak. They found that the patients' venting of experiences or impulses buried in the unconscious often acted as a cathartic, relieving their symptoms after they awoke from the hypnosis.

Freud came to the conclusion that practically all of the suppressed memories and motivations were sexual in origin. Sexual impulses tabooed by society and the child's parents were driven underground, but they still strove for expression and generated intense conflicts which were the more damaging for being unrecognized and unadmitted.

In 1894, after breaking with Breuer because the latter disagreed with his concentration on the sexual factor, Freud went on alone to develop his ideas about the causes and treatment of mental disturbances. He dropped hypnosis and urged his patients to babble in a free-association manner — to say anything that came into their minds. As the patient came to feel that the physician was listening sympathetically without any moral censure, slowly — sometimes very slowly — the individual began to unburden himself, to remember things long repressed and forgotten. Freud called this slow analysis of the "psyche" (Greek for soul or mind) "psychoanalysis."

More than half a century later, psychoanalysis still remains an art rather than a science. Rigorously controlled experiments, such as those conducted in physics and the other "hard" sciences, are, of course, impossible in psychiatry. The practitioners must base their conclusions largely on intuition or subjective judgment. Psychiatry (of which psychoanalysis is only one of the techniques) has undoubtedly helped many patients, but it has produced no spectacular cures and has not notably reduced the incidence of mental disease. Nor has it developed any all-embracing and generally accepted theory, comparable to the germ theory of infectious disease. In fact, there are almost as many schools of psychiatry as there are psychiatrists. One of Freud's students, Alfred Adler, founded a school which placed the main emphasis on man's feelings of inadequacy (the "inferiority complex") rather than on sexual repressions. Another student, Carl Gustav Jung, broke off to found a school which divided personality into "extravert" and "introvert" types and considered the unconscious and the conscious to be partners rather than in conflict. Today the more popular schools of psychoanalysis have modified Freud's ideas in various ways. The emphasis at the moment is on social pressures and "interpersonal relations," particularly the effects of the family's attitudes and behavior on the young child.

In any case, if psychiatry is not yet a science, it has at least made an important step forward by changing man's attitude toward neurotic behavior and mental disease. The mentally disturbed are now dealt with by doctors and hospitals instead of by the whip and the prison. By forcing recognition of the fact that mental illness is an illness and not a disgrace, and by inaugurating a search for methods of relieving and preventing mental illness, psychiatry has put man-kind on the road to finding ways to cope with what may become his most important problem.

In short, if Freud is not the Pasteur of mental illness, he is at least its Hippocrates.

SERIOUS MENTAL ILLNESS takes various forms, ranging from chronic depression to a complete withdrawal from reality into a world in which some, at least, of the details do not corre-spond to the way most of us see things. This form of psychosis is usually called "schizophrenia." The word covers such a multitude of disorders that it can no longer be described as a specific disease. About 60 per cent of all the chronic patients in our mental hos-pitals are diagnosed as schizophrenics.

Shock treatments with insulin or electricity, the brain-cutting operation known as "prefrontal lobotomy" (which reduces the pa-tient to something barely human) — drastic treatments such as these are about all that modern medicine has been able to come up with to make the seriously disturbed schizophrenic tractable. Psychiatry and psychoanalysis have been of little avail, except sometimes in the early stages when a physician is still able to communicate with the patient. But some recent discoveries concerning drugs and the chemistry of the brain have introduced an encouraging note.

Even the ancients knew that certain plant juices could induce hal-lucinations (fantasies of vision, hearing, and so on) and others could bring on happy states. The Delphic priestesses of ancient Greece chewed some plant before they pronounced their cryptic oracles. Indian tribes of the southwestern United States have made a religious ritual of chewing peyote or mescal buttons (which produce halluci-nations in color). Perhaps the most dramatic case was that of the Moslem sect in a mountain stronghold in Iran who used "hashish," the juice of hemp leaves. The drug, taken in their religious ceremo-nies, gave the communicants the illusion that they caught glimpses of the paradise to which their souls would go after death, and they would obey any command of their leader, called "the Old Man of the Mountains," to receive this key to heaven. His commands took the form of ordering them to kill enemy rulers and hostile Moslem government officials; this gave rise to the word "assassin," from "hashishin" (a user of hashish). The sect terrorized the region throughout the twelfth century, until the Mongol invaders in 1226 swarmed into the mountains and killed every last assassin.

The modern counterpart of the euphoric herbs of earlier times (aside from alcohol) is the group of drugs known as the "tranquilizers." As a matter of fact, one of the tranquilizers had long been known in India in the form of a plant called *Rauwolfia serpentinum*. It was from the dried roots of this plant that American chemists in 1952 extracted "reserpine," the first of the currently popular tranquilizing drugs. Several substances with similar effects but simpler chemical structure have since been synthesized.

The tranquilizers are sedatives, but with a difference. They reduce anxiety without appreciably depressing other mental activity. Nevertheless they do tend to make people sleepy, and they may have other undesirable effects. They were at once found to be immensely helpful in relieving and quieting mental patients, including some schizophrenics. They also came into use for reducing blood pressure. But where the tranquilizers had their runaway boom was among the public at large, which apparently seized upon them as a panacea to banish all cares.

Now RESERPINE TURNS OUT to have a tantalizing resemblance to an important substance in the brain. A portion of its complex molecule is rather similar to the substance called "serotonin." Serotonin was discovered in the blood in 1948, and it has greatly intrigued physiologists ever since. It was found to be present in the hypothalamus region of the human brain and proved to be widespread in the brain and nerve tissues of other animals, including invertebrates.

What is more, various other substances that affect the central nervous system have turned out to resemble serotonin closely. One of them is a compound in toad venom called "bufotenin." Another is mescaline, the active drug in mescal buttons. Most dramatic of all is a substance named "lysergic acid diethylamide." In 1943 a Swiss chemist named Albert Hofmann happened to absorb some of this compound in the laboratory and was overcome by strange sensations. A small dose of the drug, investigation later showed, will produce many of the symptoms of schizophrenia!

What can all this mean? Well, serotonin (which is structurally like the amino acid tryptophan) can be broken down by means of an enzyme called "amine oxidase," which occurs in brain cells. Suppose that this enzyme is taken out of action by a competitive substance with a structure like serotonin's — lysergic acid, for example. With the breakdown enzyme removed, serotonin will accumulate in the brain cells, and its level may rise too high. This will upset the serotonin balance in the brain and may bring on the schizophrenic state.

Is it possible that schizophrenia arises from some naturally induced upset of this sort? In 1957 Mark D. Altschule of Harvard reported that he had brought about striking improvement in schizophrenics by injecting extracts from the pineal body, a small blob of tissue (shaped like a tiny pine cone) in the brain. His extract may conceivably be a hormone-like substance that controls the serotonin balance and thus acts as an arbiter of order in the brain.

The chief previous claim to fame of the pineal body in man was that René Descartes in the seventeenth century pronounced it the seat of the soul. For centuries scientists have chuckled over Descartes' notion. It would be irony indeed if the pineal body turned out to be a material "soul," presiding over the mind's mental and emotional health.

Be that as it may, biologists seem to be on the verge of opening up a new field which might be called "biochemical psychiatry," employing drugs to restore the balance of a disordered mind. The chemistry of the brain is certainly an inviting new frontier.

725

FEEDBACK

MAN IS NOT A MACHINE and a machine is not man, but as science and technology advance, man and machine seem to be becoming less and less distinguishable from each other.

If you analyze what it is that makes a man, one of the first thoughts that strikes you is that, more than any other living organism, he is a self-regulating system. He is capable of controlling not only himself but also his environment. He copes with changes in the environment, not by yielding but by reacting according to his own desires and standards. Let's see how close a machine can come to this ability.

About the simplest form of self-regulating mechanical device is the safety valve. A very elementary version of this is exemplified in a pressure cooker invented by the French physicist Denis Papin in 1679. To keep the lid on against the steam pressure, he placed a weight on it, but he used a weight light enough so that the lid could fly off before the pressure rose to the point where the pot would explode. The present-day household pressure cooker or steam boiler has more sophisticated devices for this purpose (such as a plug that will melt when the temperature gets too high), but the principle is the same.

Of course, this is a "one-shot" sort of regulation. But it is easy to think of examples of continuous regulation. A primitive type was a device patented in 1745 by an Englishman, Edmund Lee, to keep a windmill facing squarely to the wind. He devised a "fantail" with small vanes which caught the wind whenever the wind shifted direction; the turning of these vanes operated a set of gears that rotated the windmill itself so that its main vanes were again head-on to the wind in the new quarter. In that position the fantail vanes remained motionless; they turned only when the windmill was not facing the wind.

But the archetype of all mechanical self-regulators is the "governor" invented by James Watt for his steam engine. To keep the steam output of his engine steady, Watt conceived a device consisting of a vertical shaft with two weights attached to it laterally by hinged rods, allowing the weights to move up and down. The pressure of the steam whirled the shaft. When the steam pressure rose, the shaft whirled faster and the centrifugal force drove the weights upward. In moving up they partly closed a valve, choking off the flow of steam. As the steam pressure fell, the shaft whirled less rapidly, gravity pulled the weights down, and the valve opened. Thus the governor kept the steam pressure at a pre-set level. Each departure from that level set in train a series of events that corrected the deviation. This is called "feedback": the error itself continually sends back information and serves as the measure of the correction required.

A very familiar modern example of a feedback device is the "thermostat," invented in principle by a Scottish chemist named Andrew Ure in 1830. Its essential component is a "thermocouple," which consists of two strips of different metals laid against each other and soldered together. Since the two metals expand and contract at different rates with changes in temperature, the strip bends.

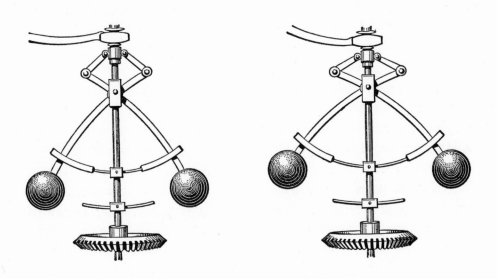

WATT'S GOVERNOR.

727

The thermostat is set, say, at 70° F. When the room temperature falls below that, the thermocouple bends in such a fashion as to make a contact that closes an electric circuit and turns on the heating system. When the temperature rises above 70 degrees, the thermocouple bends back enough to break the contact. Thus the heater regulates its own operation through feedback.

It is feedback that similarly controls the workings of the human body. To take one example of many, the glucose level in the blood is controlled by the insulin-producing pancreas just as the temperature of a house is controlled by the heater. And just as the working of the heater is regulated by the departure of the temperature from the norm, so the secretion of insulin is regulated by the departure of the glucose concentration from the norm. A too-high glucose level turns on the insulin, just as a too-low temperature turns on the heater. Likewise, as a thermostat can be turned up to higher temperature, so an internal change in the body such as the secretion of adrenalin can raise the operation of the human body to a new norm, so to speak.

Self-regulation by living organisms to maintain a constant norm was named "homeostasis" by the famous Harvard physiologist Walter Bradford Cannon, who was a leader in investigation of the phenomenon in the first decades of the twentieth century.

MOST SYSTEMS, living and non-living, lag a little in their response to feedback. For instance, after a heater has been turned off, it continues for a time to emit its residual heat; conversely, when it is turned on, it takes a little time to heat up. Therefore the room temperature does not hold to 70° F. but oscillates around that level; it is always overshooting the mark on one side or the other. This phenomenon, called "hunting," was first studied in the 1830's by George Airy, the Astronomer Royal of England, in connection with devices he had designed to turn telescopes automatically with the motion of the earth.

Hunting is characteristic of most living processes, from control of the glucose level in the blood to conscious behavior. When you reach to pick up an object, the motion of your hand is not a single movement but a series of movements continually adjusted in both speed and direction, with the muscles correcting departures from the proper line of motion, those departures being judged by the eye. The corrections are so automatic that you are not aware of them. But watch an infant, not yet practiced in visual feedback, try to pick up something. It overshoots and undershoots because the muscular corrections are not precise enough. And victims of nerve damage that interferes with the ability to utilize visual feedback go into pathetic oscillations, or wild hunting, whenever they attempt a coordinated muscular movement.

The normal, practiced hand goes smoothly to its target and stops at the right moment because the control center looks ahead and makes corrections in advance. Thus when you drive a car around a corner you begin to turn back the steering wheel before you have completed the turn, so that the wheels will be straight by the time you have rounded the corner. In other words, the correction is applied in time to avoid overshooting the mark to any significant degree. Now this principle can be applied to a machine. Matters can be arranged so that as the system approaches the desired condition, the shrinking margin between its actual state and the desired state will automatically shut off the corrective force before it overshoots. In 1868 a French engineer, Léon Farcot, used this principle to invent an automatic control for a steam-operated ship's rudder. As the rudder approached the desired position, his device automatically closed down the steam valve; by the time the rudder reached the specified position, the steam pressure had been shut off. When the rudder moved away from this position, its motion opened the appropriate valve so that it was pushed back. Farcot called his device a "servomechanism," and in a sense it ushered in the era of "automation."

Servomechanisms did not really come into their own until the arrival of electronics. The application of electronics made it possible to endow the mechanisms with a sensitivity and swiftness of response even beyond the capabilities of a living organism. Furthermore, radio extended their sphere of action over a considerable distance. The German buzz-bomb of World War II was essentially a flying servomechanism, and it introduced the possibility not only of guided missiles but also of self-operated or remotely-operated vehicles of all sorts, from subway trains to space ships. Because the military establishments had the keenest interest in these devices, and the most abundant supply of funds, servomechanisms have reached perhaps their highest development in aiming-and-firing mechanisms for guns and rockets. These systems can detect a swiftly moving target hundreds of miles away, instantly calculate its course (taking into account the target's speed of motion, the wind, the temperatures of the various layers of air, and numerous other conditions), and hit the target with pinpoint accuracy, all without any human guidance.

Automation found an ardent theoretician and advocate in the mathematician Norbert Wiener. In the 1940's he and his group at the Massachusetts Institute of Technology worked out some of the fundamental mathematical relationships governing the handling of feedback. He named this branch of study "cybernetics," from the Greek word for "helmsman," which seems appropriate, since the first use of servomechanisms was in connection with a helmsman. (Cybernetics also harks back to Watt's centrifugal governor, for "governor" comes from the Latin word for helmsman.)

Since World War II automation has progressed fairly rapidly, especially in the United States and the Soviet Union. Oil refineries and factories manufacturing objects such as radio sets and aluminum pistons have been set up on an almost completely automatic basis, taking in raw materials at one end and pouring out finished products at the other, with all the processes handled by self-regulating machines. Automation has even invaded the farm: engineers at the University of Wisconsin announced in 1960 an automated hog-feeding system in which machines would feed each hog the correct amount of the correct type of feed at the correct time.

In a sense, automation marks the beginning of a new Industrial Revolution. Like the first revolution, it may bring great pains of adjustment, not only for workers but also for the economy in general. There is a story of an automobile executive who conducted a union official on a tour of a new automatic factory and observed: "You won't be able to collect union dues from these machines, I'm afraid." The union official shot back: "And you won't be able to sell them automobiles, either."

Automation will not make the human worker obsolete, any more than the steam engine or electricity did. But it will certainly mean a great shift in emphasis. The first Industrial Revolution made it no longer necessary for a man to be a muscle-straining workhorse. The second will make it no longer necessary for him to be a mind-dulled automaton.

NATURALLY, feedback and servomechanisms have stirred up as much interest among biologists as among engineers. Self-regulating machines can serve as simplified models for studying the workings of the nervous system.

A generation ago the imagination of men was excited — and disturbed — by Karel Čapek's play *R. U. R.* (for "Rossem's Universal Robots," robot coming from the Czech word meaning "to work"). In recent years scientists have begun to experiment with various forms of robots (now usually called "automata") not as mere mechanical substitutes for men but as tools to explore the nature of living organisms. For instance, L. D. Harmon of the Bell Telephone Laboratories devised a transistorized circuit which, like a neuron, fires electrical pulses when stimulated. Such circuits can be assembled into devices that mimic some of the functions of the eye and the ear. In England the biologist W. Ross Ashby formed a system of circuits that exhibits simple reflex responses. He calls his creature a "homeostat," because it tends to maintain itself in a stable state.

The British neurologist W. Grey Walter built a more elaborate system that explores and reacts to its surroundings. His turtle-like object, which he calls a "testudo" (Latin for "tortoise"), has a photoelectric cell for an eye, a sensing device to detect touch, and two motors, one to move forward or backward and the other to turn around. In the dark, it crawls about, circling in a wide arc. When it touches an obstacle, it backs off a bit, turns slightly and moves forward again; it will do this until it gets around the obstacle. When its photoelectric eye sees a light, the turning motor shuts off and the testudo advances straight toward the light. But its phototropism is under control; as it gets close to the light the increase in brightness causes it to back away, so that it avoids the mistake of the moth. When its batteries run down, however, the now "hungry" testudo can crawl close enough to the light to make contact with a recharger placed near the light bulb. Once recharged, it is again sensitive enough to back away from the bright area around the light.

The mathematician John von Neumann, one of the authors of the theory of games, considered the problem of constructing a machine that would reproduce itself. He concluded that a machine equipped with a program of instructions (corresponding to DNA) could, in theory, assemble replicas of itself from a supply of parts. It might, in fact, build any machine for which it had a set of plans.

These are not thinking machines. They are in the true sense robots, capable of performing certain functions of a living organism. A specialized robot may easily perform a particular task more efficiently than a human being can. A generalized robot, designed to do a variety of things, would be far less efficient than a man, but such creations may well be useful and perhaps necessary in the first explorations of space. The Harvard astronomer Fred L. Whipple has suggested that robots might be used to build space platforms. The first visitor to the moon may be a robot.

THINKING MACHINES

CAN WE BUILD A MACHINE that thinks? To try to answer that question we must first define "thinking."

Certainly we can take mathematics as one form of thinking. And it is a particularly good example for our purposes. For one thing, it is distinctly a human attribute. Some lower organisms are able to distinguish between three objects and four, say, but no species except *Homo sapiens* can perform the simple operation of dividing ¾ by ⅞. Secondly, mathematics involves a type of reasoning that operates by fixed rules and includes (ideally) no undefined terms or procedures. It can be analyzed in a more definite and more precise way than can the kind of thinking that goes into, say, literary composition or high finance or industrial management or military strategy. So let us consider machines in relation to mathematics.

Tools to aid mathematical reasoning are undoubtedly as old as mathematics itself. The first tools for the purpose must have been man's own fingers. Mathematics began when man used his fingers to represent numbers and combinations of numbers. It is no accident that the word "digit" stands both for a finger (or toe) and for a numerical integer.

From that, another step leads to the use of other objects in place of fingers — small pebbles, perhaps. There are more pebbles than fingers, and intermediate results can be preserved for future reference in the course of solving the problem. Again, it is no accident that the word "calculate" comes from the Latin word for pebble.

Pebbles or beads lined up in slots or strung on wires formed the "abacus," the first really versatile mathematical tool. With this device it became easy to represent units, tens, hundreds, thousands, and so on. By manipulating the pebbles, or counters, of an abacus, one could quickly carry through an addition such as $576 + 289$. Furthermore, any instrument that can add can also multiply, for multiplication is only repeated addition. And multiplication makes raising to a power possible, because this is only repeated multiplication (*e.g.*, 4^5 is shorthand for $4 \times 4 \times 4 \times 4 \times 4$). Finally, running the instrument backward, so to speak, makes possible the operations of subtraction, division, and extracting a root.

The abacus can be considered the second "digital computer." (The first, of course, was the fingers.)

For thousands of years the abacus remained the most advanced

733

form of calculating tool. In fact, it was not replaced until someone invented a numerical notation which imitated the workings of the abacus. That is, the nine different pebbles in the units row of the abacus were represented by nine different symbols, and those same nine symbols were used for the tens row, hundreds row, and thousands row. Counters differing only in position were replaced by symbols differing only in position, so that in the written number 222, for instance, the first 2 represents 200, the second 20, and the third represents two itself; that is, $200 + 20 + 2 = 222$.

This "positional notation" was made possible by recognition of an all-important fact which the ancient users of the abacus had overlooked. Although there are only nine counters in each row of the abacus, there are actually ten possible arrangements. Besides using any number of counters from one to nine in a row, it is also possible to use *no* counter — that is, to leave the place at the counting position empty. This escaped all the great Greek mathematicians and was not recognized until the ninth century, when some unnamed Hindu thought of representing the tenth alternative by a special symbol which the Arabs called "sifr" ("empty") and which has come down to us, in consequence, as "cipher" or, in more corrupt form, "zero." The importance of the zero is recorded in the fact that the manipulation of numbers is still sometimes called "ciphering," and that to solve any hard problem is to "decipher" it.

Another powerful tool grew out of the use of the exponents to express powers of numbers. To express 100 as 10^2, 1,000 as 10^3, 100,000 as 10^5, and so on is a great convenience in several respects; not only does it simplify the writing of large numbers but it reduces multiplication and division to simple addition or subtraction of the exponents (*e.g.*, $10^2 \times 10^3 = 10^5$) and makes raising to a power or extraction of a root a simple matter of multiplying or dividing exponents (*e.g.*, the cube root of 1,000,000 is $10^{6/3} = 10^2$). Now this is all very well, but very few numbers can be put into simple exponential form. What could be done with a number such as 111? The answer to that question led to the tables of logarithms.

The first to deal with this problem was the seventeenth-century

734

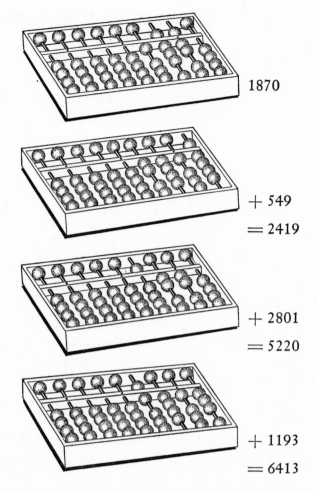

1870

+ 549

= 2419

+ 2801

= 5220

+ 1193

= 6413

ADDING WITH AN ABACUS. *Each counter below the bar counts 1; each counter above the bar counts 5. A counter registers when it is pushed to the bar. Thus in the top setting here the right-hand column reads 0; the one to the left of that reads 7 or (5 + 2); the next left reads 8 or (5 + 3); and the next left reads 1: the number shown, then, is 1870. When 549 is added to this, the right column becomes 9 or (9 + 0); the next addition (4 + 7) becomes 1 with 1 to carry, which means that one counter is pushed up in the next column; the third addition is 9 + 5, or 4 with 1 to carry; and the fourth addition is 1 + 1 or 2: the addition gives 2419, as the abacus shows. The simple maneuver of carrying 1 by pushing up a counter in the next column makes it possible to calculate very rapidly; a skilled operator can add faster than an adding machine can.*

Scottish mathematician John Napier. Obviously, expressing a number such as 111 as a power of 10 involves assigning a fractional exponent to 10 (the exponent is between 2 and 3). In more general terms, the exponent will be fractional whenever the number in question is not a multiple of the base number. Napier worked out a method of calculating the fractional exponents of numbers, and he named these exponents "logarithms." For the base he used not 10 but a quantity called e (approximately 2.71828 . . .) which evolved naturally out of the rather advanced mathematics used in calculating the exponents. Napier's logarithms therefore are called "natural logarithms." Shortly afterward the English mathematician Henry Briggs worked out logarithms with 10 as the base. The "Briggsian logarithms" are less convenient than Napier's for calculus, but they are more popular for ordinary computations.

All non-integral exponents are irrational; that is, they cannot be expressed in the form of an ordinary fraction. They can be expressed only as an indefinitely long decimal expression lacking a repeating pattern. Such a decimal can be calculated, however, to as many places as necessary for the desired precision.

For instance, let us say we wish to multiply 111 by 254. The Briggsian logarithm of 111 to five decimal places is 2.04532, and for 254 it is 2.40483. Adding these logarithms, we get $10^{2.04532} \times 10^{2.40483} = 10^{4.45015}$. That number is approximately 28,194, the actual product of 111×254. If we want to get still closer accuracy, we can use the logarithms to six or more decimal places.

Tables of logarithms simplified computation enormously. In 1622 an English mathematician named William Oughtred made things still easier by devising a "slide rule." Two rulers are marked with a "logarithmic scale," in which the distances between numbers get shorter as the numbers get larger: for example, the first division holds the numbers from 1 to 10; the second division, of the same length, holds the numbers from 11 to 100; the third from 101 to 1,000; and so on. Now by sliding one rule along the other to an appropriate position, one can read off the result of an operation involving multiplication or division. The slide rule makes such computations as easy as addition and subtraction on the abacus, though in both cases, to be sure, one must be skilled in the use of the instrument.

THE FIRST STEP toward a truly automatic calculating machine was taken in 1642 by the French mathematician Blaise Pascal. He invented an adding machine which did away with the need to move the counters separately in each row of the abacus. His machine consisted of a set of wheels connected by gears. When the first wheel—the units wheel—was turned ten notches to its 0 mark, the second wheel turned one notch to the number 1, so the two wheels together showed the number 10. When the tens wheel reached its 0, the third wheel turned a notch, showing 100, and so on. (The principle is the same as that of the mileage indicator in an automobile).

Pascal's device could add and subtract. In 1674 the mathematician Gottfried Wilhelm von Leibnitz went a step farther and arranged the wheels and gears so that multiplication and division were as automatic and easy as addition and subtraction. In 1850 a United States inventor named D. D. Parmalee patented an important advance which added greatly to the calculator's convenience: in place of moving the wheels by hand, he introduced a set of keys — pushing down a marked key with the finger turned the wheels to the correct number. This is the mechanism of what is now familiar to us as the old-fashioned cash register.

It remained only to electrify the machine (so that motors did the work dictated by the touching of keys), and the Pascal-Leibnitz device graduated into the modern desk computer.

The desk computer, however, represents a dead end, not the wave of the future. The computer that we have in mind when we consider thinking machines is an entirely different affair. Its granddaddy is an idea conceived early in the eighteenth century by an English mathematician named Charles Babbage.

A genius far in advance of his time, Babbage imagined an analytical machine that would be able to perform any mathematical operation, store numbers in a memory device, compare the results of operations, and so on. He worked for 37 years on his ideas, putting together awesomely elaborate structures of wheels, cams, levers, and wires. In the end he failed, because what he was seeking to achieve could not be accomplished with mere mechanical devices.

The machine had to wait a century for the development of electronics. And electronics in turn suggested the use of a mathematical language much easier for a machine to handle than the decimal system of numerals. It is called the "binary system." To understand the modern computer we must acquaint ourselves with this system.

The binary notation uses only two digits: 0 and 1. It expresses all numbers in terms of powers of 2. Thus the number one is 2^0, the number two is 2^1, three is $2^1 + 2^0$, four is 2^2, and so on. As in the decimal system, the power is indicated by the position of the symbol. For instance, the number four is represented by 100, read thus: $(1 \times 2^2) + (0 \times 2^1) + (0 \times 2^0)$, or $4 + 0 + 0 = 4$ in the decimal system.

As an illustration, let us consider the number 6,413. In the decimal system it can be written $(6 \times 10^3) + (4 \times 10^2) + (1 \times 10^1) + (3 \times 10^0)$ — remember that any number to the zero power equals 1. Now in the binary system we add numbers in powers of 2, instead of powers of 10, to compose a number. The highest power of 2 that leaves us short of 6,413 is 12; 2^{12} is 4,096. If we now add 2^{11}, or 2,048, we have 6,144, which is 269 short of 6,413. Next, 2^8 adds 256 more, leaving 13; we can then add 2^3, or 8, leaving 5; then 2^2, or 4, leaving 1; and 2^0 is 1. Thus we might write the number 6,413 as $(1 \times 2^{12}) + (1 \times 2^{11}) + (1 \times 2^8) + (1 \times 2^3) + (1 \times 2^2) + (1 \times 2^0)$. But as in the decimal system, each digit in a number, reading from the left, must represent the next smaller power. Just as in the decimal system we represent the additions of the third, second, first, and zero powers of 10 in stating the number 6,413, so in the binary system we must represent the additions of the powers of 2 from 12 down to 0. In the form of a table this would read:

$$1 \times 2^{12} = 4{,}096$$
$$1 \times 2^{11} = 2{,}048$$
$$0 \times 2^{10} = 0$$
$$0 \times 2^{9} = 0$$
$$1 \times 2^{8} = 256$$
$$0 \times 2^{7} = 0$$
$$0 \times 2^{6} = 0$$
$$0 \times 2^{5} = 0$$
$$0 \times 2^{4} = 0$$
$$1 \times 2^{3} = 8$$
$$1 \times 2^{2} = 4$$
$$0 \times 2^{1} = 0$$
$$1 \times 2^{0} = 1$$
$$\overline{6{,}413}$$

Taking the successive multipliers in the column at the left (as we take 6, 4, 1, and 3 as the successive multipliers in the decimal system), we write the number in the binary system as 1100100001101.

This looks pretty cumbersome. It takes 13 digits to write the number 6,413, whereas in the decimal system we need only four. But for a computing machine the system is just about the simplest imaginable. Since there are only two different digits, any operation can be carried out in terms of just the two states of an electrical circuit — on and off. On (*i.e.*, the circuit closed) can represent 1; off (the circuit open) can represent 0. With proper circuitry and

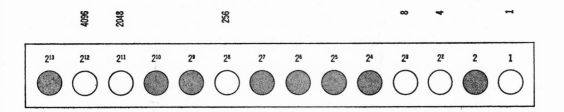

THE NUMBER 6,413 *represented by lights on a computer panel. The unshaded circles are lamps turned on.*

the use of diodes the machine can carry out all sorts of mathematical manipulations. For instance, with two switches in parallel it can perform addition: $0 + 0 = 0$ (off plus off equals off), and $0 + 1 = 1$ (off plus on equals on). Similarly, two switches in series can perform multiplication: $0 \times 0 = 0$; $0 \times 1 = 0$; $1 \times 1 = 1$.

So much for the binary system. As for electronics, its contribution to the computing machine is incredible speed. It can perform an arithmetical operation almost instantaneously: some of the electronic computers carry out billions of operations per second! Calculations that would take a man with a pencil a lifetime can be completed by a computer in a matter of days. To cite a typical case, before the coming of the computer an English mathematician named William Shanks spent 15 years calculating the value of π and carried it to 707 decimal places (getting the last hundred-odd places wrong); recently an electronic computer carried out the calculation accurately to 10,000 decimal places, taking only a few days for the job.

The first large electronic computer, built at the University of Pennsylvania during World War II, was ENIAC (for Electronic Numerical Integrator and Computer). Is ENIAC a "thinking machine?" Hardly. Essentially it is no more than a very rapid abacus. It slavishly follows instructions that are fed into it.

The basic tool for instructing most computers is the punch card. A hole punched in a definite position on such a card can signify a number; a combination of two or more holes in specific positions can signify a letter of the alphabet, an operation of mathematics, a quality — anything one chooses to let it represent. Thus the card can record a person's name, the color of his eyes and hair, his position or income, his marital status, his special talents or educational qualifications. When the card is passed between electric poles, the contacts made through the holes set up a specific electrical pattern. By scanning cards in this way and selecting only those that set up a particular pattern, the machine can pick out of a large population just those individuals, say, who are over six feet tall, have blue eyes, and speak Russian.

Similarly, a punch card carrying a "program" for a computer sets up electrical circuits that cause the machine to put certain numbers through certain operations. In all except the simplest programs, the computer has to store some numbers or data until it is ready to use them in the course of its series of operations. This means it must have a memory device. The memory in a modern computer usually is of the magnetic type: the numbers are stored in the form of magnetized spots on a drum or in some other kind of array. A particular spot may represent the digit 1 when it is magnetized and 0 when it is not magnetized. Each such item of information is a "bit" (for "binary digit"). The spots are magnetized by an electric current in recording the information and also are read off by an electric current.

The computer is, of course, the crowning instrument that makes full automation possible. Servomechanisms can only carry out the slave aspects of a task. In any complex process, such as the aiming and firing of a gun or the operation of an automatic factory, computers are necessary to calculate, interpret, coordinate, and supervise — in other words, to serve as mechanical minds to direct the mechanical muscles. And the computer is by no means limited to this sort of function. It makes out your electric bills; it handles reservations for airlines; it keeps the records of checks and banking accounts; it deals with company payrolls, maintains a running record of inventories, in short, handles a great deal of the business of large corporations today.

The mathematicians, physicists, and engineers investigating the possible uses of computers are sure that all this is only a beginning. They have programed computers to play chess, as an exercise in storing and applying information. (Of course, the machine plays only a mediocre game, but very likely it will eventually be possible to program a computer to learn from its opponent's moves.) In laboratory experiments computers have been programed to digest articles from scientific journals, to index such articles, and to translate from one language into another. For instance, with a vocabulary of Russian words and their English equivalents stored in its memory, a computer can scan Russian print, recognize key words, and render a crude translation. A great deal of research is being done on this problem of translating by machine, because the flood of technical literature the world over is so vast that human translators cannot possibly keep up with it.

Not only can a computer "read"; it can also listen. Workers at the Bell Telephone Laboratories have built a machine called "Audrey" which can distinguish words of ordinary speech. Presumably this creates the possibility that computers will some day be able to "understand" spoken instructions. And if a machine can "hear," perhaps it could also speak.

So far these developments are only suggested as distant possibilities. Computers are fast and far more efficient than a man in performing routine mathematical operations, but they do not begin to approach the flexibility of the human mind. Whereas even a child learning to read has no difficulty in recognizing that a capital B, a small b, and an italic *b* in various type sizes and styles all stand for the same letter, this is far beyond any present machine. To attain any such flexibility in a machine would call for prohibitive size and complexity.

The human brain weighs about three pounds and works on a practically negligible input of energy. In contrast, ENIAC, which is probably less than one-millionth as complex as the brain, weighs 30 tons and requires 150 kilowatts of energy. To be sure, devices such as the transistor and the "cryotron," a kind of switch employing superconducting wires at low temperatures, have miniatured computers and reduced the power requirements. But we are not yet in sight of the amazing compactness of the human brain.

WE HAVE STILL NOT ANSWERED THE QUESTION whether a machine can think. Yet we have a good part of the answer. A machine, we have seen, can calculate, remember, associate, compare, and recognize. Can it also reason? The answer again is yes.

In 1938 a young American mathematician and engineer named Claude E. Shannon pointed out in his master's thesis that deductive logic, in a form known as Boolean algebra, could be handled by means of the binary system. Boolean algebra refers to a system of "symbolic logic" suggested in 1854 by the English mathematician George Boole in a book entitled *An Investigation of the Laws of Thought*. Boole observed that the types of statements employed in deductive logic could be represented by mathematical symbols, and he went on to show how such symbols could be manipulated according to fixed rules to yield appropriate conclusions.

To take a very simple example, consider the following statement: "Both A and B are true." We are to determine the truth or falsity of this statement by a strictly logical exercise, assuming that we know whether A and B, respectively, are true or false. To handle the problem in binary terms, as Shannon suggested, let 0 represent "false" and 1 represent "true." If A and B are both false, then the statement "Both A and B are true" is false. In other words, 0 and 0 yield 0. If A is true but B is false (or vice versa), then the statement again is false. That is, 1 and 0 (or 0 and 1) yield 0. If A is true and B is true, then the statement "Both A and B are true" is true. Symbolically, 1 and 1 yield 1.

Now these three alternatives correspond to the three possible multiplications in the binary system, namely: $0 \times 0 = 0$, $1 \times 0 = 0$, and $1 \times 1 = 1$. Thus the problem in logic posed by the statement "Both A and B are true" can be manipulated by multiplication. A computer (properly programed) therefore can handle this logical problem as easily, and in the same way, as it handles ordinary calculations.

In the case of the statement "Either A or B is true," the problem is handled by addition instead of by multiplication. If neither A nor B is true, then this statement is false. In other words, $0 + 0 = 0$. If A is true and B false, or vice versa, the statement is true; in these cases $1 + 0 = 1$ and $0 + 1 = 1$. If both A and B are true, the statement is certainly true, and $1 + 1 = 10$. (The significant digit in the 10 is the 1; the fact that it is moved over one position is immaterial. In the binary system 10 represents $(1 \times 2^1) + (0 \times 2^0)$, which is equivalent to 2 in the decimal system.)

7 4 3

Boolean algebra has become important in the engineering of communications, and it forms part of what is now known as "information theory."

WHAT REMAINS OF THINKING, then, that cannot be acquired by the machine? We are left finally with creativity and the ability of the human mind to cope with the unknown: its intuition, judgment, weighing of a situation and the possible consequences — call it what you will. This, too, was put in mathematical form, after a fashion, by the mathematician John von Neumann, who with the economist Oskar Morgenstern wrote the *Theory of Games and Economic Behavior* in the early 1940's.

Von Neumann took certain simple games, such as matching coins and poker, as models for analysis of the typical situation in which one tries to find a winning strategy against an opponent who is himself selecting the best possible course of action for his own purposes. Military campaigns, business competition, many matters of great moment involve decisions of this kind. Even scientific research can be viewed as a game of man against Nature, and game theory can be helpful in selecting the optimal strategy of research, assuming that Nature stacks the cards in the way that will hamper man most (which, in fact, it often seems to do).

All these attempts to mimic the mind of man are in their earliest infancy. Not in the foreseeable future can we envision any possibility of a machine matching the human brain. The road, however, is open, and it conjures up thoughts which are exciting but also in some ways frightening. What if man eventually were to produce a mechanical creature equal or superior to himself in all respects, including intelligence and creativity? Would it replace man, as the superior organisms of the earth have replaced or subordinated the less well-adapted in the long history of evolution?

It is a queasy thought: that we represent, for the first time in the history of life on the earth, a species capable of bringing about its own possible replacement. Of course, we have it in our power to

744

prevent such a regrettable denouement by refusing to build machines that are too intelligent. But it is tempting to build them nevertheless. What achievement could be grander than the creation of
an object that surpasses the creator? How could we consummate the
victory of intelligence over Nature more gloriously than by passing
on our heritage in triumph to a greater intelligence — of our own
making?

APPENDIX

MATHEMATICS IN SCIENCE

GRAVITATION

As I explained in Chapter 1, Galileo initiated science in its modern sense by introducing the concept of reasoning back from observation and experiment to basic principles. In doing so, he also introduced the essential technique of measuring natural phenomena accurately and abandoned the practice of merely describing them in general terms. In short, he turned from the qualitative description of the Universe by the Greek thinkers to a quantitative description.

Although science depends so much on mathematical relationships and manipulations, and could not exist in the Galilean sense without it, I have nevertheless written this book non-mathematically, and done so deliberately. Mathematics, after all, is a highly-specialized tool. To have discussed the developments in science in mathematical terms would have required a prohibitive amount of space and required a sophisticated knowledge of mathematics on the part of the reader. But in this appendix I would like to present an example or two of the way in which simple mathematics has been fruitfully applied to science. How better to begin than with Galileo himself?

Galileo (like Leonardo da Vinci nearly a century earlier) suspected that falling objects steadily increased their velocity as they fell. He set out to measure exactly by how much and in what manner the velocity increased.

The measurement was anything but easy for Galileo, with the tools he had at his disposal in 1600. To measure a velocity requires the measurement of time. We speak of velocities of 60 miles *an hour*, of 13 feet *a second*. But there were no clocks in Galileo's time that could do more than strike the hour at approximately equal intervals.

Galileo resorted to a crude water clock. He let water trickle slowly from a small spout, assuming, hopefully, that it dripped at a constant rate. This water he caught in a cup, and by the weight of water caught during the interval in which an event took place, Galileo measured the elapsed time. (He also used his pulse beat for the purpose on occasion.)

One difficulty was, however, that a falling object dropped so rapidly that Galileo could not collect enough water, in the interval of falling, to weigh accurately. What he did, then, was to "dilute" the pull of gravity by having a brass ball roll down a groove in an inclined plane. The more nearly horizontal the plane, the more slowly the ball moved. Thus Galileo was able to study falling bodies in whatever degree of "slow motion" he pleased.

Galileo found that a ball rolling on a perfectly horizontal plane moved at constant speed. (This supposes a lack of friction, a condition which could be assumed within the limits of Galileo's crude measurements.) Now a body moving on a horizontal track is moving at right angles to the force of gravity. Under such conditions, the body's velocity is not affected by gravity either way. A ball resting on a horizontal plane remains at rest, as anyone can observe. A ball set to moving on a horizontal plane moves at a constant velocity, as Galileo observed.

Mathematically, then, it can be stated that the velocity v of a body, *in the absence of any external force*, is constant k, or:

$$v = k$$

If k is equal to any number other than zero, the ball is moving at constant velocity. If k is equal to zero, the ball is at rest; thus rest is a "special case" of constant velocity.

Nearly a century later, when Newton systematized the discoveries of Galileo in connection with falling bodies, this finding became the First Law of Motion (also called the "principle of inertia"). It is usually given something like this: Every body persists in a state of rest or of uniform motion in a straight line unless compelled by external force to change that state.

When a ball rolls down an inclined plane, however, it is under the continuous pull of gravity. Its velocity then, Galileo found, was not constant but increased with time. Galileo's measurements showed that the velocity increased in proportion to the lapse of time t.

In other words, when a body was under the action of constant external force, its velocity, starting at rest, could be expressed as:

$$v = kt$$

What was the value of k?

That, it was easy to find by experiment, depended on the slope of the inclined plane. The more nearly vertical the plane, the more quickly the rolling ball gained velocity and the higher the value of k. The maximum gain in speed would come when the plane was vertical — in other words, when the ball dropped freely under the undiluted pull of gravity. The symbol g (for "gravity") is used where the undiluted force of gravity is acting, so that the velocity of a ball in free fall starting from rest, was:

$$v = gt$$

Now let's consider the inclined plane in more detail. In the diagram:

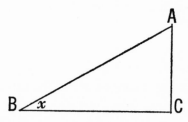

the length of the inclined plane is AB, while its height at the upper end is AC. The ratio of AC to AB is the sine of the angle x, usually abbreviated as sin x.

The value of this ratio — that is, of sin x — can be obtained approximately by constructing triangles with particular angles and actually measuring the height and length involved. Or it can be calculated by mathematical techniques to any degree of precision, and the results can be embodied in a table. By using such a table, we can find, for instance, that sin 10° is approximately equal to 0.17365, that sin 45° is approximately equal to 0.70711, and so on.

There are two important special cases. Suppose that the "inclined" plane is precisely horizontal. Angle x is then zero and as the height of the inclined plane is zero, the ratio of its height to its length is also zero. In other words, sin 0° = 0. When the "inclined" plane is precisely vertical, the angle it forms with the ground is a right angle, or 90°. Its height is then exactly equal to its length, so that the ratio of one to the other is just 1. Consequently, sin 90° = 1.

Now let's return to the equation showing that the velocity of a ball rolling down an inclined plane is proportional to time:

$$v = kt$$

It can be shown by experiment that the value of k changes with the sine of the angle so that:

$$k = k' \sin x$$

(where k' is used to indicate a constant that is different from k).

In the case of a completely vertical inclined plane, $\sin x$ becomes $\sin 90°$, which is 1, so that in free fall

$$k = k'$$

It follows that k' is the value of k in free fall under the undiluted pull of gravity, which we have already agreed to symbolize as g. We can substitute g for k' and, for any inclined plane:

$$k = g \sin x.$$

The equation for the velocity of a body rolling down an inclined plane is, therefore:

$$v = (g \sin x)\ t$$

On a horizontal plane with $\sin x = \sin 0° = 0$, the equation for velocity becomes:

$$v = 0$$

This is another way of saying that a ball on a horizontal plane, starting from rest, will remain motionless regardless of the passage of time. An object at rest tends to remain at rest, etc. That's part of the First Law of Motion, and it follows from the inclined plane equation of velocity.

Suppose that a ball doesn't start from rest but has an initial motion before it begins to fall. Suppose, in other words, you have a ball moving along a horizontal plane at five feet per second, and it suddenly finds itself at the upper end of an inclined plane and starts rolling downward.

Experiment shows that its velocity thereafter is five feet per second greater, at every moment, than it would have been if it had started rolling down the plane from rest. In other words, the equation for the motion of a ball down an inclined plane can be expressed more completely as follows:

$$v = (g \sin x)\, t + V$$

where V is the original starting velocity. If an object starts at rest, then V is equal to 0 and the equation becomes as we had it before:

$$v = (g \sin x)\, t$$

If we next consider an object with some initial velocity on a horizontal plane, so that angle x is $0°$, the equation becomes:

$$v = (g \sin 0°) + V$$

or, since $\sin 0°$ is 0:

$$v = V$$

Thus the velocity of such an object remains its initial velocity, regardless of the lapse of time. That is the rest of the First Law of Motion, again derived from observed motion on an inclined plane.

The rate at which velocity changes is called "acceleration." If, for instance, the velocity (in feet per second) of a ball rolling down an inclined plane is, at the end of successive seconds, 4, 8, 12, 16 . . . then the acceleration is four feet per second per second.

In a free fall, if we use the equation:

$$v = gt$$

each second of fall brings an increase in velocity of g feet per second. Therefore, g represents the acceleration due to gravity.

The value of g can be determined from inclined-plane experiments. By transposing the inclined-plane equation, we get:

$$g = v / (t \sin x)$$

Since v, t, and x can all be measured, g can be calculated, and it turns out to be equal to 32 feet per second per second. In free fall under normal gravity at earth's surface, then, the velocity of fall is related to time thus:

$$v = 32t$$

This is the solution to Galileo's original problem: namely, determining the rate of fall of a falling body and the manner in which that rate changes.

The next question is: how far does a body fall in a given time? From the equation relating the velocity to time, it is possible to relate distance to time by the process in calculus called "integration." It is not necessary to go into that, however, because the equation can be worked out by experiment, and, in essence, Galileo did this.

He found that a ball rolling down an inclined plane covered a distance proportional to the square of the time. In other words, doubling the time increased the distance four-fold, tripling it increased the distance nine-fold, and so on.

For a freely falling body, the equation relating distance d and time is:

$$d = \tfrac{1}{2} gt^2$$

or, since g is equal to 32:

$$d = 16t^2$$

Next suppose that instead of dropping from rest, an object is thrown horizontally from a position high in the air. Its motion would then be a compound of two motions — a horizontal one and a vertical one.

The horizontal motion, involving no force other than the single original impulse (if we disregard wind, air resistance, and so on), is one of constant velocity, in accordance with the First Law of Motion, and the distance the object covers horizontally is proportional to the time elapsed. The vertical motion, however, covers a distance, as I have just explained, that is proportional to the square of the time elapsed.

The combination of these two motions (proportional to time horizontally, and proportional to the square of the time vertically) produces a curve called a parabola. If a body is thrown not horizontally but upward or downward, the curve of motion is still a parabola.

Such curves of motion, or trajectories, apply, of course, to a projectile such as a cannon ball. The mathematical analysis of trajectories, stemming from Galileo's work, made it possible to calculate where a cannon ball would fall when fired with a given propulsive force and a given angle of elevation of the cannon. Thus, as it happened, the very first achievement of modern science proved to have a direct and immediate military application.

Isaac Newton extended the Galilean concepts of motion to the heavens and showed that the same set of laws of motion applied to the heavens and the earth alike.

He began by considering that the moon might be falling toward the earth in response to the earth's gravity but never struck the earth's surface because of the horizontal component of its motion. A projectile fired horizontally, as I said, follows a parabolically curved path downward to intersection with earth's surface. But the earth's surface curves downward, too, since the earth is a sphere. A projectile given a sufficiently rapid horizontal motion might curve downward no faster than the earth's surface and would therefore eternally circle the earth.

Now the moon's elliptical motion around the earth can be split into horizontal and vertical components. The vertical component is such that in the space of a second the moon falls a trifle more than

1/20 of an inch toward the earth. In that time it also moves about 3,300 feet in the horizontal direction, just far enough to compensate for the fall and carry it around the earth's curvature.

The question was whether this 1/20 inch fall of the moon was caused by the same gravitational attraction that caused an apple, falling from a tree, to drop 16 feet in the first second of its fall.

Newton visualized the earth's gravitational force as spreading out in all directions like a vast, expanding sphere. Now the surface area A of a sphere is proportional to the square of its radius r:

$$A = 4\pi r^2$$

He therefore reasoned that the gravitational force, spreading out over the spherical area, must weaken as the square of the radius. The intensity of light and of sound weakened as the square of the distance from the source — why not the force of gravity as well?

The distance from the earth's center to an apple on its surface is roughly 4,000 miles. The distance from the earth's center to the moon is roughly 240,000 miles. Since the distance to the moon was 60 times greater than to the apple, the force of the earth's gravity at the moon must be 60^2, or 3,600, times weaker than at the apple. Divide 16 feet by 3,600, and you come out with roughly 1/20 of an inch. It seemed clear to Newton that the moon did indeed move in the grip of the earth's gravity.

Newton was led on further to consider "mass" in relation to gravity. Ordinarily we measure mass as weight. But weight is only the result of the attraction of the earth's gravitational force. If there were no gravity, an object would be weightless; nevertheless it would still contain the same amount of matter. Mass, therefore, is independent of weight and should be capable of measurement by a means not involving weight.

Suppose you tried to pull an object on a perfectly frictionless surface in a direction horizontal to the earth's surface, so that there was no resistance from gravity. It would take effort to set the body in motion and to accelerate its motion, because of the body's inertia.

If you measured the applied force accurately, say by pulling on a spring balance attached to the object, you would find that the force f required to bring about a given acceleration a would be directly proportional to the mass m. If you doubled the mass, it would take double the force. For a given mass, the force required would be directly proportional to the acceleration desired. Mathematically all this is expressed in the equation:

$$f = ma$$

The equation is known as Newton's Second Law of Motion.

Now, as Galileo had found, the pull of the earth's gravity accelerates all bodies, heavy or light, at precisely the same rate. (Air resistance may slow the fall of very light bodies, but in a vacuum a feather will fall as rapidly as a lump of lead, as can easily be demonstrated.) If the Second Law of Motion is to hold, one must conclude that the earth's gravitational pull on a heavy body must be greater than on a light body, in order to produce the same acceleration. To accelerate a mass that is eight times as great as another, for instance, takes eight times as much force. It follows that the earth's gravitational pull on any body must be exactly proportional to the mass of that body. (That, in fact, is why mass on the earth's surface can be measured quite accurately as weight.)

Newton evolved a Third Law of Motion, too. It goes: "For every action there is an equal and opposite reaction." This applies to force. In other words, if the earth pulls at the moon with a certain force, then the moon pulls on the earth with an equal force. If the moon were suddenly doubled in mass, the earth's gravitational force upon it would also be doubled, in accordance with the Second Law, and of course the moon's gravitational force on the earth would then have to be doubled in accordance with the Third Law.

Similarly, if it were the earth rather than the moon that doubled in mass, it would be the moon's gravitational force on the earth that would double, according to the Second Law, and the earth's gravitational force on the moon that would double, in accordance with the Third.

If both the earth and the moon were to double in mass, there would be a doubled doubling, each body doubling its gravitational force twice, for a four-fold increase all told.

Newton could only conclude by this sort of reasoning that the gravitational force between any two bodies in the Universe was directly proportional to the product of the masses of the bodies. And, of course, as he had decided earlier, it is inversely proportional to the square of the distance (center to center) between the bodies. This is Newton's Law of Universal Gravitation.

If we let f represent the gravitational force, m_1 and m_2 the masses of the two bodies concerned, and d the distance between them, then the law can be stated:

$$f = \frac{Gm_1m_2}{d^2}$$

G is the "gravitational constant," the determination of which made it possible to "weigh the earth" (see Chapter 3). It was Newton's surmise that G had a fixed value throughout the Universe. As time went on, it was found that new planets, undiscovered in Newton's time, tempered their motions to the requirements of Newton's law; even double stars incredibly far away danced in time to Newton's analysis of the Universe.

All this came from the new quantitative view of the Universe pioneered by Galileo. As you see, much of the mathematics involved was really very simple. Those parts of it I have quoted here are high-school algebra.

In fact, all that was needed to introduce one of the greatest intellectual revolutions of all time was:

1) A simple set of observations any high-school student of physics might make with a little guidance.

2) A simple set of mathematical generalizations.

3) The transcendent genius of Galileo and Newton, who had the insight and originality to make these observations and generalizations for the first time.

RELATIVITY

THE LAWS OF MOTION as worked out by Galileo and Newton depended on the assumption that such a thing as absolute motion existed — that is, motion with reference to something at rest. But everything that we know of in the Universe is in motion: the earth, the sun, the Galaxy, the systems of galaxies. Where in the Universe, then, can we find absolute rest against which to measure absolute motion?

It was this line of thought that led to the Michelson-Morley experiment, which in turn led to a scientific revolution as great, in some respects, as that initiated by Galileo (see Chapter 7). Here, too, the basic mathematics is rather simple.

The experiment was an attempt to detect the absolute motion of the earth against an "ether" which was supposed to fill all space and to be at rest. The reasoning behind the experiment was as follows.

Suppose that a beam of light is sent out in the direction in which the earth is traveling through the ether, and that at a certain distance in that direction there is a fixed mirror which reflects the light back to the source. Let us symbolize the velocity of light as c, the velocity of the earth through the ether as v, and the distance of the mirror as d. The light starts with the velocity $c + v$: its own velocity plus the earth's velocity. (It is traveling with a tailwind, so to speak.) The time it takes to reach the mirror is d divided by $(c + v)$.

On the return trip, however, the situation is reversed. The reflected light now is bucking the headwind, so to speak, of the earth's velocity, and its net velocity is $c - v$. The time it takes to return to the source is d divided by $(c - v)$.

The total time for the round trip is:

$$\frac{d}{c + v} + \frac{d}{c - v}$$

Combining the terms algebraically, we get:

$$\frac{d(c-v) + d(c+v)}{(c+v)(c-v)}$$

$$= \frac{dc - dv + dc + dv}{c^2 - v^2}$$

$$= \frac{2dc}{c^2 - v^2}$$

Now suppose that the light beam is sent out to a mirror at the same distance in a direction at right angles to the earth's motion through the ether.

The beam of light is aimed from S (the source) to M (the mirror) over the distance d. However, during the time it takes the

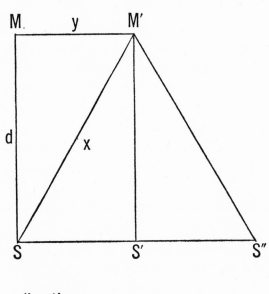

direction
of earth's
motion

759

light to reach the mirror, the earth's motion has carried the mirror from M to M', so that the actual path traveled by the light-beam is from S to M'. This distance we call x, and the distance from M to M' we call y.

While the light is moving the distance x at its velocity c, the mirror is moving the distance y at the velocity of the earth's motion v. Since both the light and the mirror arrive at M' simultaneously, the distances traveled must be exactly proportional to the respective velocities. Therefore:

$$\frac{y}{x} = \frac{v}{c}$$

or

$$y = \frac{vx}{c}$$

Now we can solve for the value of x by use of the Pythagorean theorem, which states that the sum of the squares of the sides of a right triangle is equal to the square of the hypotenuse. In the right triangle SMM', then, substituting vx/c for y:

$$x^2 = d^2 + \left(\frac{vx}{c}\right)^2$$

$$x^2 - \left(\frac{vx}{c}\right)^2 = d^2$$

$$x^2 - \frac{v^2x^2}{c^2} = d^2$$

$$\frac{c^2x^2 - v^2x^2}{c^2} = d^2$$

$$(c^2 - v^2)x^2 = d^2c^2$$

$$x^2 = \frac{d^2c^2}{c^2 - v^2}$$

$$x = \frac{dc}{\sqrt{c^2 - v^2}}$$

The light is reflected from the mirror at M' to the source, which meanwhile has traveled on to S''. Since the distance $S'S''$ is equal to SS', the distance $M'S''$ is equal to x. The total path traveled by the light beam is therefore $2x$, or $2dc \,/\, \sqrt{c^2 - v^2}$.

The time taken by the light beam to cover this distance at its velocity c is:

$$\frac{2dc}{\sqrt{c^2 - v^2}} \div c = \frac{2d}{\sqrt{c^2 - v^2}}$$

How does this compare with the time that light takes for the round trip in the direction of the earth's motion? Let's divide the time in the parallel case $(2dc \,/\, (c^2 - v^2)$ by the time in the perpendicular case $(2d \,/\, \sqrt{c^2 - v^2})$:

$$\frac{2dc}{c^2 - v^2} \div \frac{2d}{\sqrt{c^2 - v^2}}$$

$$= \frac{2dc}{c^2 - v^2} \times \frac{\sqrt{c^2 - v^2}}{2d}$$

$$= \frac{c\sqrt{c^2 - v^2}}{c^2 - v^2}$$

Now any number divided by its square root gives the same square root as a quotient — that is, $x \,/\, \sqrt{x} = \sqrt{x}$. Conversely, $\sqrt{x} \,/\, x = 1/\sqrt{x}$. So the last equation simplifies to:

$$\frac{c}{\sqrt{c^2 - v^2}}$$

This expression can be further simplified if we multiply both the numerator and the denominator by $\sqrt{1 \,/\, c^2}$ (which is equal to $1 \,/\, c$).

$$\frac{c\sqrt{1/c^2}}{\sqrt{c^2 - v^2}\sqrt{1/c^2}} = \frac{c/c}{\sqrt{c^2/c^2 - v^2/c^2}} = \frac{1}{\sqrt{1 - v^2/c^2}}$$

And there you are. That is the ratio of the time that light should take to travel in the direction of the earth's motion as compared with the time it should take in the direction perpendicular to the earth's motion. For any value of v greater than zero, the expression $1/\sqrt{1 - v^2/c^2}$ is greater than 1. Therefore, if the earth is moving through a motionless ether, it should take longer for light to travel in the direction of the earth's motion than in the perpendicular direction. (In fact, the parallel motion should take the maximum time and the perpendicular motion the minimum time.)

Michelson and Morley set up their experiment to try to detect the directional difference in the travel time of light. By trying their beam of light in all directions, and measuring the time of return by their incredibly delicate interferometer, they felt they ought to get differences in apparent velocity. The direction in which they found the velocity of light to be at a minimum should be parallel to the earth's absolute motion, and the direction in which the velocity would be at a maximum should be perpendicular to the earth's motion. From the difference in velocity, the amount (as well as the direction) of the earth's absolute motion could be calculated.

They found no differences at all in the velocity of light with changing direction! To put it another way, the velocity of light was always equal to c, regardless of the motion of the source — a clear contradiction of the Newtonian laws of motion. In attempting to measure the absolute motion of the earth, Michelson and Morley had thus managed to cast doubt not only on the existence of the ether, but on the whole concept of absolute rest and absolute motion, and upon the very basis of the Newtonian system of the universe (see Chapter 7).

The Irish physicist G. F. Fitzgerald conceived a way to save the situation. He suggested that all objects decreased in length in the direction in which they were moving by an amount equal to $\sqrt{1 - v^2/c^2}$. Thus:

$$L' = L\sqrt{1 - v^2/c^2}$$

where L' is the length of a moving body in the direction of its motion and L is what the length would be if it were at rest.

The foreshortening fraction $\sqrt{1 - v^2/c^2}$, Fitzgerald showed, would just cancel the ratio $1/\sqrt{1 - v^2/c^2}$, which related the maximum and minimum velocities of light in the Michelson-Morley experiment. The ratio would become unity, and the velocity of light would seem to our foreshortened instruments and sense organs to be equal in all directions, regardless of the movement of the source of light through the ether.

Under ordinary conditions the amount of foreshortening is very small. Even if a body were moving at one-tenth the velocity of light, or 18,628 miles per second, its length would be foreshortened by only 5 per cent, according to the Fitzgerald equations. Taking the velocity of light as 1, the equation says:

$$L' = L\sqrt{1 - \left(\frac{0.1}{1}\right)^2}$$

$$L' = L\sqrt{1 - 0.01}$$

$$L' = L\sqrt{0.99}$$

Thus L' turns out to be approximately equal to $0.995L$, a foreshortening of about half of 1 per cent.

For moving bodies, velocities such as this occur only in the realm of the subatomic particles. The foreshortening of an airplane traveling at 2,000 miles per hour is infinitesimal, as you can calculate for yourself.

At what velocity will an object be foreshortened to half its restlength? With L' equal to one-half L, the Fitzgerald equation is:

$$L/2 = L\sqrt{1 - v^2/c^2}$$

or, dividing by L:

$$1/2 = \sqrt{1 - v^2/c^2}$$

Squaring both sides of the equation:

$$1/4 = 1 - v^2/c^2$$

$$v^2/c^2 = 3/4$$

$$v = \sqrt{3/4}\ c = 0.866\ c$$

Since the velocity of light in a vacuum is 186,282 miles per second, the velocity at which an object is foreshortened to half its length is 0.866 times 186,282, or roughly 161,300 miles per second.

If a body moves at the speed of light, so that v equals c, the Fitzgerald equation becomes:

$$L' = L\sqrt{1 - c^2/c^2} = L\sqrt{0} = 0$$

At the speed of light, then, length in the direction of motion becomes zero. It follows, therefore, that no velocity faster than that of light is possible, because negative length appears meaningless in the physical world.

In the decade after Fitzgerald had advanced his equation, the electron was discovered, and scientists began to examine the properties of tiny charged particles. Lorentz worked out a theory that the mass of a particle with a given charge was inversely proportional to its radius. In other words, the smaller the volume into which a particle crowded its charge, the greater its mass.

Now if a particle is foreshortened because of its motion, its radius in the direction of motion is reduced in accordance with the Fitzgerald equation. Substituting the symbols R and R' for L and L', we write the equation:

$$R' = R\sqrt{1 - v^2/c^2}$$

$$R'/R = \sqrt{1 - v^2/c^2}$$

The mass of a particle is inversely proportional to its radius. Therefore:

$$\frac{R'}{R} = \frac{M}{M'}$$

where M is the mass of the particle at rest and M' is its mass when in motion.

Substituting M / M' for R' / R in the preceding equation, we have:

$$\frac{M}{M'} = \sqrt{1 - v^2/c^2}$$

$$M' = \frac{M}{\sqrt{1 - v^2/c^2}}$$

The Lorentz equation can be handled just as the Fitzgerald equation was. It shows, for instance, that for a particle moving at a velocity of 18,628 miles per second (one-tenth the speed of light) the mass M' would appear to be 0.5 per cent higher than the rest mass M. At a velocity of 161,300 miles per second the apparent mass of the particle would be twice the rest mass.

Finally, for a particle moving at a velocity equal to that of light, so that v is equal to c, the Lorentz equation becomes:

$$M' = \frac{M}{\sqrt{1 - c^2/c^2}} = \frac{M}{O}$$

Now as the denominator of any fraction with a fixed numerator becomes smaller and smaller ("approaches zero"), the value of the fraction itself becomes larger and larger without limit. In other words, from the equation above, it would seem that the mass of any object traveling at a velocity approaching that of light becomes infinitely large. Again, the velocity of light would seem to be the maximum possible, for a mass greater than infinity appears meaningless.

All this led Einstein to recast the laws of motion and of gravitation into new and broader forms which dispensed with absolute motion and treated all motion as relative, leaving only the velocity of light constant. He considered a universe, in other words, in which the results of the Michelson-Morley experiments were to be expected.

One consequence of the Lorentz equation was worked out by Einstein to produce what has become perhaps the most famous scientific equation of all time.

The Lorentz equation can be written in the form:

$$M' = M\ (1 - v^2/c^2)^{-1/2}$$

since in algebraic notation $1/\sqrt{x}$ can be written $x^{-1/2}$. This puts the equation into a form which can be expanded (that is, converted into a series of terms) by a formula discovered by, of all people, Newton. The formula is the binomial theorem.

The number of terms into which the Lorentz equation can be expanded is infinite, but since each term is smaller than the one before, if you take only the first two terms you are approximately correct, the sum of all the remaining terms being small enough to be neglected. The expansion becomes:

$$(1 - v^2/c^2)^{-1/2} = 1 + \frac{\frac{1}{2}v^2}{c^2} \cdots$$

Substituting that in the Lorentz equation, we get:

$$M' = M\left(1 + \frac{\frac{1}{2}v^2}{c^2}\right) = M + \frac{\frac{1}{2}Mv^2}{c^2}$$

Now in classical physics the expression $\frac{1}{2}Mv^2$ represents the energy of a moving body. If we let the symbol e stand for energy, the equation above becomes:

$$M' = M + e/c^2$$

or

$$M' - M = e/c^2$$

The increase in mass due to motion $(M' - M)$ can be represented as m, so:

$$m = e/c^2$$

or

$$e = mc^2$$

It was this equation that for the first time indicated mass to be
a form of energy. Einstein went on to show that the equation applied to all mass, not merely to the increase in mass due to motion.

Here again, most of the mathematics involved is only at the high-
school level. Yet it presented the world with the beginnings of a
view of the Universe greater and broader even than that of Newton, and also pointed the way to concrete consequences. It pointed
the way to the nuclear reactor and the atom bomb, for instance.

Bibliography

A "guide to science" would be incomplete without a guide to more reading. I am setting down here a brief selection of books. The list is a miscellaneous one and does not pretend to be a comprehensive collection of the best modern books about science, but I have read most of them myself and can highly recommend all of them.

CHAPTER 1 — *What Is Science?*

CLAGETT, MARSHALL, *Greek Science in Antiquity*. Abelard-Schuman, New York, 1955.

CROMBIE, A. C., *Medieval and Early Modern Science* (2 vols.). Doubleday & Company, New York, 1959.

DAMPIER, SIR WILLIAM CECIL, *A History of Science*. Cambridge University Press, New York, 1958.

DREYER, J. L. E., *A History of Astronomy from Thales to Kepler*. Dover Publications, New York, 1953.

MASON, S. F., *Main Currents of Scientific Thought*. Abelard-Schuman, New York, 1953.

SARTON, GEORGE, *Six Wings: Men of Science in the Renaissance*. Indiana University Press, Bloomington, Ind., 1957.

CHAPTER 2 — *The Universe*

ABETTI, GIORGIO, *The History of Astronomy*. Sidgwick and Jackson, London, 1954.

ASIMOV, ISAAC, *Kingdom of the Sun*. Abelard-Schuman, New York, 1960.

BIZONY, M. T. (general editor), *The Space Encyclopedia*. Dutton & Company, New York, 1957.

BOK, BART J., *The Astronomer's Universe*. Cambridge University Press, New York, 1958.

CLASON, CLYDE B., *Exploring the Distant Stars*. G. P. Putnam's Sons, New York, 1958.

GAMOW, GEORGE, *The Creation of the Universe*. Viking Press, New York, 1955.

HOYLE, FRED, *Frontiers of Astronomy*. New American Library, New York, 1955.

JOHNSON, MARTIN, *Astronomy of Stellar Energy and Decay*. Dover Publications, New York, 1959.

KRUSE, W. and DIECKVOSS, W., *The Stars*. University of Michigan Press, Ann Arbor, 1957.

MUNITZ, MILTON K. (editor), *Theories of the Universe*. The Free Press, Glencoe, Ill., 1957.

OPIK, ERNST J., *The Oscillating Universe*. New American Library, New York, 1960.

PAYNE-GAPOSCHKIN, CECILIA, *Introduction to Astronomy*. Prentice-Hall, New York, 1954.

PFEIFFER, JOHN, *The Changing Universe*. Random House, New York, 1956.

SCIAMA, D. W., *The Unity of the Universe*. Doubleday & Company, New York, 1959.

SCIENTIFIC AMERICAN (editors), *The Universe* and *The New Astronomy*. Simon and Schuster, New York, 1955.

WHITROW, G. J., *The Structure and Evolution of the Universe,* Harper & Brothers, 1959.

CHAPTER 3 — *The Earth*

ADAMS, FRANK DAWSON, *The Birth and Development of the Geological Sciences.* Dover Publications, New York, 1938.

BURTON, MAURICE, *Life in the Deep.* Roy Publishers, New York, 1958.

GAMOW, GEORGE, *Biography of the Earth.* New American Library, New York, 1948.

GILLULY, J., WATERS, A. C., and WOODFORD, A. O., *Principles of Geology.* W. H. Freeman & Company, San Francisco, Calif., 1958.

GUTENBERG, B. (editor), *Internal Constitution of the Earth.* Dover Publications, New York, 1951.

HURLEY, PATRICK M., *How Old Is the Earth?* Doubleday & Company, New York, 1959.

MASON, BRIAN, *Principles of Geochemistry.* John Wiley & Sons, New York, 1958.

MOORE, RUTH, *The Earth We Live On.* Alfred A. Knopf, New York, 1956.

CHAPTER 4 — *The Atmosphere*

ADLER, IRVING, *Weather in Your Life.* John Day Company, New York, 1959.

BATES, D. R. (editor), *The Earth and Its Atmosphere.* Basic Books, New York, 1957.

LEY, WILLY, *Rockets, Missiles, and Space Travel.* Viking Press, New York, 1957.

NEWELL, HOMER E., JR., *Window in the Sky.* McGraw-Hill Book Company, New York, 1959.

NININGER, H. H., *Out of the Sky.* Dover Publications, New York, 1952.

CHAPTER 5 — *The Elements*

ALEXANDER, W. and STREET, A., *Metals in the Service of Man*. Penguin Books, New York, 1954.

ASIMOV, ISAAC, *Building Blocks of the Universe*. Abelard-Schuman, New York, 1957.

DAVIS, HELEN MILES, *The Chemical Elements*. Ballantine Books, Boston, Mass., 1959.

HOLDEN, ALAN and SINGER, PHYLIS, *Crystals and Crystal Growing*. Doubleday & Company, New York, 1960.

LEICESTER, HENRY M., *The Historical Background of Chemistry*. John Wiley & Sons, New York, 1956.

PAULING, LINUS, *General Chemistry*. W. H. Freeman & Company, San Francisco, Calif., 1958.

SCIENTIFIC AMERICAN (editors), *New Chemistry*. Simon & Schuster, New York, 1957.

WEAVER, E. C. and FOSTER, L. S., *Chemistry for Our Times*. Mc-Graw-Hill Book Company, New York, 1947.

CHAPTER 6 — *The Particles*

ASIMOV, ISAAC, *Inside the Atom*. Abelard-Schuman, New York, 1958.

ASIMOV, ISAAC, *Only a Trillion*. Abelard-Schuman, New York, 1957.

GAMOW, GEORGE, *Mr. Tompkins Explores the Atom*. Cambridge University Press, New York, 1955.

GLASSTONE, SAMUEL, *Sourcebook on Atomic Energy* (2nd ed.). D. Van Nostrand Company, Princeton, N.J., 1958.

HECHT, SELIG, *Explaining the Atom*. Viking Press, New York, 1955.

HUGHES, DONALD J., *The Neutron Story*. Doubleday & Company, New York, 1959.

SHAMOS, M. H. and MURPHY, G. M. (editors), *Recent Advances in Science*. New York University Press, New York, 1956.

CHAPTER 7 — *The Waves*

BLACK, N. H. and LITTLE, E. P., *An Introductory Course in College Physics*. The Macmillan Company, New York, 1957.

EDDINGTON, SIR ARTHUR S., *The Nature of the Physical World*. Cambridge University Press, New York, 1953.

EINSTEIN, ALBERT and INFELD, LEOPOLD, *The Evolution of Physics*. Simon and Schuster, New York, 1938.

FREEMAN, IRA M., *Physics Made Simple*. Made Simple Books, Inc., New York, 1954.

HOFFMAN, BANESH, *The Strange Story of the Quantum*. Dover Publications, New York, 1959.

SHAMOS, MORRIS H., *Great Experiments in Physics*. Henry Holt & Company, New York, 1959.

CHAPTER 8 — *The Machine*

BITTER, FRANCIS, *Magnets*. Doubleday & Company, New York, 1959.

DE VILLE, ERIC, *Electricity*. Penguin Books, New York, 1955.

LARSEN, EGON, *Transport*. Roy Publishers, New York, 1959.

LEY, WILLY, *Engineers' Dreams*. Viking Press, New York, 1954.

NEAL, HARRY EDWARD, *Communication*. Julius Messner, New York, 1960.

PIERCE, JOHN R., *Electrons, Waves and Messages*. Doubleday & Company, New York, 1956.

SINGER, CHARLES, HOLMYARD, E. J., and HALL, A. R. (editors), *A History of Technology* (5 vols.). Oxford University Press, New York, 1954.

TAYLOR, F. SHERWOOD, *A History of Industrial Chemistry*. Abelard-Schuman, New York, 1957.

THOMPSON, SIR GEORGE, *The Foreseeable Future*. Cambridge University Press, New York, 1955.

UPTON, MONROE, *Electronics for Everyone*. New American Library, New York, 1957.

USHER, ABBOTT PAYSON, *A History of Mechanical Inventions*. Beacon Press, Boston, 1959.

CHAPTER 9 — *The Reactor*

ALEXANDER, PETER, *Atomic Radiation and Life*. Penguin Books, New York, 1957.

BISHOP, AMASA S., *Project Sherwood*. Addison-Wesley Publishing Company, Reading, Mass., 1958.

FOWLER, JOHN M., *Fallout: A Study of Superbombs, Strontium 90, and Survival*. Basic Books, New York, 1960.

JUKES, JOHN, *Man-Made Sun*. Abelard-Schuman, New York, 1959.

JUNGK, ROBERT, *Brighter Than a Thousand Suns*. Harcourt, Brace and Company, New York, 1958.

RIEDMAN, SARAH R., *Men and Women Behind the Atom*. Abelard-Schuman, New York, 1958.

SCIENTIFIC AMERICAN (editors), *Atomic Power*. Simon and Schuster, New York, 1955.

CHAPTER 10 — *The Molecule*

ASIMOV, ISAAC, *The World of Carbon*. Abelard-Schuman, New York, 1958.

ASIMOV, ISAAC, *The World of Nitrogen*. Abelard-Schuman, New York, 1958.

FIESER, L. F. and FIESER, M., *Organic Chemistry*. D. C. Heath & Company, Boston, 1956.

HUTTON, KENNETH, *Chemistry*. Penguin Books, New York, 1957.

PAULING, LINUS, *The Nature of the Chemical Bond* (3rd ed.). Cornell University Press, Ithaca, N.Y., 1960.

CHAPTER 11 — *The Proteins*

ASIMOV, ISAAC, *The Chemicals of Life*. Abelard-Schuman, New York, 1954.

BALDWIN, ERNEST, *Dynamic Aspects of Biochemistry*. Cambridge University Press, New York, 1952.

KAMEN, MARTIN D., *Isotopic Tracers in Biology*. Academic Press, New York, 1957.

SCIENTIFIC AMERICAN (editors), *The Physics and Chemistry of Life*. Simon and Schuster, New York, 1955.

CHAPTER 12 — *The Cell*

ANFINSEN, CHRISTIAN B., *The Molecular Basis of Evolution*. John Wiley & Sons, New York, 1959.

ASIMOV, ISAAC, *The Living River*. Abelard-Schuman, New York, 1960.

BOYD, WILLIAM C., *Genetics and the Races of Man*. Little, Brown & Company, Boston, 1950.

BOYD, W. C. and ASIMOV, ISAAC, *Races and People*. Abelard-Schuman, New York, 1955.

BUTLER, J. A. V., *Inside the Living Cell*. Basic Books, New York, 1959.

HUGHES, ARTHUR, *A History of Cytology*. Abelard-Schuman, New York, 1959.

NEEL, J. V. and SCHULL, W. J., *Human Heredity*. University of Chicago Press, Chicago, 1954.

OPARIN, A. I., *The Origin of Life on the Earth*. Academic Press, New York, 1957.

SINGER, CHARLES, *A Short History of Anatomy and Physiology from the Greeks to Harvey*. Dover Publications, New York, 1957.

WALKER, KENNETH, *Human Physiology*. Penguin Books, New York, 1956.

CHAPTER 13 — *The Microorganism*

DE KRUIF, PAUL, *Microbe Hunters*. Harcourt, Brace and Company, New York, 1932.

DUBOS, RENÉ, *Louis Pasteur*. Little, Brown & Company, Boston, 1950.

LUDOVICI, L. J., *The World of the Microscope*. G. P. Putnam's Sons, New York, 1959.

RIEDMAN, SARAH R., *Shots Without Guns*. Rand, McNally & Company, Chicago, 1960.

WILLIAMS, GREER, *Virus Hunters*. Alfred A. Knopf, New York, 1959.

ZINSSER, HANS, *Rats, Lice and History*. Little, Brown & Company, Boston, 1935.

CHAPTER 14 — *The Body*

CARLSON, ANTON J. and JOHNSON, VICTOR, *The Machinery of the Body*. University of Chicago Press, Chicago, 1953.

CHANEY, MARGARET S., *Nutrition*. Houghton Mifflin Company, Boston, 1954.

McCOLLUM, ELMER VERNER, *A History of Nutrition*. Houghton Mifflin Company, Boston, 1957.

WALKER, B. S., ASIMOV, ISAAC, and NICHOLAS, M. K., *Chemistry and Human Health*. McGraw-Hill Book Company, New York, 1956.

CHAPTER 15 — *The Species*

ASIMOV, ISAAC, *Wellsprings of Life*. Abelard-Schuman, New York, 1960.

BOULE, M. and VALLOIS, H. V., *Fossil Men*. The Dryden Press, New York, 1957.

CARRINGTON, RICHARD, *A Biography of the Sea*. Basic Books, New York, 1960.

CARTER, L. J. (editor), *Realities of Space Travel*. Putnam & Company, London, 1957.

DARWIN, FRANCIS (editor), *The Life and Letters of Charles Darwin* (2 vols.). Basic Books, New York, 1959.

HANRAHAN, JAMES S. and BUSHNELL, DAVID, *Space Biology*. Basic Books, New York, 1960.

HARRISON, R. J., *Man, the Peculiar Animal*. Penguin Books, New York, 1958.

HOWELLS, WILLIAM, *Mankind in the Making*. Doubleday & Company, New York, 1959.

HUXLEY, T. H., *Man's Place in Nature*. University of Michigan Press, Ann Arbor, 1959.

MEDAWAR, P. B., *The Future of Man*. Basic Books, Inc., New York, 1960.

MILNE, L. J. and M. J., *The Biotic World and Man*. Prentice-Hall, New York, 1958.

ROMER, A. S., *Man and the Vertebrates* (2 vols.). Penguin Books, New York, 1954.

ROSTAND, JEAN, *Can Man Be Modified?* Basic Books, New York, 1959.

SAX, KARL, *Standing Room Only*. Beacon Press, Boston, 1955.

SIMPSON, GEORGE G., PITTENDRIGH, C. S., and TIFFANY, L. H., *Life: An Introduction to College Biology*. Harcourt, Brace and Company, New York, 1957.

TINBERGEN, NIKO, *Curious Naturalists*. Basic Books, New York, 1960.

CHAPTER 16 — *The Mind*

ANSBACHER, H. and R. (editors), *The Individual Psychology of Alfred Adler*. Basic Books, New York, 1956.

ARIETI, SILVANO (editor), *American Handbook of Psychiatry* (2 vols.). Basic Books, New York, 1959.

BERKELEY, EDMUND C., *Symbolic Logic and Intelligent Machines*. Reinhold Publishing Corporation, New York, 1959.

DE LATIL, PIERRE, *Thinking by Machine*. Houghton Mifflin Company, Boston, 1957.

FREUD, SIGMUND, *Collected Papers* (5 vols.). Basic Books, New York, 1959.

JONES, ERNEST, *The Life and Work of Sigmund Freud* (3 vols.). Basic Books, New York, 1957.

LASSEK, A. M., *The Human Brain*. Charles C. Thomas, Springfield, Ill., 1957.

MENNINGER, KARL, *Theory of Psychoanalytic Technique*. Basic Books, New York, 1958.

MURPHY, GARDNER, *Human Potentialities*. Basic Books, New York, 1958.

RAWCLIFFE, D. H., *Illusions and Delusions of the Supernatural and Occult*. Dover Publications, New York, 1959.

SCIENTIFIC AMERICAN (editors), *Automatic Control*. Simon and Schuster, New York, 1955.

SCOTT, JOHN PAUL, *Animal Behavior*. University of Chicago Press, Chicago, 1957.

THOMPSON, CLARA and MULLAHY, PATRICK, *Psychoanalysis: Evolution and Development*. Grove Press, New York, 1950.

APPENDIX — *Mathematics in Science*

ASIMOV, ISAAC, *Realm of Measure*. Houghton Mifflin Company, Boston, 1960.

COURANT, RICHARD and ROBBINS, HERBERT, *What is Mathematics?* Oxford University Press, New York, 1941.

DANTZIG, TOBIAS, *Number, the Language of Science*. The Macmillan Company, New York, 1954.

FELIX, LUCIENNE, *The Modern Aspect of Mathematics*. Basic Books, New York, 1960.

FREUND, JOHN E., *A Modern Introduction to Mathematics*. Prentice-Hall, New York, 1956.

KLINE, MORRIS, *Mathematics and the Physical World*. Thomas Y. Crowell Company, New York, 1959.

KLINE, MORRIS, *Mathematics in Western Culture*. Oxford University Press, New York, 1953.

NEWMAN, JAMES R., *The World of Mathematics* (4 vols.). Simon and Schuster, New York, 1956.

General

ASIMOV, ISAAC, *The Words of Science*. Houghton Mifflin Company, Boston, 1959.

CABLE, E. J., and others, *The Physical Sciences*. Prentice-Hall, New York, 1959.

GAMOW, GEORGE, *Matter, Earth, and Sky*. Prentice-Hall, New York, 1958.

HUTCHINGS, EDWARD, JR. (editor), *Frontiers in Science*. Basic Books, New York, 1958.

SHAPLEY, HARLOW, RAPPORT, SAMUEL, and WRIGHT, HELEN (editors), *A Treasury of Science* (4th ed.). Harper & Brothers, New York, 1958.

SLABAUGH, W. H. and BUTLER, A. B., *College Physical Science*. Prentice-Hall, New York, 1958.

WATSON, JANE WERNER, *The World of Science*. Simon and Schuster, New York, 1958.

Illustrations

PLATES

781

STELLAR POPULATIONS I AND II: — California Institute of Technology.

A SPIRAL GALAXY: — California Institute of Technology.

THE CRAB NEBULA: — California Institute of Technology.

A SPIRAL GALAXY: — Mt. Wilson Observatory, California.

A BARRED SPIRAL GALAXY: — California Institute of Technology.

TWO COLLIDING GALAXIES: — California Institute of Technology.

FOLLOWING PAGE 66

RED-SHIFTS OF DISTANT GALAXIES: — California Institute of Technology.

A GLOBULAR CLUSTER: — California Institute of Technology.

THE SMALL MAGELLANIC CLOUD: — Harvard College Observatory.

THE LARGE MAGELLANIC CLOUD: — Harvard College Observatory.

THE JODRELL BANK RADIO TELESCOPE: — National Aeronautics and Space Administration.

CHAPTER 3 — *The Earth*

FOLLOWING PAGE 98

SATURN AND ITS RINGS: — California Institute of Technology.

THE MOON: — California Institute of Technology.

THE FAR SIDE OF THE MOON: — SOVFOTO.

FOUCAULT'S FAMOUS EXPERIMENT: — The Bettmann Archive.

GLACIAL STRATA: — The American Geographical Society.

GLACIAL FORMATION: — Richard U. Light, The American Geographical Society.

SEDIMENTARY FORMATION: — American Geographical Society.

GRAND CANYON: — U.S. Air Force, American Geographical Society.

CHAPTER 5 — *The Elements*

FOLLOWING PAGE 194

A SINGLE ICE CRYSTAL: — Franklyn Branley, Ed., *Scientists' Choice*, published by Basic Books, Inc.
URANIUM ORE: — American Museum of Natural History.
MOLECULAR MODEL: — National Bureau of Standards.
TYPICAL CRYSTALS: — National Bureau of Standards.

CHAPTER 6 — *The Particles*

FOLLOWING PAGE 242

LINEAR ACCELERATOR: — United Press International.
THE SOVIET UNION'S PHASOTRON: — SOVFOTO.
TRACKS OF ELECTRONS AND POSITRONS: — University of California, Berkeley.
TRACKS OF NUCLEAR PARTICLES: — United Press International.
BROOKHAVEN'S NEW SYNCHROTRON: — Brookhaven National Laboratory.
LINEAR ACCELERATOR: — Brookhaven National Laboratory.

FOLLOWING PAGE 258

RADIOACTIVE TRACERS: — National Bureau of Standards.
SMASHING OF A SILVER ATOM: — United Press International.
MESON COLLISION: — Brookhaven National Laboratory.
ANTI-PROTONS AND LAMBDA PARTICLES: — Lawrence Radiation Laboratory, Berkeley, California.
SPINNING PROTONS: — National Bureau of Standards.
PROTONS LINED UP: — National Bureau of Standards.

CHAPTER 7 — *The Waves*

FOLLOWING PAGE 290

MAGNETIC DOMAINS: — National Bureau of Standards.
CONTOUR MAP: — National Bureau of Standards.
SURFACE OF A HUMAN HAIR: — United Press International.
ELECTRON MICROGRAPH: — Carl Zeiss, Jena.
ELECTRIC FIELD: — National Bureau of Standards.

CHAPTER 8 — *The Machine*

FOLLOWING PAGE 338

JAMES WATT'S STEAM ENGINE: — The Bettmann Archive.
JOHN FITCH'S STEAMBOAT: — The Bettmann Archive.
GEORGE STEPHENSON'S STEAM LOCOMOTIVE: — The Bettmann
    Archive.
GALVANI'S EXPERIMENT: — The Bettmann Archive.
A JET PLANE: — U.S. Air Force.
THE X-15 ROCKET PLANE: — U.S. Air Force.

CHAPTER 9 — *The Reactor*

FOLLOWING PAGE 354

FISSION OF A URANIUM ATOM: — United Press International.
RADIOACTIVITY MADE VISIBLE: — Brookhaven National Laboratory.
DRAWING OF THE FIRST CHAIN REACTOR: — Argonne National
    Laboratory.

THE CHICAGO REACTOR UNDER CONSTRUCTION: — Argonne National Laboratory.

THE FIRST HYDROGEN BOMB: — U.S. Air Force.

THE REACTOR CORE: — Westinghouse Atomic Power Division.

FOLLOWING PAGE 370

SOVIET EXPERIMENTS IN FUSION: — SOVFOTO.

LOS ALAMOS EXPERIMENTS IN FUSION: — Los Alamos Scientific Laboratory.

PINCHED PLASMA: — Los Alamos Scientific Laboratory.

THE LIFE AND DEATH OF A PINCH: — Los Alamos Scientific Laboratory.

THE BELL SOLAR BATTERY: — Bell Telephone Laboratories.

A THERMOELECTRIC CELL: — United Press International.

CHAPTER 10 — *The Molecule*

FOLLOWING PAGE 410

STRUCTURE OF UREA: — Dr. Benjamin Post, Brooklyn Polytechnical Institute.

EIGHT-SIDED RING: — Dr. Benjamin Post, Brooklyn Polytechnical Institute.

SILK FIBERS: — Siemens New York, Inc.

COLLAGEN FIBERS: — The Rockefeller Institute.

SECTION OF A MUSCLE FIBER: — Dr. David S. Smith, The Rockefeller Institute.

FOLLOWING PAGE 426

THE RUBBER MOLECULE: — U.S. Rubber Company.

VULCANIZATION OF RUBBER: — U.S. Rubber Company.

A MODERN PLASTICS PLANT: — U.S. Rubber Company.
GLASSWARE: — U.S. Rubber Company.

CHAPTER 12 — *The Cell*

FOLLOWING PAGE 506

NORMAL CHROMOSOMES: — Franklyn Branley, Ed., *Scientists'*
    Choice, published by Basic Books, Inc.
CHROMOSOMES DAMAGED BY RADIATION: — Brookhaven National
    Laboratory.
RADIATION DAMAGE: — Brookhaven National Laboratory.
MUTATIONS IN FRUIT FLIES: — Brookhaven National Laboratory.
SPERM CELL: — Siemens New York, Inc.
HEART CELL: — The Rockefeller Institute.
LIVER CELL: — The Rockefeller Institute.
MITOCHONDRIA: — The Rockefeller Institute.
MICROSOMES: — The Rockefeller Institute.

FOLLOWING PAGE 522

RIBONUCLEOPROTEIN PARTICLES: — Dr. J. F. Kirsch,
    The Rockefeller Institute.
DNA-PROTEIN COMPLEX: — United Press International.
THE PLANET MARS: — California Institute of Technology.
STANLEY MILLER'S HISTORIC EXPERIMENT: — United Press
    International.

CHAPTER 13 — *The Microorganism*

FOLLOWING PAGE 570

LOUIS PASTEUR: — The Bettmann Archive.
JOSEPH LISTER: — The Bettmann Archive.

STAPHYLOCOCCUS BACTERIA: — National Institutes of Health.

THE ROD-SHAPED BACILLUS: — Siemens New York, Inc.

THE TOBACCO MOSAIC VIRUS: — Siemens New York, Inc.

THE INFLUENZA VIRUS: — National Institutes of Health.

BACTERIOPHAGES: — Franklyn Branley, Ed., *Scientists' Choice*, published by Basic Books, Inc.

AN X-RAY MICROGRAPH OF A BEETLE: — Dr. David S. Smith, Cavendish Physics Laboratory, University of Cambridge.

CANCER-PRODUCING PARTICLES: — Dr. Dan H. Moore, The Rockefeller Institute.

CHAPTER 15 — *The Species*

FOLLOWING PAGE 666

FOSSIL OF A CRINOID: — American Museum of Natural History.

A PALM-LEAF FOSSIL: — American Museum of Natural History.

FOSSIL OF A BRYOZOAN: — United Press International.

FOSSIL OF A FORAMINIFER: — United Press International.

A 3,000-YEAR-OLD CRUSTACEAN: — SOVFOTO.

AN ANCIENT ANT: — American Museum of Natural History.

FOSSIL OF A TRILOBITE: — American Museum of Natural History.

FOSSIL OF A CORAL: — American Museum of Natural History.

A FOSSILIZED FISH: — American Museum of Natural History.

MODEL OF AN EXTINCT LUNG-FISH: — American Museum of Natural History.

CAST OF A COELACANTH: — American Museum of Natural History.

SKELETON OF A PTERODACTYL: — American Museum of Natural History.

FOLLOWING PAGE 698

TRACKS OF DINOSAUR: — American Museum of Natural History.

THE EVOLUTION OF THE HORSE: — American Museum of Natural History.

SKULL OF PITHECANTHROPUS: — American Museum of Natural History.
SKULL OF SINANTHROPUS: — American Museum of Natural History.
NEANDERTHAL MAN: — American Museum of Natural History.
CRO-MAGNON MAN: — American Museum of Natural History.
AUSTRALOPITHECUS: — American Museum of Natural History.
SINANTHROPUS WOMAN: — American Museum of Natural History.
STONE TOOLS: — American Museum of Natural History.

CHAPTER 16 — *The Mind*

FOLLOWING PAGE 714

THE ORIGINAL UNIVAC: — Remington Rand–Univac.
PROGRAM ON TAPE: — Remington Rand–Univac.
DISK MEMORY UNIT: — International Business Machines, Inc.
TAPE MEMORIES: — Remington Rand–Univac.
AN ARRAY OF FERRITE CORES: — International Business Machines, Inc.
READING BY MACHINE: — International Business Machines, Inc.

DRAWINGS

By BUNJI TAGAWA: — Pages 27, 37, 47, 61, 65, 67, 70–71, 79, 83, 90, 94, 108–109, 112, 114, 115, 124, 126, 133, 143, 145, 151, 153.
By CHESTER A. REEDS, American Museum of Natural History: — Page 96.
By JAMES EGLESON: — Pages 191, 198, 199, 236, 242, 244, 246, 249, 262, 272, 273, 276, 288, 303.
By DONALD McKAY: — Pages 311, 314, 317, 319, 320, 321, 325, 326, 334, 335, 337, 339, 344, 349, 351, 357, 369, 377, 381.

By HILDA SIMON: — Pages 397, 400, 425, 451, 458, 460, 480, 727, 735, 739.

By ERIC MOSE: — Pages 501, 503, 505, 511, 512, 532, 538, 557, 570, 642, 660, 667, 686, 704, 708, 712.

Index of Names

A

Abderhalden, Emil, 450
Abelson, Philip, 184
Adams, John Couch, 287
Adams, Walter Sydney, 57
Addison, Thomas, 643
Adler, Alfred, 722
Agassiz, Jean Louis Rodolphe, 116
Airy, George Biddell, 554, 728
Albert (Prince), 409
Alburger, David E., 62
Allison, Fred, 181
Altschule, Mark D., 725
Amagat, E. H., 211
Amontons, Guillaume, 291
Amundsen, Roald, 112
Anderson, Carl David, 238, 256
Andrews, Thomas, 205
Ångstrom, Anders Jonas, 270
Appleton, Edward Victor, 139

Aquinas, Thomas, 14, 536
Archimedes, 12, 553
Aristarchus, 23
Aristotle, 9, 14, 53, 84, 123, 153, 170, 536, 654, 665, 708
Armstrong, Edwin Howard, 338
Arrhenius, Svante August, 138, 537
Aschheim, S., 641
Ashby, W. Ross, 731
Asshurbanipal, 680
Astbury, W. T., 453
Aston, Francis William, 231, 299
Atlas, 21
Avery, Oswald T., 530

B

Baade, Walter, 38, 71
Babbage, Charles, 737
Bacon, Francis, 16

Index of Subjects

W